Calculus

D1455681

NINTH EDITION

Ron Larson

The Pennsylvania State University
The Behrend College

Bruce Edwards

University of Florida

With the Assistance of

Frank C. Wilson
Chandler-Gilbert Community College
Stella Ollarsaba
Dobson High School
Rick Vaughn
Scottsdale Community College
Sue Steele
Chandler-Gilbert Community College
Stephen Heiser
Mountain Pointe High School
Jacqueline Hartrick
Chandler High School
Carol Baldwin
Chandler High School
Richard Franzen
Mesquite High School

BROOKS/COLE
CENGAGE Learning

Australia • Brazil • Japan • Korea • Mexico • Singapore • Spain • United Kingdom • United States

ISBN-13: 978-0-547-21296-8
ISBN-10: 0-547-21296-8

Brooks/Cole
20 Channel Center Street
Boston, MA 02210
USA

Cengage Learning products are represented in Canada by Nelson Education, Ltd.

For your course and learning solutions, visit **academic.cengage.com**

Printed in the United States of America
2 3 4 5 6 7 13 12 11 10

Contents

Part I

Part II

Introduction

Homework Quizzes

PREFACE

This AP* Teacher's Resource Guide is a supplement to *Calculus*, Ninth Edition, by Ron Larson and Bruce H. Edwards. All references to chapters, sections, and other specific content relate to this text.

Part I of the guide contains valuable information and tips for teaching Calculus. Within this section, you will find three types of content: chapter summaries, Calc Chat findings and tips, and Capstone problem explanations. The **chapter summaries** contain teaching strategies; key points and suggestions for teaching the topics are broken down to the section level.

In the **Calc Chat** online study guide (available at www.calcchat.com), students can access the worked-out solutions to all odd-numbered exercises in the book. We keep track of how many times each solution is accessed, and we look for trends as well as "spikes" in this data for each set. Many of the changes we made to the exercises for the Ninth Edition were made as the result of a large number of "hits" on a particular Eighth Edition exercise or exercise block. In this section of the guide, we outline our *findings*, explain how we changed or rearranged the exercises for the Ninth Edition as a result of these findings, and provide the instructor with *teaching tips and suggestions* for each section of the text.

The **Capstone** problems are synthesis exercises that appear once in each numbered exercise set. They always appear in the last third of the exercise set, and are always even-numbered, so the solutions are in the Complete Solutions Manual. Capstone problems provide students and teachers with the opportunity to review key concepts in the section, and can be easily integrated into a review of the section. Capstone problems are not "number-messy," that is, they do not involve tedious calculations that are time-consuming for the teacher to go over in class. Rather, they are more conceptual in nature. Each Capstone problem has an accompanying PPT transparency with graphs and/or figures for the instructor to use.

Part II is tailored even more specifically to the AP* teacher and student. This section includes introductory letters with detailed tips for both teachers and students, Homework Quizzes, and Sample Exams. There is a **Homework Quiz** for every section, consisting of three to four questions that can be used to test students' understanding of the homework assignment, or for additional practice. Answers are included, following each quiz. We also include four complete **Sample Exams**: two for Calculus AB and two for Calculus BC, with both multiple choice and free response questions. Solutions are provided on the Teacher Resource CD.

We hope that this guide becomes a valuable resource for teachers and students alike. If there is anything that we can do to improve this guide, please let us know.

AP and Advanced Placement Program are registered trademarks of the College Entrance Examination Board, which was not involved in the production of, and does not endorse, this product.*

Chapter P   Preparation for Calculus

Chapter Summary
Section Topics

P.1   **Graphs and Models**—Sketch the graph of an equation. Find the intercepts of a
graph. Test a graph for symmetry with respect to an axis and the origin. Find the
points of intersection of two graphs. Interpret mathematical models for real-life data.

P.2   **Linear Models and Rates of Change**—Find the slope of a line passing through
two points. Write the equation of a line with a given point and slope. Interpret slope
as a ratio or as a rate in a real-life application. Sketch the graph of a linear equation
in slope-intercept form. Write equations of lines that are parallel or perpendicular to
a given line.

P.3   **Functions and Their Graphs**—Use function notation to represent and evaluate a
function. Find the domain and range of a function. Sketch the graph of a function.
Identify different types of transformations of functions. Classify functions and
recognize combinations of functions.

P.4   **Fitting Model to Data**—Fit a linear model to a real-life data set. Fit a quadratic
model to a real-life data set. Fit a trigonometric model to a real-life data set.

Chapter Comments

Chapter P is a review chapter and, therefore, should be covered quickly. Spend about 3 or 4 days
on this chapter, placing most of the emphasis on Section 3. Of course, you cannot cover every
single item that is in this chapter in that time, so this is a good opportunity to encourage your
students to read the book. To convince your students of this, assign homework problems or give a
quiz on some of the material that is in this chapter but that you do not go over in class. Although
you will not hold your students responsible for everything in all 16 chapters, the tools in this
chapter need to be readily at hand, i.e., memorized.

Sections P.1 and P.2 can be covered in a day. Students at this level of mathematics have graphed
equations before so let them read about that information on their own. Discuss intercepts,
emphasizing that they are points, not numbers, and, so, should be written as ordered pairs. Also
discuss symmetry with respect to the x-axis, the y-axis, and the origin. Be sure to do a problem
like Example 5 in Section P.1. Students need to be able to find the points of intersection of graphs
in order to calculate the area between two curves in Chapter 7.

In Section P.2, discuss the slope of a line, the point-slope form of a line, equations of vertical and
horizontal lines, and the slopes of parallel and perpendicular lines. You need to emphasize the
point-slope form of a straight line because this is needed to write the equation of a tangent line in
Chapter 2.

Students need to know everything in Section P.3, so carefully go over the definition of a function,
domain and range, function notation, transformations, the terms algebraic and transcendental, and
the composition of functions. Note that the authors assume a knowledge of trigonometric
functions. If necessary to review these functions, refer to Appendix C. Because students need
practice handling Δx, be sure to do an example calculating $f(x + \Delta x)$. Your students should
know the graphs of eight basic functions in Figure P.27. A knowledge of even and odd functions
will be helpful with definite integrals.

Section P.4 introduces the idea of fitting models to data. Because a basic premise of science is
that much of the physical world can be described mathematically, you and your students would
benefit from looking at the three models presented in this section.

1

The authors assume students have a working knowledge of inequalities, the formula for the distance between two points, absolute value, etc. If needed, you can find a review of these concepts in Appendix C.

Section P.1 Graphs and Models

Tips and Tools for Problem Solving

CalcChat.com

We noticed in the data that students are having trouble with concepts taught or reviewed in a precalculus course. You may want to spend time reviewing these concepts: factoring, solving equations involving square roots, and solving polynomial equations. For further review, encourage students to study the following material in *Precalculus*, 7th edition, by Larson and Hostetler.

- Factoring: Appendix A.3

- Solving equations involving square roots: Appendix A.5

- Solving polynomial equations: Appendix A.5

Encourage students who have access to a graphing utility or computer algebra system to use the technology to check their answers.

Exercises 19–28 (19–26 in *Calculus* 8/e)
According to the data, students had difficulty finding the intercepts of the graph of an equation. To give students more practice, we added Exercises 19 and 20. Also, consider doing an in class example of finding the intercepts of the graph of an equation with a radical, such as $y = \sqrt{x + 4}$ or $y = x\sqrt{4 - x^2}$. Note that the latter suggestion is similar to Exercise 23.

Exercises 29–40 (27–38 in *Calculus* 8/e)
Because students had difficulty with this exercise block, we rewrote Example 3 and added a test for y-axis symmetry. Further demonstration of how to perform symmetry tests should help students to complete these exercises successfully.

Capstone

Page 9, Exercise 82 You can use this exercise to review the following concepts.

- Finding the x-intercept(s) of a graph

- Finding the y-intercept(s) of a graph

- Testing a graph for symmetry with respect to the x-axis

- Testing a graph for symmetry with respect to the y-axis

- Testing a graph for symmetry with respect to the origin

- Finding the points of intersection of two graphs

- Identifying several characteristics of a graph of an equation

These concepts will arise later in the text. It is important that students grasp them now so they are able to learn more advanced material later. Some of the sections where these concepts will be used are shown in the table.

Concept	Section
Finding intercepts	3.6, 3.8, 11.5
Testing for symmetry	P.3, 3.6, 4.5, 5.6, 7.6, 7.7, 10.6, 11.7
Finding points of intersection	7.1, 10.5, 11.5

The graph of each equation given in Exercise 82 is provided on a transparency. Using these graphs, ask students which graph has a given characteristic. For instance, show the graph of $y = 3x^3 - 3x$ to the students and then ask them whether the graph is symmetric with respect to the y-axis. Then continue through the other characteristics. Finally, ask them how to verify their conclusions analytically. You can then perform the calculations. (See solution given below.) Repeat this process for each graph. In part (d), note that $(-2, 1)$ is a point of intersection of graphs ii and vi.

Solution

Sketch the graph of each equation. Use the graph to reinforce the characteristic. Then verify analytically as shown below.

(a) v $\left(\text{Because } 3(-x)^2 + 3 = 3x^2 + 3 = y.\right)$

(b) i $\left(\text{Because } y = 3x^3 - 3x = 3x(x - 1)(x + 1) \text{ has } x\text{-intercepts at } (0, 0), (1, 0), (-1, 0).\right)$

(c) None of the equations are symmetric with respect to the x-axis.

(d) ii $\left(\text{Because } (-2 + 3)^2 = 1.\right)$ and vi $\left(\text{Because } \sqrt{-2 + 3} = 1.\right)$

(e) i $\left(\text{Because } 3(-x)^3 - 3(-x) = -3x^3 + 3x = -y.\right)$ and iv $\left(\text{Because } \sqrt[3]{-x} = -\sqrt[3]{x} = -y.\right)$

(f) i $\left(\text{Because } 3(0)^3 - 3(0) = 0.\right)$ and iv $\left(\text{Because } \sqrt[3]{0} = 0.\right)$

Section P.2   Linear Models and Rates of Change
Tips and Tools for Problem Solving

CalcChat.com

We noticed in the data that students are having trouble with concepts taught or reviewed in a precalculus course. You may want to spend time reviewing these concepts: slope, writing equations of lines, and slope as a rate of change. For further review, encourage students to study the following material in *Precalculus*, 7th edition, by Larson and Hostetler.

- Slope: Section 1.3

- Finding the slope of a line: Section 1.3

- Writing linear equations in two variables: Section 1.3

- Parallel and perpendicular lines: Section 1.3

- Slope as a rate of change: Section 1.3

Encourage students who have access to a graphing utility or computer algebra system to use the technology to check their answers.

Exercises 19–22, 67–70 (19–22, 65–68 in *Calculus* 8/e)
Students had difficulty with these exercises, so you may need to review slope as a rate of change. Rate of change is an important topic in calculus.

Exercises 23–28 (23–26 in *Calculus* 8/e)
According to the data, students had difficulty finding the slope and y-intercept of a line. To give students more practice, we added Exercises 23 and 24. Also, consider doing an example in class to remind students how to rewrite an equation such as $x + 3y = 12$ in slope-intercept form.

Then show them how to identify the slope and y-intercept. Remind students that the slope of a vertical line is undefined and the slope of a horizontal line is 0. (As mentioned before, you can also direct students to the appropriate material in *Precalculus*.)

3

Exercises 47–50 (45–48 in *Calculus* 8/e)
We revised the direction line to instruct students to write the equation of the line in *general form*. In the eighth edition, the answers were listed in general form, but the direction line did not specify the form of the equation. This caused some confusion for students who expected the form of the equation to be $\dfrac{x}{a} + \dfrac{y}{b} = 1$ (see Exercise 46).

Exercises 61–66 (59–64 in *Calculus* 8/e)
Exercise 63 (59 in *Calculus* 8/e) had the greatest number of hits in Section P.2. We reordered these exercises to improve the grading, created a new exercise (61), and revised an existing exercise (66). We also revised the direction line to specify that the equations of the lines should be written in *general form*. Consider doing an example in class that is similar to Exercise 63, using the point $(2, -1)$ and the line $2y - 3y = 5$. (As mentioned before, you can also direct students to the appropriate material in *Precalculus*.)

Capstone

Page 17, Exercise 60 You can use this exercise to review the following concepts.

- Writing equations of lines that are parallel or perpendicular to a given line
- Writing the equation of a line with a given slope
- Writing the equation of a line such that the line coincides with the graph of a given line

Some of these concepts will arise later in the text. It is important that students grasp them now so they are able to learn more advanced material later. Some of the sections where these concepts will be used are shown in the table.

Concept	Section
Writing an equation of a line that is parallel to a given line	2.1, 2.3, 3.2
Writing an equation of a line that is perpendicular to a given line	2.5
Writing an equation of a line with a given slope	2.1–2.5, 3.8

For part (a) the line is parallel to the x-axis when $a = 0$ and $b \neq 0$. You can either ask students to write an equation of this line or you can show them that it is $by = 4$ or $y = b/4$. [See transparency for part (a)]. You can do likewise for part (b), which also has a transparency. You can use part (b) to remind students that all vertical lines are parallel. Transparencies for the sample answers in parts (c)–(e) are also provided. There are many correct answers, so reassure students that they should not feel discouraged if they did not get the same answer(s) as those given in the solution below. You could ask students for the equations they got and graph them.

Solution

$ax + by = 4$

(a) The line is parallel to the x-axis if $a = 0$ and $b \neq 0$.

(b) The line is parallel to the y-axis if $b = 0$ and $a \neq 0$.

(c) Answers will vary. *Sample answer:* $a = -5$ and $b = 8$.

$$-5x + 8y = 4$$
$$y = \tfrac{1}{8}(5x + 4) = \tfrac{5}{8}x + \tfrac{1}{2}$$

4

(d) The slope must be $-\frac{5}{2}$.

Answers will vary. *Sample answer:* $a = 5$ and $b = 2$.

$$5x + 2y = 4$$
$$y = \tfrac{1}{2}(-5x + 4) = -\tfrac{5}{2}x + 2$$

(e) $a = \frac{5}{2}$ and $b = 3$.

$$\tfrac{5}{2}x + 3y = 4$$
$$5x + 6y = 8$$

Section P.3 Functions and Their Graphs
Tips and Tools for Problem Solving

CalcChat.com

We noticed in the data that students are having trouble with concepts taught or reviewed in a precalculus course. You may want to spend time reviewing these concepts: evaluating a function and the domain and range of a function. For further review, encourage students to study the following material in *Precalculus*, 7th edition, by Larson and Hostetler.

- Evaluating a function: Section 1.4

- Domain and range of a function: Section 1.4

Encourage students who have access to a graphing utility or computer algebra system to use the technology to check their answers.

Exercises 9–12 (9–12 in *Calculus* 8/e)
Because students had difficulty doing Exercise 9, we recommend you cover Example 1(c) in class. This is an important concept because difference quotients will come up again in Chapter 2.

Exercises 13–30 (13–28 in *Calculus* 8/e)
According to the data, students had difficulty finding the domains and ranges of these functions, particularly those involving radicals. To give students more practice with these concepts, we added Exercises 13 and 15. We also reordered some of the exercises to improve the grading. Be sure to cover Examples 2 and 3 in class. (As mentioned before, you can also direct students to the appropriate material in *Precalculus*.)

Capstone

Page 29, Exercise 88 You can use this exercise to review the following concepts.

- Determining whether a relation is a function

- Finding the domain and range of a function

- Sketching the graph of a function

- Evaluating a function

Students need to know these concepts because they are used throughout the text.

Note that the water runs into the vase at a *constant* rate. So for each time t, there corresponds a depth d. After discussing the domain and range, sketch a possible graph of the function. (This graph is available as a transparency.) You can use the graph to reinforce the conclusion in part (a) using the Vertical Line Test. Because the width of the vase widens then narrows and then widens again, the rate of change of the depth of the water slows then quickens and then slows again. You may want to point this out as a preview of Chapter 2. Then use the graph to answer part (d). [See transparency for part (d).]

5

Solution

(a) For each time t, there corresponds a depth d.

(b) Domain: $0 \le t \le 5$

Range: $0 \le d \le 30$

(c)

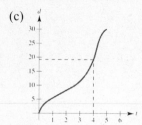

(d) $d(4) \approx 18$. At 4 seconds, the depth is approximately 18 cm.

Section P.4 Fitting Models to Data
Tips and Tools for Problem Solving

CalcChat.com

Although we made changes to the section exercises, no changes were made based on the data.

Capstone

Page 35, Exercise 14 You can use this exercise to review the following concepts.

- Fitting a linear model to a real-life data set

- Fitting a quadratic model to a real-life data set

- Fitting a cubic model to a real-life data set

Much of the physical world can be described mathematically, so students will benefit from reviewing these models. Also, students need to know these concepts because they are used throughout the text.

Students should obtain models similar to the ones given in part (a) below. Use the transparency to show the models and the data together. It is clear from the graph that the cubic model is better than the linear model. Next, give the quadratic model and show its graph using the second transparency. From the graph, the quadratic model does not appear to be a good fit. Part (e) will give you an opportunity to show students that a model can be a poor predictor using values outside the domain of the given data set. If there is another model you wish to investigate (for example, higher-order polynomials), you can do part (f).

Solution

(a) $N_1 = 3.72t + 31.6$

$N_3 = -0.0932t^3 + 1.735t^2 - 3.77t + 35.1$

(b)

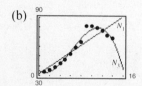

(c) The cubic model is better.

(d) $N_2 = -0.221t^2 + 6.81t + 24.9$

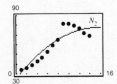

The model does not fit the data well.

(e) For 2007, $t = 17$, and $N_1 \approx 94.8$ million and $N_3 \approx 14.5$ million. Neither seems accurate.
The linear model's estimate is too high and the cubic model's estimate is too low.

(f) Answers will vary.

Chapter P Project

Height of a Ferris Wheel Car

The Ferris wheel was designed by American engineer George Ferris (1859–1896). The first Ferris wheel was built for the 1893 World's Columbian Exposition in Chicago, and later used at the 1904 World's Fair in St. Louis. It had a diameter of 250 feet, and each of its 36 cars could hold 60 passengers.

Exercises

In Exercises 1–3, use the following information. A Ferris wheel with a diameter of 100 feet rotates at a constant rate of 4 revolutions per minute. Let the center of the Ferris wheel be at the origin.

1. Each of the Ferris wheel's cars travels around a circle.

    (a) Write an equation of the circle where x and y are measured in feet.

    (b) Sketch a graph of the equation you wrote in part (a).

    (c) Use the Vertical Line Test to determine whether y is a function of x.

    (d) What does your answer to part (c) mean in the context of the problem?

2. The height h (in feet) of a Ferris wheel car located at the point (x, y) is given by

    $$h = 50 + y$$

    where y is related to the angle θ (in radians) by the equation

    $$y = 50 \sin \theta$$

    as shown in the figure.

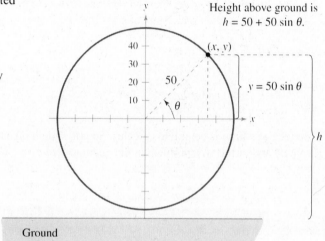

Height above ground is $h = 50 + 50 \sin \theta$.

$y = 50 \sin \theta$

Ground

    (a) Write an equation of the height h in terms of time t (in minutes). (*Hint:* One revolution is 2π radians.)

    (b) Sketch a graph of the equation you wrote in part (a).

    (c) Use the Vertical Line Test to determine whether h is a function of t.

    (d) What does your answer to part (c) mean in the context of the problem?

3. The model in Exercise 2 yields a height of 50 feet when $t = 0$. Alter the model so that the height of the car is 0 feet when $t = 0$. Explain your reasoning.

Chapter 1   Limits and Their Properties

Chapter Summary

Section Topics

1.1   **A Preview of Calculus**—Understand what calculus is and how it compares with precalculus. Understand that the tangent line problem is basic to calculus. Understand that the area problem is also basic to calculus.

1.2   **Finding Limits Graphically and Numerically**—Estimate a limit using a numerical or graphical approach. Learn different ways that a limit can fail to exist. Study and use a formal definition of limit.

1.3   **Evaluating Limits Analytically**—Evaluate a limit using properties of limits. Develop and use a strategy for finding limits. Evaluate a limit using dividing out and rationalizing techniques. Evaluate a limit using the Squeeze Theorem.

1.4   **Continuity and One-Sided Limits**—Determine continuity at a point and continuity on an open interval. Determine one-sided limits and continuity on a closed interval. Use properties of continuity. Understand and use the Intermediate Value Theorem.

1.5   **Infinite Limits**—Determine infinite limits from the left and from the right. Find and sketch the vertical asymptotes of the graph of a function.

Chapter Comments

Section 1.1 gives a preview of calculus. On pages 43 and 44 of the textbook are examples of some of the concepts from precalculus extended to ideas that require the use of calculus. Review these ideas with your students to give them a feel for where the course is heading.

The idea of a limit is central to calculus. So you should take the time to discuss the tangent line problem and/or the area problem in this section. Exercise 11 of Section 1.1 is yet another example of how limits will be used in calculus. A review of the formula for the distance between two points can be found in Appendix C.

The discussion of limits is difficult for most students the first time that they see it. For this reason you should carefully go over the examples and the informal definition of a limit presented in Section 1.2. Stress to your students that a limit exists only if the answer is a real number. Otherwise, the limit fails to exist, as shown in Examples 3, 4, and 5 of this section. You might want to work Exercise 67 of Section 1.2 with your students in preparation for the definition of the number e coming up in Section 5.1. You may choose to omit the formal definition of a limit.

Carefully go over the properties of limits found in Section 1.3 to ensure that your students are comfortable with the idea of a limit and also with the notation used for limits. By the time you get to Theorem 1.6, it should be obvious to your students that all of these properties amount to direct substitution.

When direct substitution for the limit of a quotient yields the indeterminate form $\frac{0}{0}$, tell your students that they must rewrite the fraction using legitimate algebra. Then, do at least one problem using dividing out techniques and another using rationalizing techniques. Exercises 60 and 62 of Section 1.3 are examples of other algebraic techniques needed for the limit problems. You need to go over the Squeeze Theorem, Theorem 1.8, with your students so that you can use it to prove

$\lim\limits_{x \to 0} \dfrac{\sin x}{x} = 1$. The proof of Theorem 1.8 and many other theorems can be found in Appendix A.

Your students need to memorize both of the results in Theorem 1.9 as they will need these facts to do problems throughout the textbook. Most of your students will need help with Exercises 65–76 in this section.

Continuity, Section 1.4, is another idea that often puzzles students. However, if you describe a continuous function as one in which you can draw the entire graph without lifting your pencil, the idea seems to stay with them. Distinguishing between removable and non-removable discontinuities will help students to determine vertical asymptotes.

To discuss infinite limits, Section 1.5, remind your students of the graph of the function $f(x) = 1/x$ studied in Section P.3. Be sure to make your students write a vertical asymptote as an equation, not just a number. For example, for the function $y = 1/x$, the vertical asymptote is $x = 0$.

Section 1.1 A Preview of Calculus

Tips and Tools for Problem Solving

CalcChat.com

Although we made changes to the section exercises, no changes were made based on the data.

Capstone

Page 47, Exercise 10 You can use this exercise to review the following concepts.

- Understanding what calculus is
- Instantaneous rate of change

Instantaneous rate of change will be discussed in later chapters (e.g., Chapters 2 and 3) and in numerous exercises.

While the answers to this question may vary, a sample answer is given in the solution below. You may want to ask students to define instantaneous rate of change. (We discussed average rate of change in Section P.2. You may want to contrast instantaneous rate of change with average rate of change.) Ask students if instantaneous rate of change is found with or without calculus. (See chart on page 43 of the text.)

Solution

Answers will vary. *Sample answer:* The instantaneous rate of change of an automobile's position is the velocity of the automobile, and can be determined by the speedometer.

Section 1.2 Finding Limits Graphically and Numerically

Tips and Tools for Problem Solving

CalcChat.com

Although we made changes to the section exercises, no changes were made based on the data.

Capstone

Page 57, Exercise 64 You can use this exercise to review the following concepts.

- The value of f at c has no bearing on the existence of the limit of $f(x)$ as x approaches c.
- The value of the limit of $f(x)$ as x approaches c has no bearing on the value of f at c.

Students need to know these concepts because the idea of a limit is central to calculus.

In addition to the solution given below, you could ask students for examples. For part (a), you could ask students to create functions such that $f(2) = 4$ where $\lim_{x \to 2} f(x)$ exists and $\lim_{x \to 2} f(x)$ does not exist. For part (b), you could ask students to create functions such that $\lim_{x \to 2} f(x) = 4$ where $f(2) = 4$ and $f(2) \neq 4$. Finally, take the opportunity to emphasize the following point (see page 49 of the text): the existence or nonexistence of $f(x)$ at $x = c$ has no bearing on the existence of the limit of $f(x)$ as x approaches c.

Solution

(a) No. The fact that $f(2) = 4$ has no bearing on the existence of the limit of $f(x)$ as
    x approaches 2.

(b) No. The fact that $\lim_{x \to 2} f(x) = 4$ has no bearing on the value of f at 2.

Section 1.3   Evaluating Limits Analytically

Tips and Tools for Problem Solving

CalcChat.com

We noticed in the data that students are having trouble with limits involving trigonometric functions (see note on Exercises 65–76, 81–84) and rationalizing numerators (see Exercises 55–58, 77, 78). If you do not have time to review these concepts, encourage students to study the following material in the appendix or in *Precalculus*, 7th edition, by Larson and Hostetler.

- Trigonometric functions: Appendix C.3

- Rationalizing numerators: *Precalculus* Appendix A.2

Exercises 5–22 (5–22 in *Calculus* 8/e)
We revised Exercises 19–22 and reordered the block of exercises to improve the grading.

Exercises 49–64 (49–62 in *Calculus* 8/e)
To give students more practice, we added Exercises 49 and 50. We also revised Exercises 51 and 52 and reordered Exercises 55 and 57 (formerly 53 and 55, respectively) to improve the grading.

Exercises 65–76, 81–84 (67–82 in *Calculus* 8/e)
Most of your students will need help with Exercises 65–76. These exercises require the ability to rewrite trigonometric expressions using algebra, and the proper application of Theorem 1.9. If necessary, have your students study Appendix C.3: Review of Trigonometric Functions.

Capstone

Page 69, Exercise 116 You can use this exercise to review the following concept.

- Using a strategy for finding limits

Students need to know this concept because the idea of a limit is central to calculus.

Ask students if the limit of $f(x)$ as x approaches 2 can be evaluated by direct substitution. They should understand that this limit *cannot* be evaluated by direct substitution. Ask them how to evaluate this limit. One way is to redefine the function and then use Theorem 1.7. Let $g(x) = 3$ for all values of x. Because $\lim_{x \to 2} g(x) = 3$, by Theorem 1.7 $\lim_{x \to 2} f(x) = 3$. (You can also use the approach suggested in the solution on the next page.) You can reinforce this conclusion using the graph of f (see the transparency) and by creating a table. Point out to students that the value of f at $x = 2$ is irrelevant. (You may want to do this by asking students if this value is relevant. If you do this, ask them before finding the limit. This reviews a concept taught in Section 1.2.)

Solution

$$\lim_{x \to 2^-} f(x) = \lim_{x \to 2^+} f(x) = \lim_{x \to 2} f(x) = 3$$

The value of f at $x = 2$ is irrelevant.

Section 1.4 Continuity and One-Sided Limits

Tips and Tools for Problem Solving

CalcChat.com

As in Section 1.3, we noticed in the data that students are having trouble with limits involving trigonometric functions and rationalizing denominators and numerators. Students also had trouble with limits involving rational functions. Encourage students to sharpen their algebra skills by studying the following material in the appendix or in *Precalculus*, 7th edition, by Larson and Hostetler.

- Trigonometric functions: Appendix C.3

- Rationalizing numerators: *Precalculus* Appendix A.2

- Simplifying rational expressions: *Precalculus* Appendix A.4

Exercises 7–26 (7–24 in *Calculus* 8/e)
To give students more practice, we added Exercises 7 and 8.

Exercises 35–60 (33–54 in *Calculus* 8/e)
To give students more practice, we added Exercises 35–37 and 39.

Exercises 63–68 (57–60 in *Calculus* 8/e)
To give students more practice, we added Exercises 63 and 64.

Capstone

Page 81, Exercise 98 You can use this exercise to review the following concepts.

- Describing the difference between a removable discontinuity and a nonremovable discontinuity

- Writing a function that has a removable discontinuity

- Writing a function that has a nonremovable discontinuity

- Writing a function that has a removable discontinuity and a nonremovable discontinuity

Students will need to know these concepts when they study concepts such as vertical asymptotes (Section 1.5), improper integrals (Section 8.8), and functions of several variables (Section 13.2).

Discuss the difference between a removable discontinuity and a nonremovable discontinuity. Use the solution for part (a) given on the next page to illustrate a function with a nonremovable discontinuity. (The graph of this function and the others in the solution are available as transparencies.) Note that it is not possible to remove the discontinuity by redefining the function. When you illustrate a removable discontinuity in part (b), note that the function can be redefined to remove the discontinuity. Ask students how they would do this. $\left(\text{Let } f(-4) = 1.\right)$ Finally, illustrate part (c). Show students the function and the graph, and then ask them if there are any removable or nonremovable discontinuities. Once they have properly identified $x = -4$ as removable and $x = 4$ as nonremovable, ask them to redefine f to remove the discontinuity at $x = -4$. $\left(\text{Let } f(-4) = 0.\right)$

Solution

A discontinuity at c is removable if the function f can be made continuous at c by appropriately defining (or redefining) $f(c)$. Otherwise, the discontinuity is nonremovable.

(a) $f(x) = \dfrac{|x-4|}{x-4}$

(b) $f(x) = \dfrac{\sin(x+4)}{x+4}$

(c) $f(x) = \begin{cases} 0, & x < -4 \\ 1, & x = -4 \\ 0, & -4 < x < 4 \\ 1, & x \geq 4 \end{cases}$

    $x = 4$ is nonremovable. $x = -4$ is removable.

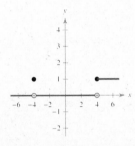

Section 1.5 Infinite Limits

Tips and Tools for Problem Solving

CalcChat.com

As in Section 1.4, we noticed in the data that students are having trouble with limits involving trigonometric functions, rationalizing denominators and numerators, and limits involving rational functions. Refer to the notes in Section 1.4 for the material students should review.

Exercises 13–32, 37–54 (9–28, 33–48 in *Calculus* 8/e)
In Exercises 13–32, we reordered the exercises to improve the grading. In Exercises 37–54, we added Exercises 37 and 38 and revised Exercises 39, 41, 43, and 45. Also, we revised Example 1 on page 84 by adding an analytical approach as well as showing a graphical approach to determining an infinite limit. We feel this approach will give students a better understanding of the concept.

Capstone

Page 89, Exercise 64 You can use this exercise to review the following concept.

- Finding the vertical asymptotes of the graph of a function

Students need to understand this concept because it will be used many times as they study calculus.

In class, you can ask students that believe the graph of f has a vertical asymptote at $x = 1$ to prove it. For those that think this is not always true, ask them to provide a counterexample. A sample answer is given in the solution, and you can use the transparency to illustrate a counterexample. If desired, you could also ask students the following.

(a) At which x-values (if any) is f not continuous?

(b) Which of the discontinuities are removable?

Solution

No, it is not always true. Consider $p(x) = x^2 - 1$. The function

$$f(x) = \frac{x^2 - 1}{x - 1} = \frac{p(x)}{x - 1}$$

has a hole at $(1, 2)$, not a vertical asymptote.

Chapter 1 Project

Medicine in the Bloodstream

A patient's kidneys purify 25% of the blood in her body in 4 hours.

Exercises

In Exercises 1–3, a patient takes one 16-milliliter dose of a medication.

1. Determine the amount of medication left in the patient's body after 4, 8, 12, and 16 hours.

2. Notice that after the first 4-hour period, $\frac{3}{4}$ of the 16 milliliters of medication is left in the body, after the second 4-hour period, $\frac{9}{16}$ of the 16 milliliters of medication is left in the body, and so on. Use this information to write an equation that represents the amount a of medication left in the patient's body after n 4-hour periods.

3. Can you find a value of n for which a equals 0? Explain.

In Exercises 4–9, the patient takes an additional 16-milliliter dose every 4 hours.

4. Determine the amount of medication in the patient's body immediately after taking the second dose.

5. Determine the amount of medication in the patient's body immediately after taking the third and fourth doses. What is happening to the amount of medication in the patient's body over time?

6. The medication is eliminated from the patient's body at a constant rate. Sketch a graph that shows the amount of medication in the patient's body during the first 16 hours. Let x represent the number of hours and y represent the amount of medication in the patient's body in milliliters.

7. Use the graph in Exercise 6 to find the limits.

   (a) $\lim\limits_{x \to 4^-} f(x)$

   (b) $\lim\limits_{x \to 4^+} f(x)$

   (c) $\lim\limits_{x \to 12^-} f(x)$

   (d) $\lim\limits_{x \to 12^+} f(x)$

8. Discuss the continuity of the function represented by the graph in Exercise 6. Interpret any discontinuities in the context of the problem.

9. The amount of medication in the patient's body remains constant when the amount eliminated in 4 hours is equal to the additional dose taken at the end of the 4-hour period. Write and solve an equation to find this amount.

Chapter 2   Differentiation

Chapter Summary

Section Topics

2.1   **The Derivative and the Tangent Line Problem**—Find the slope of the tangent line to a curve at a point. Use the limit definition to find the derivative of a function. Understand the relationship between differentiability and continuity.

2.2   **Basic Differentiation Rules and Rates of Change**—Find the derivative of a function using the Constant Rule. Find the derivative of a function using the Power Rule. Find the derivative of a function using the Constant Multiple Rule. Find the derivative of a function using the Sum and Difference Rules. Find the derivatives of the sine function and of the cosine function. Use derivatives to find rates of change.

2.3   **The Product and Quotient Rules and Higher-Order Derivatives**—Find the derivative of a function using the Product Rule. Find the derivative of a function using the Quotient Rule. Find the derivative of a trigonometric function. Find a higher-order derivative of a function.

2.4   **The Chain Rule**—Find the derivative of a composite function using the Chain Rule. Find the derivative of a function using the General Power Rule. Simplify the derivative of a function using algebra. Find the derivative of a trigonometric function using the Chain Rule.

2.5   **Implicit Differentiation**—Distinguish between functions written in implicit form and explicit form. Use implicit differentiation to find the derivative of a function.

2.6   **Related Rates**—Find a related rate. Use related rates to solve real-life problems.

Chapter Comments

The material presented in Chapter 2 forms the basis for the remainder of calculus. Much of it needs to be memorized, beginning with the definition of a derivative of a function found on page 99. Your students need to have a thorough understanding of the tangent line problem and they need to be able to find an equation of a tangent line. Frequently, students will use the function $f'(x)$ as the slope of the tangent line. They need to understand that $f'(x)$ is the formula for the slope and the actual value of the slope can be found by substituting into $f'(x)$ the appropriate value for x. On page 102 of Section 2.1, you will find a discussion of situations where the derivative fails to exist. These examples (or similar ones) should be discussed in class.

As you teach this chapter, vary your notations for the derivative. One time write y', another time write dy/dx or $f'(x)$. Terminology is also important: instead of saying "find the derivative," sometimes say, "differentiate." This would be an appropriate time, also, to talk a little about Leibnitz and Newton and the discovery of calculus.

Sections 2.2, 2.3, and 2.4 present a number of rules for differentiation. Have your students memorize the Product Rule and the Quotient Rule (Theorems 2.7 and 2.8) in words rather than symbols. Students tend to be lazy when it comes to trigonometry and therefore, you need to impress upon them that the formulas for the derivatives of the six trigonometric functions need to be memorized also. You will probably not have enough time in class to prove every one of these differentiation rules, so choose several to do in class and perhaps assign a few of the other proofs as homework.

The Chain Rule, in Section 2.4, will require two days of your class time. Students need a lot of practice with this and the algebra involved in these problems. Many students can find the derivative of $f(x) = x^2\sqrt{1 - x^2}$ without much trouble, but simplifying the answer is often very difficult for them. Insist that they learn to factor and write the answer without negative exponents. Strive to get the answer in the form given in the back of the book. This will help them later on when the derivative is set equal to zero.

Implicit differentiation is often difficult for students. Have your students think of y as a function of x and therefore y^3 is $\left[f(x)\right]^3$. This way they can relate implicit differentiation to the Chain Rule studied in the previous section.

Try to get your students to see that Related Rates, discussed in Section 2.6, are another use of the Chain Rule.

Section 2.1 The Derivative and the Tangent Line Problem

Tips and Tools for Problem Solving

CalcChat.com

Exercises 33–38 (33–36 in *Calculus* 8/e)
To give students more practice, we added Exercises 33 and 34. We also suggest doing the following. After going over Example 3, return to Example 2 where $f(x) = x^2 + 1$ and note that $f'(x) = 2x$. How can we find the equation of the line tangent to f and parallel to $4x - y = 0$? Because the slope of the line is 4,

$$2x = 4$$

$$x = 2.$$

So, at the point $(2, 5)$ the tangent line is parallel to $4x - y = 0$. The equation of the tangent line is $y - 5 = 4(x - 2)$ or $y = 4x - 3$.

Capstone

Page 105, Exercise 64 You can use this exercise to review (or discover) the following concepts.

- Estimating values on a graph

- Interpreting values of the derivative of a function

- Discovering relationships between a function and its derivative

This *Capstone* involves using the derivative of an unknown function. You can use this exercise to introduce concepts such as increasing and decreasing.

Parts (a) and (b) can be answered using the graph of g'. (See the transparency.) You can use parts (c) and (d) to introduce the terms increasing and decreasing (or you can just say rising and falling, terms familiar from our study of slope). When $g'(x)$ is negative, g is decreasing (or falling) and when $g'(x)$ is positive, g is increasing (or rising). Remind students that we know this because the derivative tells us the slope of the tangent line at each point. Alternatively, you can demonstrate this by graphing $g(x) = \frac{1}{9}x^3 - 3x$ and noting the behavior of g at $x = 1$ and $x = -4$. For part (e), note that $g'(x)$ is positive on the interval $[4, 6]$. This means that g is increasing from $x = 4$ to $x = 6$. So,

$g(6) > g(4)$ and $g(6) - g(4) > 0$. $\left(\text{You can demonstrate this numerically using } g(x) = \frac{1}{9}x^3 - 3x.\right)$

Finally, it is not possible to find $g(2)$ from the graph, but you can say that g is decreasing at $x = 2$ using the same reasoning as in part (c).

Solution

(a) $g'(0) = -3$

(b) $g'(3) = 0$

(c) Because $g'(1) = -\frac{8}{3}$, g is decreasing (falling) at $x = 1$.

(d) Because $g'(-4) = \frac{7}{3}$, g is increasing (rising) at $x = -4$.

(e) Because $g'(4)$ and $g'(6)$ are both positive, $g(6)$ is greater than $g(4)$, and $g(6) - g(4) > 0$.

(f) No, it is not possible. All you can say is that g is decreasing (falling) at $x = 2$.

Section 2.2   Basic Differentiation Rules and Rates of Change

Tips and Tools for Problem Solving

CalcChat.com

Exercises 3–24 (3–24 in *Calculus* 8/e)
We rewrote the direction line to clarify that the derivatives should be found using rules of differentiation.

Exercises 39–54 (39–52 in *Calculus* 8/e)
To give students more practice, we added Exercises 43 and 44. Some students need to be reminded that they can rewrite the function before differentiating. We suggest you go over an example in class like $f(x) = \dfrac{5x^2 + x}{x}$. Show students that before differentiating they can rewrite the function as $f(x) = 5x + 1$. Then they can differentiate to obtain $f'(x) = 5$.

Use this example to emphasize the prudence of examining the function first before differentiating. Rewriting the function in a simpler, equivalent form can expedite the differentiating process.

Exercises 59–64 (57–62 in *Calculus* 8/e)
Students had trouble with these exercises. Students may need to review finding the zeros of a polynomial function and solving trigonometric equations. See Sections 2.2 and Section 5.3 of *Precalculus*, 7th edition, by Larson and Hostetler respectively.

Exercises 65–70 (63–66 in *Calculus* 8/e)
To give students more practice, we added Exercises 69 and 70.

Capstone

Page 116, Exercise 72 You can use this exercise to review the following concepts.

- Analyzing the graph of a function to determine when the average rate of change of the function is greatest

- Analyzing the graph of a function to compare the average rate of change and instantaneous rate of change of the function

- Sketching the graph of a tangent line so that the slope is the same as the average rate of change over a given interval

Use the graph of f given on the transparency to reinforce the solution on the next page. A transparency is also provided for part (c).

Solution

(a) The slope appears to be steepest between A and B.

(b) The average rate of change between A and B is greater than the instantaneous rate of change at B.

(c)

Section 2.3   Product and Quotient Rules and Higher-Order Derivatives

Tips and Tools for Problem Solving

CalcChat.com

We noticed in the data that after applying differentiation rules, some students are having difficulty simplifying polynomial and rational expressions. Students should review these concepts by studying Appendices A.2–A.4 and A.7 in *Precalculus*, 7th edition, by Larson and Hostetler.

Exercises 73–76 (73–76 in *Calculus* 8/e)
We revised Exercise 73 and reordered the exercises to improve the grading.

Exercises 93–100 (93–98 in *Calculus* 8/e)
To give students more practice, we added Exercises 93 and 94.

Capstone

Page 129, Exercise 120 You can use this exercise to review the following concepts.

- Analyzing the graph of a function and the graphs of its first and second derivatives

- Identifying the graphs of position, velocity, and acceleration functions

- Using the graphs of position, velocity, and acceleration functions to identify when a particle speeds up and when it slows down

This exercise will help you to review higher-order derivatives as well as the relationship between position, velocity, and acceleration functions. Using the transparency for part (a), note that the function that looks cubic is the position function, the function that looks quadratic is the velocity function, and the function that is a line is the acceleration function. You can demonstrate this for students using the cubic function $f(x) = x^3$. Note that the first derivative is $f'(x) = x^2$ and the second derivative is $f''(x) = x$. Recall from Section 2.2, page 114, that the speed of an object is the absolute value of its velocity. Show the transparency for part (b), which shows the graph of the absolute value of the velocity. (Note that the graph is obtained by reflecting in the x-axis the negative portion of the graph of v.) From this graph, show the intervals where the particle speeds up and when it slows down (see the solution on the next page).

Solution

(a)

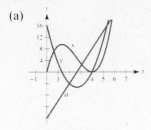

s position function
v velocity function
a acceleration function

(b) The speed of the particle is the absolute value of its velocity. So, the particle's speed is slowing down on the intervals $(0, 4/3)$ and $(8/3, 4)$ and it speeds up on the intervals $(4/3, 8/3)$ and $(4, 6)$.

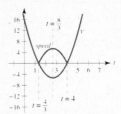

Section 2.4 The Chain Rule

Tips and Tools for Problem Solving

CalcChat.com

Exercises 7–36 (7–32 in *Calculus* 8/e)
To give students more practice, we added Exercises 33–36. Students need a lot of practice with the Chain Rule and the algebra involved in these problems. For students with poor algebra skills, have them review Appendix A.7: Errors and the Algebra of Calculus of *Precalculus*, 7th edition, by Larson and Hostetler.

Exercises 45–66 (41–58 in *Calculus* 8/e)
To give students more practice, we added Exercises 57, 58, 65, and 66.

Exercises 91–96 (83–86 in *Calculus* 8/e)
To give students more practice, we added Exercises 91 and 94. We also revised Exercises 92 and 93 and reordered the block of exercises to improve the grading.

Capstone

Page 139, Exercise 108 You can use this exercise to review the following concepts.

- Product Rule

- Chain Rule

- Quotient Rule

- General Power Rule

Students need to understand these rules because they are the foundation of our study of differentiation.

Use the solution to show students how to solve each problem. As you apply each rule, give the definition of the rule verbally. Note that part (b) is not possible because we are not given $g'(3)$.

Solution

(a) $f(x) = g(x)h(x)$

$f'(x) = g(x)h'(x) + g'(x)h(x)$

$f'(5) = (-3)(-2) + (6)(3) = 24$

(b) $f(x) = g(h(x))$

$f'(x) = g'(h(x))h'(x)$

$f'(5) = g'(3)(-2) = -2g'(3)$

Not possible. You need $g'(3)$ to find $f'(5)$.

(c) $f(x) = \dfrac{g(x)}{h(x)}$

$f'(x) = \dfrac{h(x)g'(x) - g(x)h'(x)}{\left[h(x)\right]^2}$

$f'(5) = \dfrac{(3)(6) - (-3)(-2)}{(3)^2} = \dfrac{12}{9} = \dfrac{4}{3}$

(d) $f(x) = \left[g(x)\right]^3$

$f'(x) = 3\left[g(x)\right]^2 g'(x)$

$f'(5) = 3(-3)^2(6) = 162$

Section 2.5   Implicit Differentiation

Tips and Tools for Problem Solving

CalcChat.com

Although we made changes to the section exercises, no changes were made based on the data.

Capstone

Page 148, Exercise 74 You can use this exercise to review the following concepts.

- Finding derivatives when the variables agree and when they disagree

- Using implicit differentiation to find the derivative of a function

Implicit differentiation is often difficult for students, so as you review this concept remind students to think of y as a function of x. Part (a) is true, and part (b) can be corrected as shown below. Part (c) requires implicit differentiation. Note that the result can also be written as $-2y\,\sin(y^2)\,\dfrac{dy}{dx}$.

Solution

(a) True

(b) False. $\dfrac{d}{dy}\cos(y^2) = -2y\,\sin(y^2)$.

(c) False. $\dfrac{d}{dx}\cos(y^2) = -2yy'\,\sin(y^2)$.

Section 2.6   Related Rates

Tips and Tools for Problem Solving

CalcChat.com

Although we made changes to the section exercises, no changes were made based on the data.

Capstone

Page 156, Exercise 38 You can use this exercise to review the following concepts.

- Finding a related rate

- Using graphical reasoning

You can use this exercise to use a graphical approach to determining the sign of a related rate. Because you do not have to find any derivatives, you can use the graphs to reinforce the concept of related rates.

The graphs in this exercise are available as transparencies. Use each graph of *f* to show that when the rate of change of *x* is negative (*x* is decreasing) that the rate of change of *y* is positive (*y* is increasing) in graph (i) and negative (*y* is decreasing) in graph (ii). Then use the graphs to show that when the rate of change of *y* is positive (*y* is increasing) that the rate of change of *x* is negative (*x* is decreasing) in graph (i) and positive (*x* is increasing) in graph (ii).

Solution

(i)   (a) $\dfrac{dx}{dt}$ negative $\Rightarrow$ $\dfrac{dy}{dt}$ positive

(b) $\dfrac{dy}{dt}$ positive $\Rightarrow$ $\dfrac{dx}{dt}$ negative

(ii) (a) $\dfrac{dx}{dt}$ negative $\Rightarrow$ $\dfrac{dy}{dt}$ negative

(b) $\dfrac{dy}{dt}$ positive $\Rightarrow$ $\dfrac{dx}{dt}$ positive

22

Chapter 2 Project

Timing a Handoff

You are a competitive bicyclist. During a race, you bike at a constant velocity of k meters per second. A chase car waits for you at the ten-mile mark of a course. When you cross the ten-mile mark, the car immediately accelerates to catch you. The position function of the chase car is given by the equation $s(t) = \frac{15}{4}t^2 - \frac{5}{12}t^3$, for $0 \leq t \leq 6$, where t is the time in seconds and s is the distance traveled in meters. When the car catches you, you and the car are traveling at the same velocity, and the driver hands you a cup of water while you continue to bike at k meters per second.

Exercises

1. Write an equation that represents your position s (in meters) at time t (in seconds).

2. Use your answer to Exercise 1 and the given information to write an equation that represents the velocity k at which the chase car catches you in terms of t.

3. Find the velocity function of the car.

4. Use your answers to Exercises 2 and 3 to find how many seconds it takes the chase car to catch you.

5. What is your velocity when the car catches you?

6. Use a graphing utility to graph the chase car's position function and your position function in the same viewing window.

7. Find the point of intersection of the two graphs in Exercise 6. What does this point represent in the context of the problem?

8. Describe the graphs in Exercise 6 at the point of intersection. Why is this important for a successful handoff?

9. Suppose you bike at a constant velocity of 9 meters per second and the chase car's position function is unchanged.

    (a) Use a graphing utility to graph the chase car's position function and your position function in the same viewing window.

    (b) In this scenario, how many times will the chase car be in the same position as you after the 10-mile mark?

    (c) In this scenario, would the driver of the car be able to successfully handoff a cup of water to you? Explain.

10. Suppose you bike at a constant velocity of 8 meters per second and the chase car's position function is unchanged.

    (a) Use a graphing utility to graph the chase car's position function and your position function in the same viewing window.

    (b) In this scenario, how many times will the chase car be in the same position as you after the 10-mile mark?

    (c) In this scenario, why might it be difficult for the driver of the chase car to successfully handoff a cup of water to you? Explain.

23

Chapter 3   Applications of Differentiation

Chapter Summary

Section Topics

3.1   **Extrema on an Interval**—Understand the definition of extrema of a function on an interval. Understand the definition of relative extrema of a function on an open interval. Find extrema on a closed interval.

3.2   **Rolle's Theorem and the Mean Value Theorem**—Understand and use Rolle's Theorem. Understand and use the Mean Value Theorem.

3.3   **Increasing and Decreasing Functions and the First Derivative Test**—Determine intervals on which a function is increasing or decreasing. Apply the First Derivative Test to find relative extrema of a function.

3.4   **Concavity and the Second Derivative Test**—Determine intervals on which a function is concave upward or concave downward. Find any points of inflection of the graph of a function. Apply the Second Derivative Test to find relative extrema of a function.

3.5   **Limits at Infinity**—Determine (finite) limits at infinity. Determine the horizontal asymptotes, if any, of the graph of a function. Determine infinite limits at infinity.

3.6   **A Summary of Curve Sketching**—Analyze and sketch the graph of a function.

3.7   **Optimization Problems**—Solve applied minimum and maximum problems.

3.8   **Newton's Method**—Approximate a zero of a function using Newton's Method.

3.9   **Differentials**—Understand the concept of a tangent line approximation. Compare the value of the differential, dy, with the actual change in y, Δy. Estimate a propagated error using a differential. Find the differential of a function using differentiation formulas.

Chapter Comments

Chapter 3 considers some of the applications of a derivative. The first five sections in this chapter lead up to analyzing the graph of a function in Section 3.6. Before beginning this material, you may want to quickly review with your students the ideas of intercepts, vertical asymptotes and symmetry with respect to the x-axis, the y-axis and the origin. These algebraic tools covered in Chapter P are needed, along with those from calculus, in order to analyze the graph of a function.

Don't get bogged down in Section 3.1. The students need to know the terminology, so stress the definitions of critical numbers and extrema. Section 3.2 covers Rolle's Theorem and the Mean Value Theorem. Rolle's Theorem is used to prove the Mean Value Theorem.

Sections 3.3 and 3.4 cover the bulk of the material necessary to analyze the graphs of functions. Go over these sections carefully.

In Section 3.5, limits at infinity, as well as horizontal asymptotes, are discussed. Be sure to require that your students write horizontal asymptotes as lines: for example, $y = 3$.

Section 3.6 contains a summary of all of the ideas involved in analyzing the graph of a function. Note that slant asymptotes are covered in the comment after Example 2. After this material is covered, each day until you finish the chapter, assign one or two carefully chosen graphing problems. Have your students make a list of all of the tools useful in sketching a graph: intercepts, asymptotes, symmetry, critical numbers, increasing and decreasing intervals, extrema, concavity and inflection points. Only after this list is completed should the function be sketched.

If your students know the material in Sections 3.1 through 3.6 well, then the optimization problems in Section 3.7 should go fairly well for them. Stress the difference between a primary and a secondary equation. Also, stress the need to have the function in one independent variable before attempting to maximize or minimize it.

Newton's Method, covered in Section 3.8, is a tool that students of future math and science courses will be expected to know. A calculator is needed.

You should be able to cover Differentials, Section 3.9, quickly. Students need to understand that a differential is a reasonable approximation for the actual difference in function values. Following Examples 2 and 7 there is a brief discussion of the tangent line approximation of the graph of a function at a point.

Section 3.1   Extrema on an Interval

Tips and Tools for Problem Solving

CalcChat.com

We noticed in the data that students are having trouble with concepts taught or reviewed in a precalculus course. You may want to spend time reviewing these concepts: factoring, solving equations involving square roots, and solving polynomial equations. For further review, encourage students to study the following material in *Precalculus*, 7th edition, by Larson and Hostetler.

- Factoring: Appendix A.3

- Solving equations involving square roots: Appendix A.5

- Solving polynomial equations: Appendix A.5

- Finding the zeros of a polynomial function: Section 2.2

- Solving trigonometric equations: Section 5.3

Exercises 17–36 (19–36 in *Calculus* 8/e)
To give students more practice, we added Exercises 30 and 32. We also revised exercises 17, 19, 20, 35, and 36.

Capstone

Page 170, Exercise 54 You can use this exercise to review the following concepts.

- Definition of extrema

- The Extreme Value Theorem

- Definition of relative extrema

Students must understand relative extrema to successfully complete this chapter.

As you go over this in class, use the transparency graph. By the Extreme Value Theorem, we know that the graphed function has both a minimum and a maximum on the interval shown. Refer to the definitions of extrema and relative extrema to explain the reasoning used to decide the classification of each point (see solution).

Solution

A: absolute minimum (definition of extrema, part 1)

B: relative maximum (definition of relative extrema, part 1)

C: neither (there is no open interval containing c on which the value of the graphed function is a minimum or a maximum)

D: relative minimum (definition of relative extrema, part 2)

E: relative maximum (definition of relative extrema, part 1)

F: relative minimum (definition of relative extrema, part 2)

G: neither (f is not defined at G)

Section 3.2   Rolle's Theorem and the Mean Value Theorem

Tips and Tools for Problem Solving

CalcChat.com

Exercises 11–24 (11–24 in *Calculus* 8/e)
We added "If Rolle's Theorem cannot be applied, explain why not." to the direction line.

Exercises 39–48 (39–46 in *Calculus* 8/e)
We added "If the Mean Value Theorem cannot be applied, explain why not." to the direction line. We added Exercises 41 and 45, and revised Exercises 42, 44, and 48. Also, we revised Example 3 on page 175 to extend the explanation of why the function satisfies the conditions of the Mean Value Theorem.

Capstone

Page 178, Exercise 64 You can use this exercise to review the following concepts.

- Rolle's Theorem
- Mean Value Theorem

Before going over the exercise, restate Rolle's Theorem and the Mean Value Theorem. Also, it should be stressed that the figure shows two parts of the graph of a *continuous differentiable* function f on $[-10, 4]$. The figure is available as a transparency, as are the figures used in parts (c) and (d). Go over each part using the solution given below. Use the figure to sketch $y = 2$ to illustrate that $f(a) = f(b) = 2$ in part (b). Make several possible sketches of the function to reinforce this point.

Solution

(a) f is continuous on $[-10, 4]$ and changes sign, $(f(-8) > 0, f(3) < 0)$. By the Intermediate Value Theorem, there exists at least one value of x in $[-10, 4]$ satisfying $f(x) = 0$.

(b) There exist real numbers a and b such that $-10 < a < b < 4$ and $f(a) = f(b) = 2$. Therefore, by Rolle's Theorem there exists at least one number c in $(-10, 4)$ such that $f'(c) = 0$. This is called a critical number.

(c)

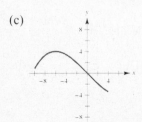

(d)

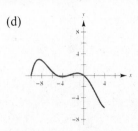

(e) No, f' did not have to be continuous on $[-10, 4]$.

Section 3.3   Increasing and Decreasing Functions and the First Derivative Test

Tips and Tools for Problem Solving

CalcChat.com

Exercises 3–8 (3–6 in *Calculus* 8/e)
We revised the direction line to get students to use a graphical approach and an analytic approach. To give students more practice, we added Exercises 7 and 8.

Exercises 17–42 (17–38 in *Calculus* 8/e)
We noticed in the data that students are having difficulty with Exercises 17 and 21. We feel this is the result of poor algebra skills. Make sure to cover Example 1 in class and emphasize the justification of each algebraic step. You may need to tell struggling students to study the following material in *Precalculus*, 7th edition, by Larson and Hostetler.

- Finding the zeros of a polynomial function: Section 2.2

To give students more practice with piecewise-defined functions, we added Exercises 39–42.

Capstone

Page 187, Exercise 78 You can use this exercise to review the following concepts.

- Increasing and decreasing functions
- Theorem 3.5
- Guidelines for finding intervals on which a function is increasing or decreasing
- Therorem 3.6
- Applying the First Derivative Test

These concepts, along with those taught in Section 3.4, cover most of the material necessary to analyze graphs of functions. Before going over this exercise, you may want to restate Theorems 3.5 and 3.6.

You can use this exercise to show students how to apply the guidelines for finding intervals on which a function is increasing or decreasing (see page 180). As you go over the following, make a table similar to the one given in Example 1 on page 180.

1. Note that the only critical number of the differentiable function f is $x = 5$. So, the test intervals are $-\infty < x < 5$ and $5 < x < \infty$.

2. We are given the value of the derivative of f at two test values, $x = 4$ and $x = 6$. In the interval $-\infty < x < 5$, we know $f'(4) = -2.5$. In the interval $5 < x < \infty$, we know $f'(6) = 3$.

3. By Theorem 3.5, f is decreasing on $(-\infty, 5)$ and increasing on $(5, \infty)$.

We can now apply the First Derivative Test to conclude that f has a relative minimum at the point where $x = 5$.

Solution

Critical number: $x = 5$

$f'(4) = -2.5 \Rightarrow f$ is decreasing at $x = 4$.

$\quad f'(6) = 3 \Rightarrow f$ is increasing at $x = 6$.

$\left(5, f(5)\right)$ is a relative minimum.

Section 3.4 Concavity and the Second Derivative Test

Tips and Tools for Problem Solving

CalcChat.com

Exercises 19–36 (11–26 in *Calculus* 8/e)
We noticed in the data that students are having difficulty with these exercises. We feel part of this is the result of poor algebra skills. Make sure when you cover the examples to emphasize the justification of each algebraic step. You may need to tell struggling students to study the following material in *Precalculus*, 7th edition, by Larson and Hostetler.

- Finding the zeros of a polynomial function: Section 2.2

To give students more practice, we added Exercises 19 and 20. We also revised Exercises 26, 28, and 29.

Exercises 37–52 (27–40 in *Calculus* 8/e)
The data show that students had more trouble with Exercise 43 (27 in *Calculus* 8/e) than any other exercise in this block. We feel students struggled with this exercise because the Second Derivative Test is not applicable, which makes it harder than some of the exercises that follow it. We reordered the exercises in this block to improve the grading. We also added Exercises 39 and 44 to give students more practice and revised Exercise 42.

Capstone

Page 196, Exercise 70 You can use this exercise to review the following concepts.

- Interpreting the inflection points of a graph

- Analyzing the graph of a function for relative extrema

Assume the depth of the vase is 12 inches and that it is full after 10 seconds. You can then show the graph below which is provided on a transparency. Justify the graph by noting that $f'(x) > 0$

(the water runs in at a constant rate) and use the explanation given in part (c). The depth is always increasing, so there are no relative extrema. The endpoints of the graph are absolute extrema.

Solution

(a)

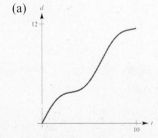

28

(b) Because the depth d is always increasing, there are no relative extrema (of course, the endpoints are absolute extrema). $f'(x) > 0$

(c) The rate of change of d is decreasing until you reach the widest point of the vase, then the rate increases until you reach the narrowest part of the vase's neck, then the rate decreases until you reach the top of the vase.

Section 3.5   Limits at Infinity

Tips and Tools for Problem Solving

CalcChat.com

Exercises 19–38 (21–34 in *Calculus* 8/e)
To give students more practice, we added Exercises 20, 22, and 31–34. We also revised Exercise 24 and reordered the exercises to improve the grading.

Capstone

Page 206, Exercise 58 You can use this exercise to review the following concepts.

- Given the graph of a function f, sketch f'.

- Using a graph to estimate limits at infinity

To sketch f', use the graph of f. The graph is available as a transparency. Note from the graph that f is decreasing on $-4 < x < 0$, so $f' < 0$ on $-4 < x < 0$. Because f is increasing on $0 < x < 4$, $f' > 0$ on $0 < x < 4$. The graph of f' should also reflect the rate of change of f. The graph of f changes rapidly as it approaches 0 from the left, slows at 0, and then the rate increases and then slows again as f nears the line $y = 3$. As x increases, f approaches the line $y = 3$ and the rate of change of f approaches 0. Make sure students realize that $y = 3$ is a horizontal asymptote of the graph of f.

Solution

(a)

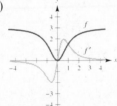

(b) $\lim_{x \to \infty} f(x) = 3$ $\lim_{x \to \infty} f'(x) = 0$

(c) Because $\lim_{x \to \infty} f(x) = 3$, the graph approaches that of a horizontal line, $\lim_{x \to \infty} f'(x) = 0$.

Section 3.6   A Summary of Curve Sketching

Tips and Tools for Problem Solving

CalcChat.com

Exercises 5–32 (7–34 in *Calculus* 8/e)
We reordered the exercises to improve the grading. We also revised Exercises 8–11, 14, 19, and 20.

Page 217, Exercise 72 You can use this exercise to review the following concepts.

- Critical numbers

- Horizontal tangent

- Relative extrema

- Points of inflection

- Concavity

You can use this exercise to review the important definitions and theorems taught in Sections 3.1–3.5. Note in part (c) that x_1 is a critical number. Some students miss this and answer "none" for part (d).

Solution

(a) $f'(x) = 0$ at x_0, x_2 and x_4. (Horizontal tangent)

(b) $f''(x) = 0$ at x_2 and x_3. (Point of inflection)

(c) $f'(x)$ does not exist at x_1. (Sharp corner)

(d) f has a relative maximum at x_1.

(e) f has a point of inflection at x_2 and x_3. (Change in concavity)

Section 3.7   Optimization Problems

Tips and Tools for Problem Solving

CalcChat.com

Exercises 13–18 (13–16, 29, 30 in *Calculus* 8/e)
We reordered the exercises to improve the grading.

Capstone

Page 225, Exercise 38 You can use this exercise to review the following concepts.

- Analyzing an optimization problem

- Reviewing the guidelines for solving applied minimum and maximum problems

You can use this exercise to show students that not all optimization problems have a maximum and a minimum. Draw several rectangles that have a perimeter of 20 feet, such as $l = 6$ and $w = 4$. Also draw a rectangle where the length and width are both 5 feet. For rectangles with a perimeter of 20 feet, this rectangle yields the maximum area. Ask students "What dimensions will yield a minimum area?" Use the solution below to show students that no such dimensions exist. Use the solution as an opportunity to review the guidelines for solving applied minimum and maximum problems. Note in Step 4 of the guidelines that no values exist for which the stated problem will make sense.

Solution

No, there is no minimum area. If the sides are x and y, then $2x + 2y = 20 \Rightarrow y = 10 - x$. The area is $A(x) = x(10 - x) = 10x - x^2$. This can be made arbitrarily small by selecting $x \approx 0$.

Section 3.8   Newton's Method

Tips and Tools for Problem Solving

CalcChat.com

Exercises 5–14 (5–14 in *Calculus* 8/e)
We reordered the exercises to improve the grading and revised Exercises 5, 6, 9, 12, and 13.

Capstone

Page 234, Exercise 32   You can use this exercise to review the following concept.

- Newton's Method

Review Newton's Method on page 229. Note in Step 2 that Newton's Method fails if $f'(x_n) = 0$ (division by 0). You can illustrate this using Exercise 21. Newton's Method also fails when the limit of the sequence of x_n's does not exist. You can illustrate this using Example 3 or Exercise 23.

Solution

Newton's Method could fail if $f'(c) \approx 0$, or if the initial value x_1 is far from c.

Section 3.9   Differentials

Tips and Tools for Problem Solving

CalcChat.com

Although we made changes to the section exercises, no changes were made based on the data.

Capstone

Page 241, Exercise 52   You can use this exercise to review the following concept.

- Understanding the concept of a tangent line approximation

Use the solution below. (You may want to model your presentation of this solution after the one used in Example 1 on page 235.) Also, sketch the graph of f and $y = x$ near $x = 0$.

Solution

Yes. $y = x$ is the tangent line approximation to $f(x) = \sin x$ at $(0, 0)$.

$f'(x) = \cos x$

$f'(0) = 1$

Tangent line: $y - 0 = 1(x - 0)$

$$y = x$$

31

Chapter 3 Project

Maximum and Minimum Temperature

In a 24-hour period, a human's body temperature will vary about 3 degrees. When at rest (usually at night), the body conserves heat and the body temperature drops. During activity (usually in the daytime), the body produces heat and the body temperature rises. This situation can be modeled by the periodic function $y = 1.8 \sin^3\left(\frac{\pi}{12}x - \frac{\pi}{2}\right) + 98.6$ where y represents the body's temperature in degrees Fahrenheit and x represents time, with $x = 0$ corresponding to 12 A.M.

Exercises

1. Find the derivative of $y = 1.8 \sin^3\left(\frac{\pi}{12}x - \frac{\pi}{2}\right) + 98.6$.

2. Find the critical numbers of $y = 1.8 \sin^3\left(\frac{\pi}{12}x - \frac{\pi}{2}\right) + 98.6$ on the interval $[0, 24]$.

3. During the course of a 24-hour period, at what time(s) is a human's body temperature greatest? During the course of a 24-hour period, at what time(s) is a human's body temperature least? What theorem did you use?

4. Use a graphing utility to graph $y = 1.8 \sin^3\left(\frac{\pi}{12}x - \frac{\pi}{2}\right) + 98.6$. What occurs when $x = 6$ and $x = 18$? What does this mean in the context of the problem?

5. A person who works third shift rests during the day and is active at night. Alter the function to model the body temperature of a third shift worker.

6. Find the critical numbers of the function you wrote in Exercise 5 on the interval $[0, 24]$.

7. During the course of a 24-hour period, at what time(s) is the body temperature of a third shift worker greatest? During the course of a 24-hour period, at what time(s) is the body temperature of a third shift worker least?

8. Use a graphing utility to graph the equation you wrote in Exercise 5. What occurs when $x = 6$ and $x = 18$? Compare this to your answer to Exercise 4. What is different about these points for the third shift worker?

9. Suppose the body temperature of a second shift worker can be modeled by shifting $y = 1.8 \sin^3\left(\frac{\pi}{12}x - \frac{\pi}{2}\right) + 98.6$ six units to the right. Write an equation to model the body temperature of a second shift worker.

10. Find the critical numbers of the function you wrote in Exercise 9 on the interval $[0, 24]$.

11. During the course of a 24-hour period, at what time(s) is the body temperature of a second shift worker greatest? During the course of a 24-hour period, at what time(s) is the body temperature of a second shift worker least?

Chapter 4 Integration

Chapter Summary

Section Topics

4.1 **Antiderivatives and Indefinite Integration**—Write the general solution of a differential equation. Use indefinite integral notation for antiderivatives. Use basic integration rules to find antiderivatives. Find a particular solution of a differential equation.

4.2 **Area**—Use sigma notation to write and evaluate a sum. Understand the concept of area. Approximate the area of a plane region. Find the area of a plane region using limits.

4.3 **Riemann Sums and Definite Integrals**—Understand the definition of a Riemann sum. Evaluate a definite integral using limits. Evaluate a definite integral using properties of definite integrals.

4.4 **The Fundamental Theorem of Calculus**—Evaluate a definite integral using the Fundamental Theorem of Calculus. Understand and use the Mean Value Theorem for Integrals. Find the average value of a function over a closed interval. Understand and use the Second Fundamental Theorem of Calculus. Understand and use the Net Change Theorem.

4.5 **Integration by Substitution**—Use pattern recognition to find an indefinite integral. Use a change of variables to find an indefinite integral. Use the General Power Rule for Integration to find an indefinite integral. Use a change of variables to evaluate a definite integral. Evaluate a definite integral involving an even or odd function.

4.6 **Numerical Integration**—Approximate a definite integral using the Trapezoidal Rule. Approximate a definite integral using Simpson's Rule. Analyze the approximate errors in the Trapezoidal Rule and Simpson's Rule.

Chapter Comments

The first section of this chapter stresses correct terminology and notation. Recognizing the different ways to express the same algebraic expression is very important here. Algebra will get a workout. As you introduce antiderivatives, insist that your students write the proper differential when they write an integral problem. Deduct points on homework and quizzes for incorrect notation.

Some of your students may not have seen sigma notation previously, so introduce it as though it is a new topic. The idea of the limit of a sum as n approaches infinity should go quickly if the students learned the rules for limits at infinity from Section 3.5. If you are pressed for time you may want to go over area using a limit definition (as done in Section 4.2) briefly. For example, you could do one problem to show the idea and the technique and then move on to Section 4.3.

The amount of time spent on Riemann Sums will depend on your schedule and your class. The definite integral is defined in Section 4.3, as is area. Be sure that your students set up the limits for area properly. Do not accept integrals for area with the upper and lower limits interchanged.

Students should know the Fundamental Theorem of Calculus by name and have it memorized. The Mean Value Theorem for Integrals and the Average Value of a Function are covered in Section 4.4. The Second Fundamental Theorem of Calculus is used in the definition of the natural logarithmic function, so be sure to go over it.

It is very important for your students to be comfortable with all of the integration techniques covered in Section 4.5. Allow two days to cover these ideas and go over each carefully. Be sure to do some change of variable problems, a technique that many students are reluctant to use.

To introduce the approximation techniques of Simpson's Rule and Trapezoidal Rule, present an integral problem for which there is no antiderivative that is an elementary function, such as $\int_{\pi/4}^{\pi/2} \sin x^2 \, dx$. This is a good opportunity to convince your students that not all functions have antiderivatives that are elementary functions. If you are pressed for time, the development of Simpson's Rule could be eliminated, but not the rule itself.

Section 4.1 Antiderivatives and Indefinite Integration

Tips and Tools for Problem Solving

CalcChat.com

Exercises 15–34 (15–34 in *Calculus* 8/e)
The data suggests that students are having trouble rewriting the integrand in a form that fits the basic integration rules. You may want to cover the examples given on page 255 (before the section exercises) in class. Students are having a lot of trouble with integrands like the one in Exercise 27, so do an example like the following.

$$\int \frac{x^3 + 1}{\sqrt{x}} \, dx = \int \left(x^{5/2} + x^{-1/2} \right) dx = \frac{x^{7/2}}{7/2} + \frac{x^{1/2}}{1/2} + C = \frac{2}{7}x^{7/2} + 2x^{1/2} + C$$

Exercises 35–44 (35–42 in *Calculus* 8/e)
To give students more practice, we added Exercises 42 and 44. We also revised Exercises 35 and 36.

Capstone

Page 257, Exercise 70 You can use this exercise to review the following concepts.

- Using the graph of f' to make conclusions about f

- First Derivative Test

- Increasing and decreasing functions

- Concavity

- Relative extrema

- Discovering relationships between a function and its antiderivative

This *Capstone* will allow you to review concepts taught in Chapter 3.

Part (a) can be answered using the graph of f'. (See the transparency.)

For part (b), note that the graph of f' tells us that f is increasing $(f' > 0)$ and the slopes of the tangent lines are greater than 2 on the interval $[0, 2]$. Because f must increase at least 4 units on $[0, 2]$ and we know $f(0) = -4$, it is not possible for $f(2) = -1$.

For part (c), note that the graph of f' tells us that f is decreasing $(f' < 0)$ on $[4, 5]$. Therefore, $f(5) < f(4)$.

For part (d), show on the graph that $f'(3.5) \approx 0$ and that by the First Derivative Test, f has a maximum at $x = 3.5$.

For part (e), note the intervals where f' is increasing and decreasing, then state the solution given on the next page.

For part (f), note that f' is concave downward on $(-\infty, 3)$, so by the definition of concavity, f'' is decreasing on $(-\infty, 3)$. Because f' is concave upward on $(3, \infty)$, f'' is increasing on $(3, \infty)$. So, f'' is a minimum at $x = 3$.

An approximate graph of f is given in the solution. Use the given information and the results of (a)–(f) to explain how to obtain the graph.

Solution

$f(0) = -4$. Graph of f' is given.

(a) $f'(4) \approx -1.0$

(b) No. The slopes of the tangent lines are greater than 2 on $[0, 2]$. Therefore, f must increase more than 4 units on $[0, 2]$.

(c) No, $f(5) < f(4)$ because f is decreasing on $[4, 5]$.

(d) f is a maximum at $x = 3.5$ because $f'(3.5) \approx 0$ and the First Derivative Test.

(e) f is concave upward when f' is increasing on $(-\infty, 1)$ and $(5, \infty)$. f is concave downward on $(1, 5)$. Points of inflection at $x = 1, 5$.

(f) f'' is a minimum at $x = 3$.

(g)

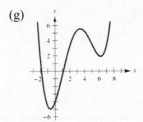

Section 4.2   Area

Tips and Tools for Problem Solving

CalcChat.com

Exercises 15–22 (15–20 in *Calculus* 8/e)
We added Exercises 15 and 16 to give students more practice and to cover all summation formulas given in Theorem 4.2.

Capstone

Page 270, Exercise 86 You can use this exercise to review the following concepts.

- Finding endpoints of subintervals
- Determining whether rectangles are inscribed or circumscribed

This exercise will give you another opportunity to show students how to divide an interval into subintervals, find the endpoints of subintervals, and how to draw the rectangles corresponding to the right endpoints. The graph is provided on a transparency.

Solution

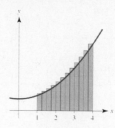

$$\Delta x = \frac{4-1}{12} = \frac{1}{4}$$

(a) The left endpoint of the first subinterval is 1, and the left endpoint of the last subinterval is $4 - \frac{1}{4} = \frac{15}{4}$.

(b) The right endpoints of the first two subintervals are $1 + \frac{1}{4} = \frac{5}{4}$ and $1 + 2\left(\frac{1}{4}\right) = \frac{3}{2}$.

(c) When using right endpoints, the rectangles will be above the curve.

(d) For a constant function, the heights of the rectangles are the same.

Section 4.3   Riemann Sums and Definite Integrals

Tips and Tools for Problem Solving

CalcChat.com

Although we made changes to the section exercises, no changes were made based on the data.

Capstone

Page 280, Exercise 52 You can use this exercise to review the following concepts.

- Definitions of Two Special Integrals (page 276)

- Theorem 4.6

- Using a graph to represent a definite integral

Part (a) uses Theorem 4.6 (see solution below). Use a graph similar to Figure 4.25 to support the answer.

Part (b) uses Theorem 4.6 to combine the first two integrals. Use part two of the definitions of two special integrals (page 276) to rewrite the third term (see the solution on the next page). Finally, use Theorem 4.6 again to identify the values of a and b.

For part (c), show the graph of $\sin x$ on $\left[0,\ 2\pi\right]$ (see transparency) and use the solution on the next page.

One possible solution for part (d) is given on the next page. The graph is provided on a transparency. Another solution is to let $a = k$ and $b = k$, where k is any real number. Then by using part one of the definitions of two special integrals (page 276), we can write $\int_{k}^{k} \cos x \, dx = 0$.

Solution

(a) $\int_{-2}^{1} f(x) \, dx + \int_{1}^{5} f(x) \, dx = \int_{-2}^{5} f(x) \, dx$

   $a = -2,\ b = 5$

(b) $\int_{-3}^{3} f(x)\,dx + \int_{3}^{6} f(x)\,dx - \int_{a}^{b} f(x)\,dx = \int_{-1}^{6} f(x)\,dx$

$$\int_{-3}^{6} f(x)\,dx + \int_{b}^{a} f(x)\,dx = \int_{-1}^{6} f(x)\,dx$$

$a = -3,\ b = -1$

(c) Answers will vary. *Sample answer:* $a = \pi,\ b = 2\pi$

$$\int_{\pi}^{2\pi} \sin x\,dx < 0$$

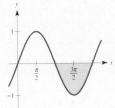

(d) Answers will vary. *Sample answer:* $a = 0,\ b = \pi$

$$\int_{0}^{\pi} \cos x\,dx = 0$$

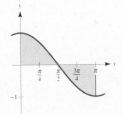

Section 4.4 The Fundamental Theorem of Calculus

Tips and Tools for Problem Solving

CalcChat.com

Exercises 27–34 (27–32 in *Calculus* 8/e)
The data suggests that students need more practice on this concept, so we added Exercises 28 and 30.

Exercises 39–44 (39–42 in *Calculus* 8/e)
The data suggests that students need more practice on this concept, so we added Exercises 42 and 44.

Exercises 45–50 (43–46 in *Calculus* 8/e)
According to the data, Exercise 48 (43 in *Calculus* 8/e) was too difficult to start the block. So we reordered
the exercises to improve the grading and added Exercises 45 and 47 to give students more practice.

Exercises 51–56 (47–50 in *Calculus* 8/e)
The data suggests that students need more practice on this concept, so we added Exercises 53 and 54.

Capstone

Page 294, Exercise 66 You can use this exercise to review the following concepts.

- Using properties of definite integrals

- Using the Fundamental Theorem of Calculus

- Finding the average value of a function

37

Because of their importance, the properties of definite integrals given in Section 4.3 are reviewed here (see pages 276–278). You can also go over the Fundamental Theorem of Calculus and finding the average value of a function.

Solution

(a) Because $y < 0$ on $[0, 2]$. $\int_0^2 f(x)\,dx = -(\text{area of region } A) = -1.5$

(b) $\int_2^6 f(x)\,dx = (\text{area of region } B) = \int_0^6 f(x)\,dx - \int_0^2 f(x)\,dx = 3.5 - (-1.5) = 5.0$

(c) $\int_0^6 |f(x)|\,dx = -\int_0^2 f(x)\,dx + \int_2^6 f(x)\,dx = 1.5 + 5.0 = 6.5$

(d) $\int_0^2 -2f(x)\,dx = -2\int_0^2 f(x)\,dx = -2(-1.5) = 3.0$

(e) $\int_0^6 [2 + f(x)]\,dx = \int_0^6 2\,dx + \int_0^6 f(x)\,dx = 12 + 3.5 = 15.5$

(f) Average value $= \frac{1}{6}\int_0^6 f(x)\,dx = \frac{1}{6}(3.5) \approx 0.5833$

Section 4.5   Integration by Substitution

Tips and Tools for Problem Solving

CalcChat.com

Exercises 7–10 (New)
The data suggests that students need more practice determining whether it is necessary to use substitution to evaluate an integral. We added Exercises 7–10 to address this need. Your students may benefit by going over these exercises in class before assigning the homework.

Capstone

Page 308, Exercise 114 You can use this exercise to review the following concepts.

- Using pattern recognition to find an indefinite integral
- Theorem 4.12
- Using the Constant Multiple Rule to rewrite an integrand
- Using the General Power Rule for Integration to find an indefinite integral

It is very important for students to be comfortable with these integration techniques. In part (a), note the use of the Constant Multiple Rule to rewrite the integrand to obtain the pattern $f(g(x))g'(x)$ where $g(x) = 2x - 1$. Then use the Power Rule for Integration and Theorem 4.12 as shown. The second way is to expand the binomial and then integrate the polynomial function (see Section 4.1).

In parts (b) and (c), you can demonstrate substitution and the General Power Rule. (See Example 7.) You may need to review the differentiation rules for sine, cosine, tangent and secant to help students see the $u^n\,du$ pattern. Also, you will need to use the identities $\sin^2 x + \cos^2 x = 1$ and $\tan^2 x + 1 = \sec^2 x$ to explain the difference in the forms of the answers.

Solution

(a) $\int (2x - 1)^2\,dx = \frac{1}{2}\int (2x - 1)^2 2\,dx = \frac{1}{6}(2x - 1)^3 + C_1 = \frac{4}{3}x^3 - 2x^2 + x - \frac{1}{6} + C_1$

$\int (2x - 1)^2\,dx = \int (4x^2 - 4x + 1)\,dx = \frac{4}{3}x^3 - 2x^2 + x + C_2$

They differ by a constant: $C_2 = C_1 - \frac{1}{6}$.

38

(b) $\int \sin x \cos x \, dx = \int (\sin x)^1 (\cos x \, dx) = \dfrac{\sin^2 x}{2} + C_1$

$\int \sin x \cos x \, dx = -\int (\cos x)^1 (-\sin x \, dx) = -\dfrac{\cos^2 x}{2} + C_2$

$-\dfrac{\cos^2 x}{2} + C_2 = -\dfrac{(1 - \sin^2 x)}{2} + C_2 = \dfrac{\sin^2 x}{2} - \dfrac{1}{2} + C_2$

They differ by a constant: $C_2 = C_1 + \frac{1}{2}$.

(c) $\int \tan x \sec^2 x \, dx = \dfrac{\tan^2 x}{2} + C_1$

$\int \tan x \sec^2 x \, dx = \int \sec x (\sec x \tan x) \, dx = \dfrac{\sec^2 x}{2} + C_2$

$\dfrac{\tan^2 x}{2} + C_1 = \dfrac{\sec^2 x - 1}{2} + C_1 = \dfrac{\sec^2 x}{2} + \dfrac{1}{2} + C_1$

They differ by a constant: $C_2 = C_1 + \frac{1}{2}$.

Section 4.6 Numerical Integration

Tips and Tools for Problem Solving

CalcChat.com

Although we made changes to the section exercises, no changes were made based on the data.

Capstone

Page 317, Exercise 46 You can use this exercise to review the following concepts.

- Trapezoidal Rule

- Simpson's Rule

Use the graphs and explanations below (see transparency). This exercise will help you highlight the differences between the Trapezoidal Rule and Simpson's Rule.

Solution

f is concave upward on $[0, 2]$.

g is concave downward on $[0, 2]$.

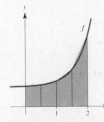 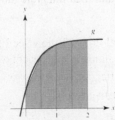

(a) The integral $\int_0^2 f(x) \, dx$ would be overestimated, and the integral $\int_0^2 g(x) \, dx$ would be underestimated.

(b) Simpson's Rule would give a more accurate approximation because it takes into account the curvature of the graph.

Chapter 4 Project

Ordering Siding

You need to determine the amount of wood siding needed for the barn.

Exercises

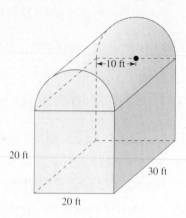

1. The curve that forms the roof of the barn is a semicircle.

   (a) Write an equation of the semicircle. Let the center of the circle be at the origin.

   (b) Approximate the area of the semicircle using the formula for the area of a circle.

   (c) Set up a definite integral that yields the area of the semicircle.

   (d) Use a graphing utility to evaluate the integral you wrote in part (c). Compare this to your answer from part (b).

2. Based on your findings in Exercise 1, determine the total area to be sided. (The roof of the barn does not need siding.)

3. One-foot wide siding is laid vertically as shown in the figure.

   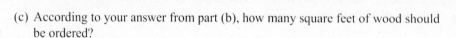

   (a) Graph the equation of the semicircle from Exercise 1 and draw the rectangles representing the upper sum for this situation. Explain why it is important to use an upper sum in this context.

   (b) Find the lengths of the wood pieces that must be ordered to completely side the barn. Because the wood must be cut to the nearest foot, round all lengths up to the nearest foot. Organize the lengths in a table as shown.

Dimensions of board	Number of pieces
1 ft by _____	

   (c) According to your answer from part (b), how many square feet of wood should be ordered?

   (d) Use your answers from Exercise 2 and part (c) to determine how much wood is wasted.

   (e) What happens to the amount of wasted wood if the width of the siding increases? decreases? Explain.

4. Repeat Exercise 3. One-foot wide siding is laid horizontally as shown in the figure.

   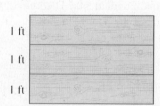

5. What recommendations would you make in order to side the barn most efficiently? Explain.

Chapter 5   Logarithmic, Exponential, and Other Transcendental Functions

Chapter Summary
Section Topics

5.1   **The Natural Logarithmic Function: Differentiation**—Develop and use properties of the natural logarithmic function. Understand the definition of the number e. Find derivatives of functions involving the natural logarithmic function.

5.2   **The Natural Logarithmic Function: Integration**—Use the Log Rule for Integration to integrate a rational function. Integrate trigonometric functions.

5.3   **Inverse Functions**—Verify that one function is the inverse function of another function. Determine whether a function has an inverse function. Find the derivative of an inverse function.

5.4   **Exponential Functions: Differentiation and Integration**—Develop properties of the natural exponential function. Differentiate natural exponential functions. Integrate natural exponential functions.

5.5   **Bases Other than e and Applications**—Define exponential functions that have bases other than e. Differentiate and integrate exponential functions that have bases other than e. Use exponential functions to model compound interest and exponential growth.

5.6   **Inverse Trigonometric Functions: Differentiation**—Develop properties of the six inverse trigonometric functions. Differentiate an inverse trigonometric function. Review the basic differentiation rules for elementary functions.

5.7   **Inverse Trigonometric Functions: Integration**—Integrate functions whose antiderivatives involve inverse trigonometric functions. Use the method of completing the square to integrate a function. Review the basic integration rules involving elementary functions.

5.8   **Hyperbolic Functions**—Develop properties of hyperbolic functions. Differentiate and integrate hyperbolic functions. Develop properties of inverse hyperbolic functions. Differentiate and integrate functions involving inverse hyperbolic functions.

Chapter Comments

Although students should be familiar and comfortable with both the logarithmic and exponential functions, they frequently are not. So present these functions as though they are new ideas. Have your students commit to memory the graphs and properties of these functions. You should review the Second Fundamental Theorem of Calculus, covered in Section 4.4, before introducing the definition of the natural logarithmic function. Be sure to go over logarithmic differentiation as done in Example 6 of Section 5.1.

Integrals that yield a natural logarithmic function are hard for the students to see at first. You must tell your students that whenever the problem is $\int f(x)/g(x)\ dx$ there are two things to consider before anything else:

(1) if degree of $f(x) \geq$ degree of $g(x)$, then perform algebraic long division to rewrite the integrand;

(2) investigate for the possibility of u'/u.

Notice that with Theorem 5.5 we can now integrate all six of the trigonometric functions. These integration rules, found on page 339, are important; have your students memorize them. The problems in the exercises for Section 5.2 bring out a number of important concepts for integration. Be sure to allow enough time to go over these thoroughly.

Students should be familiar with the inverses of functions from their algebra courses, so perhaps Section 5.3 could be covered quickly. However, a thorough discussion of Section 5.4, Exponential Functions, is necessary. This section covers the definition, properties, derivative and integral of the natural exponential function. Although not especially difficult, it is a lot of new material at one time; so go over it carefully. Be sure to do a problem involving previously covered ideas, such as extrema or area.

Section 5.5 could be covered lightly if time is a problem. However, your students will need to be able to differentiate a^u in Chapter 9, so be sure to cover Theorem 5.13.

Inverse Trigonometric Functions, covered in Sections 5.6 and 5.7, will not appeal to your students. They tend to get lazy when the trigonometry gets this involved. Section 5.6 contains a table of Basic Differentiation Rules for Elementary Functions that all students of calculus should know.

In Section 5.7 there are some examples that demonstrate important tools that will be needed for future work with integration. The rewriting of the integrand as the sum of two quotients is shown in Example 3. Completing the square on a quadratic expression is demonstrated in Examples 4 and 5. These examples should be done in class. Again, remind your students of the need to divide if the degree of the polynomial in the numerator is greater than or equal to the degree of the polynomial in the denominator. The problems for Section 5.7 contain a significant amount of information, reviewing all that we know about integration so far. You should plan to spend quite a bit of time covering them. Exercise 45 would be a good example to do with your students in class after they have attempted Exercises 1–43 on their own.

Section 5.8 discusses hyperbolic functions and could be covered lightly if you are pressed for time. Do not omit completely, however, because the students will see these functions again. A familiar example of a hyperbolic cosine function is the St. Louis Arch, discussed in the Section Project on page 400.

Section 5.1   The Natural Logarithmic Function: Differentiation

Tips and Tools for Problem Solving

CalcChat.com

Exercises 43–46, 77–82 (41–44, 71–76 in *Calculus* 8/e)
We noticed in the data that students are having trouble with these exercises. You may want to do an example in class on finding an equation of a tangent line to the graph of a logarithmic function. Also, you can assign the *CAS Investigation* for Example 3. This investigation allows students to use the derivative of a natural logarithmic function and review finding a tangent line to the graph of a function, open intervals on which a function is increasing or decreasing, and relative extrema of a function.

Exercises 47–76 (45–70 in *Calculus* 8/e)
To give students more practice, we added Exercises 47, 48, 53, and 56. Also, remind students that the logarithmic properties given in Theorem 5.2 can be used to simplify differentiation involving products, quotients, and powers (see Example 4).

Exercises 83–86 (77 and 78 in *Calculus* 8/e)
Students are having difficulty using implicit differentiation. To give students more practice, we added Exercises 85 and 86.

Students are having difficulty using logarithmic differentiation. Be sure to go over logarithmic differentiation as done in Example 6. Also, we revised each of these exercises.

Capstone

Page 333, Exercise 120 You can use this exercise to review the following concepts.

- Using properties of the natural logarithmic function
- Finding a derivative of a function involving the natural logarithmic function
- Using a derivative to find rates of change

Note in the solution the use of Property 3 from Theorem 5.2 (see page 325) to rewrite $\ln x^a$ as $a \ln x$. Students tend to forget to use Theorem 5.2 to simplify functions before differentiating. After simplifying, you can show students how to apply Theorem 5.3 (see page 328). Now use the derivative to find rates of change (see Section 2.2). After studying antiderivatives in Chapter 4, students may need a refresher on this and other previously covered ideas, such as extrema (see Example 8, page 330).

Solution

$$f(x) = \ln x^a = a \ln x$$

$$f'(x) = \frac{a}{x}$$

(a) When $x = 10$, $f'(x) = \frac{a}{10}$.

(b) When $x = 100$, $f'(x) = \frac{a}{100}$.

Section 5.2   The Natural Logarithmic Function: Integration

Tips and Tools for Problem Solving

CalcChat.com

Exercises 1–26 (1–24 in *Calculus* 8/e)
The data show that students struggled with this block of exercises, so we revised Exercises 5–8 and added Exercises 9 and 10 to give students more practice.

Exercises 31–40 (29–36 in *Calculus* 8/e)
Students are having difficulty with integrals involving trigonometric functions. Be sure that your students memorize the integration rules given on page 339 and go over Example 10. We revised Exercises 31 and 40, and added Exercises 35 and 36 to give students more practice.

Capstone

Page 341, Exercise 90 You can use this exercise to review the following concepts.

- Definition of the natural logarithmic function
- Log Rule for Integration
- Definition of e

Assume $x > 0$ and note that the integral is the definition of the natural logarithmic function (see page 324). Apply the Log Rule for Integration to obtain $\ln x$. Then solve the logarithmic equations in parts (a) and (b) as shown on the next page. Note the use of the definition of e (see page 327) in part (b).

Solution

$$\int_1^x \frac{1}{t} \, dt = \Big[\ln|t|\Big]_1^x = \ln x \quad (\text{Assume } x > 0.)$$

(a) $\ln x = \ln 5 \implies x = 5$

(b) $\ln x = 1 \implies x = e$

Section 5.3   Inverse Functions

Tips and Tools for Problem Solving

CalcChat.com

Exercises 71–80 (71–76 in *Calculus* 8/e)
Students had more trouble with these exercises than with any of the other exercises in this section. Be sure to go over Theorem 5.9 and evaluating the derivative of an inverse function as done in Example 5. We have rewritten the direction line to have students verify that the

function has an inverse and to use the function f and the given real number a to find $\left(f^{-1}\right)'(a)$.

We have also added a hint to see Example 5. To give students more practice evaluating the derivative of an inverse function, we added Exercises 71, 72, 77, and 78.

Capstone

Page 351, Exercise 100   You can use this exercise to review the following concepts.

  • Definition of inverse function

  • Theorems 5.6 and 5.9

  • Graphs of inverse functions have reciprocal slopes

Students should be familiar with the inverses of functions from their algebra courses. Because of this, you may be covering this material quickly. If so, you can use this exercise to quickly review the definition of inverse function (see page 343). Because the point $(1, 3)$ lies on the graph of f and by Theorem 5.6, we know that the point $(3, 1)$ lies on the graph of f^{-1}. It follows from Theorem 5.9 (see pages 347 and 348) that the slope of f^{-1} at $(3, 1)$ is $1/2$.

Solution

Because the slope of f at $(1, 3)$ is $m = 2$, the slope of f^{-1} at $(3, 1)$ is $1/2$.

Section 5.4   Exponential Functions: Differentiation and Integration

Tips and Tools for Problem Solving

CalcChat.com

Be thorough in your coverage of the definition, properties, derivative, and integral of the natural exponential function. This is a lot of new material at one time. Students struggled the most with the exercises listed below.

Exercises 39–60 (35–48 in *Calculus* 8/e)
To give students more practice, we added Exercises 40, 43–47, 55, and 56.

Exercises 99–116 (85–98 in *Calculus* 8/e)
To give students more practice, we added Exercises 101–104.

Page 361, Exercise 148 You can use this exercise to review the following concept.

- The inverse relationship between the natural logarithmic function and the natural exponential function

Review the definition of the natural exponential function on page 352. Use a graph like Figure 5.19 and include the line $y = x$.

Solution

The graphs of $f(x) = \ln x$ and $g(x) = e^x$ are mirror images across the line $y = x$.

Section 5.5   Bases Other than *e* and Applications

Tips and Tools for Problem Solving

CalcChat.com

Exercises 41–62 (37–48 in *Calculus* 8/e)
Because students struggled with these exercises, we added a hint to remind them to apply logarithmic properties *before* differentiating and added 10 new exercises for more practice (Exercises 42–45, 51–54, 56, and 60). Also, be sure students are able to differentiate a^u (for example, see Exercises 41–44). They will need this skill in Chapter 9.

Exercises 75–82 (61–66 in *Calculus* 8/e)
To give students more practice, we added Exercises 77 and 78.

Capstone

Page 369, Exercise 94 You can use this exercise to review the following concepts.

- Defining an exponential function that has a base other than *e*
- Defining a logarithmic function to base *a*
- Finding an exponential function to model a table of values
- Finding a logarithmic function to model a table of values

Review the definitions of exponential and logarithmic functions to base *a* on pages 362 and 363. Use the transparency to show the graph of the table of values.

For part (a), the model is $y = a^x$. When $(x, y) = (1, 0)$, $a = 0$. This value of *a* in $y = a^x$ does not produce the other values in the table. So, *y* is *not* an exponential function of *x*.

For part (b), the model is $y = \log_a x$. When $(x, y) = (2, 1)$, $a = 2$. This value of *a* in $y = \log_a x$ does produce the other values in the table. So, *y* is a logarithmic function of *x*.

For part (c), the model is $x = a^y$. When $(x, y) = (2, 1)$, $a = 2$. This value of *a* in $x = a^y$ does produce the other values in the table. So, *x* is an exponential function of *y*.

For part (d), the points in the graph clearly do not lie on a line. This can be shown several ways, such as using slope.

Solution

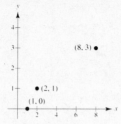

x	1	2	8
y	0	1	3

(a) y is an exponential function of x: False

(b) y is a logarithmic function of x: True; $y = \log_2 x$

(c) x is a exponential function of y: True; $2^y = x$

(d) y is a linear function of x: False

Section 5.6   Inverse Trigonometric Functions: Differentiation

Tips and Tools for Problem Solving

CalcChat.com

Exercises 21–34 (21–28 in *Calculus* 8/e)
Exercise 27 (21 in *Calculus* 8/e) was ranked as one of the hardest exercises in this section. So, we added a hint to sketch a right triangle as shown in Example 3(a). Also, we added Exercises 21–26 to give students practice solving a similar problem where the sketch of a right triangle is given.

Capstone

Page 380, Exercise 90   You can use this exercise to review the following concepts.

- Definition of inverse function
- Domain and range of the cosine and arccosine functions
- Properties of inverse trigonometric functions

Review the definition of inverse function (see page 343), and the domain and range of the cosine (see Appendix C.3) and arccosine functions (see page 373). Use the transparency graph of $y = \cos x$ and $y = \arccos x$. Note that the point $\left(\dfrac{3\pi}{2}, 0\right)$ lies on the graph of

$y = \cos x$, but $\left(0, \dfrac{3\pi}{2}\right)$ does not lie on $y = \arccos x$. This does not contradict the definition of

inverse function because the domain of $y = \arccos x$ is $[-1, 1]$ and its range is $[0, \pi]$. Be sure to cover the material at the top of page 375 and the following properties of inverse trigonometric functions.

Solution

No, $(0, 3\pi/2)$ is not on the graph of $y = \arccos x$. The domain of $y = \arccos x$ is $[-1, 1]$, and its range is $[0, \pi]$. So, $\arccos(0) = \pi/2$.

Section 5.7 Inverse Trigonometric Functions: Integration

Tips and Tools for Problem Solving

CalcChat.com

Exercises 1–24 (1–20 in *Calculus* 8/e)
We reordered the exercises to improve the grading and added Exercises 11, 12, 15, and 16 to give students more practice.

Exercises 25–38 (21–30 in *Calculus* 8/e)
We reordered the exercises to improve the grading and added Exercises 31–34 to give students more practice.

Capstone

Page 388, Exercise 60 You can use this exercise to review the following concepts.

- Integrating functions whose antiderivatives involve inverse trigonometric functions
- Using the Log Rule for Integration to integrate a rational function
- Rewriting the integrand using the Constant Multiple Rule

The integral in part (a) cannot be evaluated using basic integration rules. Have students scan the list of basic integration rules on page 385 to verify this conclusion.

$\left(\text{Some students mistakenly believe that the rule of } \int \dfrac{du}{a^2 + u^2} \text{ applies.} \right)$

The integrals in parts (b) and (c) can be evaluated using the basic integration rules.

Part (b) can be evaluated using $\int \dfrac{du}{a^2 + u^2}$ with $u = x^2$. Part (c) can be evaluated

using $\int \dfrac{du}{u}$ with $u = 1 + x^4$. Note in both cases the use of the Constant Multiple Rule

to rewrite the integrand.

Solution

(a) $\displaystyle\int \dfrac{1}{1 + x^4}\, dx$ cannot be evaluated using the basic integration rules.

(b) $\displaystyle\int \dfrac{x}{1 + x^4}\, dx = \dfrac{1}{2} \int \dfrac{2x}{1 + \left(x^2\right)^2}\, dx$

$\qquad\qquad\qquad = \dfrac{1}{2} \arctan\left(x^2\right) + C, \; u = x^2$

(c) $\displaystyle\int \dfrac{x^3}{1 + x^4}\, dx = \dfrac{1}{4} \int \dfrac{4x^3}{1 + x^4}\, dx$

$\qquad\qquad\qquad = \dfrac{1}{4} \ln\left(1 + x^4\right) + C, \; u = 1 + x^4$

Section 5.8 Hyperbolic Functions

Tips and Tools for Problem Solving

CalcChat.com

Exercises 7–16 (7–12 in *Calculus* 8/e)
To give students more practice, we added Exercises 7, 8, 10, and 12.

Exercises 19–30 (15–24 in *Calculus* 8/e)
To give students more practice, we added Exercises 19 and 20.

Exercises 45–58 (39–50 in *Calculus* 8/e)
To give students more practice, we added Exercises 45 and 46.

Exercises 65–74 (57–64 in *Calculus* 8/e)
We reordered the exercises to improve the grading and added Exercises 67 and 68 to give students more practice.

Exercises 79–86 (67–72 in *Calculus* 8/e)
We reordered the exercises to improve the grading and added Exercises 80 and 82 to give students more practice.

Exercises 87–96 (73–80 in *Calculus* 8/e)
To give students more practice, we added Exercises 87 and 88.

Exercises 97–100 (New)
To give students more practice using the formulas from Theorem 5.20, we added Exercises 97–100.

Exercises 119–124 (98–102 in *Calculus* 8/e)
We reordered the exercises to improve the grading and added Exercise 123 to give students more practice.

Capstone

Page 399, Exercise 78 You can use this exercise to review the following concept.

- Properties of the hyperbolic functions

Review the domains and ranges of the hyperbolic functions (see page 391). Note that $y = \cosh x$ and $y = \operatorname{sech} x$ take on only positive values, and $y = \sinh x$ and $y = \tanh x$ are increasing on their domains.

Solution

$f(x) = \cosh x$ and $f(x) = \operatorname{sech} x$ take on only positive values.

$f(x) = \sinh x$ and $f(x) = \tanh x$ are increasing functions.

Chapter 5 Project

Exponential Growth

The revenue for Dell Computer Corporation from 1985 through 1993 can be modeled by the equation $y = 42.575(1.707)^x$, where x is the time in years with $x = 0$ corresponding to 1985, and y is the revenue in millions of dollars.

Exercises

1. Use the model $y = 42.575(1.707)^x$. to answer the following questions.

   (a) What was Dell Computer Corporation's revenue in 1985?

   (b) What was Dell Computer Corporation's revenue in 1992?

   (c) In what year was the revenue approximately $3 billion?

2. Find the inverse function of $y = 42.575(1.707)^x$. What does the inverse function represent?

3. Use the inverse function you wrote in Exercise 2 to determine the year when revenue was approximately $3 billion. Compare this to your answer from Exercise 1.

4. Differentiate $y = 42.575(1.707)^x$.

5. What is the rate of change of revenue in 1985? in 1988?

6. Because the revenue follows an exponential growth model, what is true about the revenue's rate of change over time? Explain.

7. Set up a definite integral to determine the total revenue from 1985 through 1993.

8. Evaluate the integral you wrote in Exercise 7 to determine the total revenue from 1985 through 1993.

9. Determine the average monthly revenue from 1985 through 1993.

10. Assuming there are 52 weeks in a year, determine the average weekly revenue from 1985 through 1993.

11. Assuming there are 365 days in a year, determine the average daily revenue from 1985 through 1993.

12. If the revenue continued to follow the same growth model, what would the revenue be in 2006?

13. Based on your answer to Exercise 12, what is the likelihood that the revenue continues to follow this growth model? Explain.

14. Use the Internet to find Dell Computer Corporation's actual revenue in 2006.

15. Based on your findings in Exercises 12 and 14, what conclusions can you make about the growth of the revenue? Does the revenue continue to increase? Does the rate of change continue to increase? Explain.

Chapter 6 Differential Equations

Chapter Summary
Section Topics

6.1 **Slope Fields and Euler's Method**—Use initial conditions to find particular solutions of differential equations. Use slope fields to approximate solutions of differential equations. Use Euler's Method to approximate solutions of differential equations.

6.2 **Differential Equations: Growth and Decay**—Use separation of variables to solve a simple differential equation. Use exponential functions to model growth and decay in applied problems.

6.3 **Separation of Variables and the Logistic Equation**—Recognize and solve differential equations that can be solved by separation of variables. Recognize and solve homogeneous differential equations. Use differential equations to model and solve applied problems. Solve and analyze logistic differential equations.

6.4 **First-Order Linear Differential Equations**—Solve a first-order linear differential equation. Use linear differential equations to solve applied problems. Solve a Bernoulli differential equation.

Chapter Comments

Section 6.1 introduces the student to the notation and terminology of differential equations. Because solving differential equations analytically can be very difficult, this section considers two other ways of looking at the solution. The first is a slope field, which is a graphical approach. The second is Euler's Method, an approximation technique for initial value problems. Your students should be familiar with all of the ideas in this section.

Be sure to cover Section 6.2 thoroughly. Here the technique of separation of variables is discussed as well as applications involving exponential growth and decay. This is an excellent opportunity to expose your students to a practical use of the exponential function.

Section 6.3 and 6.4 explore some of the other types of differential equations. You should cover these as time allows. Students frequently become frustrated checking their answers to homework problems in differential equations. Be sure to point out that there are many correct ways that an answer to a differential equation could be written. As the students become more familiar with this work, they will have a better idea of what is expected for an answer.

Section 6.1   Slope Fields and Euler's Method

Tips and Tools for Problem Solving

CalcChat.com

Exercises 13–20 (13–18 in *Calculus* 8/e)
To give students more practice, we added Exercises 14 and 16.

Exercises 21–28 (19–24 in *Calculus* 8/e)
To give students more practice, we added Exercises 22 and 26.

Capstone

Page 413, Exercise 84 You can use this exercise to review the following concepts.

- Matching a solution with the correct differential equation
- Determining intervals on which a function is increasing or decreasing

This exercise shows students another way to check an answer by analyzing the graph of the solution. As you go over this in class, use the transparency graph.

Note that the graph shows a solution of one of the given differential equations—in other words, the graph of y. When $x < 0$ the graph of y is increasing, and when $x > 0$ the graph of y is decreasing. So, the graph of y has a maximum when $x = 0$. Therefore, $y' = 0$ when $x = 0$. This means (d) is not possible. When $x > 0$, $y > 0$ and the graph of y is decreasing, which means $y' < 0$. This means (a) and (b) are not possible. Therefore, (c) is the correct equation.

You can also verify this result by graphing the slope field for each differential equation.

Solution

When $x = 0$, $y' = 0$, therefore (d) is not possible.

When $x, y > 0$, $y' < 0$ (decreasing function) therefore (c) is the equation.

Section 6.2 Differential Equations: Growth and Decay

Tips and Tools for Problem Solving

CalcChat.com

Although we made changes to the section exercises, no changes were made based on the data.

Capstone

Page 421, Exercise 62 You can use this exercise to review the following concepts.

- Describing why a linear function is appropriate to model a real-life situation
- Describing why an exponential function is appropriate to model a real-life situation

Appropriate explanations are given below. This exercise gives students practice communicating their understanding of mathematical concepts while seeing a practical application of the exponential function. When you go over each part, you may want to use a graph to illustrate each explanation. For part (b), you could refer to Figure 6.9 on page 418.

Solution

(a) Because the population increases by a constant each month, the rate of change from month to month will always be the same. So, the slope is constant, and the model is linear.

(b) Although the percentage increase is constant each month, the rate of growth is not constant. The rate of change of y is given by

$$\frac{dy}{dt} = ry$$

which is an exponential model.

Section 6.3 Separation of Variables and the Logistic Equation

Tips and Tools for Problem Solving

CalcChat.com

Exercises 1–14 (1–12 in *Calculus* 8/e)
To give students more practice, we added Exercises 2 and 3.

Exercises 25–28 (23 and 24 in *Calculus* 8/e)
To give students more practice, we added Exercises 25 and 27.

Capstone

Page 433, Exercise 88 You can use this exercise to review the following concepts.

- Logistic equation
- Real-life situations

There are many ways for students to answer this question. A sample answer is given below. This exercise gives students the opportunity to communicate in words their understanding of a mathematical concept and to discover practical applications of the logistic equation.

Solution

Answers will vary. *Sample answer:* There might be limits on available food or space.

Section 6.4   First-Order Linear Differential Equations

Tips and Tools for Problem Solving

CalcChat.com

Although we made changes to the section exercises, no changes were made based on the data.

Capstone

Page 441, Exercise 36 You can use this exercise to review the following concepts.

- First-order linear differential equations
- Integrating factor
- Derivative of a product

Refer to the note on page 434. In the solution below, note when both sides of the equation are multiplied by the integrating factor $u(x)$, the left-hand side becomes the derivative of a product.

So, the derivative of the product $uy = y' \cdot u + P(x)u \cdot y$. Therefore, $u'(x) = P(x)u$. The answer is (a).

Solution

$$y' + P(x)y = Q(x)$$

Integrating factor: $u = e^{\int P(x)\,dx}$

$$y'u + P(x)yu = Q(x)u$$

$$(uy)' = Q(x)u$$

So $u'(x) = P(x)u$.

Answer (a)

Chapter 6 Project

Finding the Height of a Fall

A detective is investigating a man's death. The man was seen falling from the roof of a building, hitting the ground after exactly 3 seconds. The suspect, who was on the roof with the man, claims the man jumped, but the detective suspects foul play. Assume that acceleration due to gravity is -32 feet per second per second.

Exercises

In Exercises 1–4, the man accidentally fell from the roof.

1. Write a differential equation with initial conditions to model the situation.

2. Solve the differential equation to find the velocity function for the fall.

3. Determine the position function for the fall.

4. Based on the function you wrote in Exercise 3, how tall is the building?

In Exercises 5–8, the man jumped from the roof. Use an initial velocity of 2 feet per second.

5. Write a differential equation with initial conditions to model the situation.

6. Solve the differential equation to find the velocity function for the fall.

7. Determine the position function for the fall.

8. Based on the function you wrote in Exercise 7, how tall is the building?

In Exercises 9–12, the man was pushed off the roof. Use an initial velocity of -3 feet per second.

9. Write a differential equation with initial conditions to model the situation.

10. Solve the differential equation to find the velocity function for the fall.

11. Determine the position function for the fall.

12. Based on the function you wrote in Exercise 11, how tall is the building?

13. What additional information is needed to determine whether foul play was involved?

14. Suppose the building is 144 feet tall. Should the detective suspect foul play? Explain.

15. Suppose the building is more than 144 feet tall. Which of the three scenarios should the detective suspect? Explain.

16. Suppose the building is less than 144 feet tall. Which of the three scenarios should the detective suspect? Explain.

17. The detective discovers that the building is 20 stories tall and each story is about 8 feet. What should the detective conclude?

Chapter 7   Applications of Integration

Chapter Summary

Section Topics

7.1   **Area of a Region Between Two Curves**—Find the area of a region between two curves using integration. Find the area of a region between intersecting curves using integration. Describe integration as an accumulation process.

7.2   **Volume: The Disk Method**—Find the volume of a solid of revolution using the disk method. Find the volume of a solid of revolution using the washer method. Find the volume of a solid with known cross sections.

7.3   **Volume: The Shell Method**—Find the volume of a solid of revolution using the shell method. Compare the uses of the disk method and the shell method.

7.4   **Arc Length and Surfaces of Revolution**—Find the arc length of a smooth curve. Find the area of a surface of revolution.

7.5   **Work**—Find the work done by a constant force. Find the work done by a variable force.

7.6   **Moments, Centers of Mass, and Centroids**—Understand the definition of mass. Find the center of mass in a one-dimensional system. Find the center of mass in a two-dimensional system. Find the center of mass of a planar lamina. Use the Theorem of Pappus to find the volume of a solid of revolution.

7.7   **Fluid Pressure and Fluid Force**—Find fluid pressure and fluid force.

Chapter Comments

Chapter 7 covers many applications to the definite integral. There are far too many problems in this chapter to cover in a normal calculus course. You would be better off assigning just a few carefully chosen problems from each section covered.

Because you may not have the time to cover each topic in this chapter, you should cover the area between two curves carefully so that the students get used to the idea of using a representative rectangle in the given region. Remind your students that they are expected to know how to sketch a graph (Chapter 3) and how to find points of intersection (Chapter P).

Both the disk and the shell methods, Sections 7.2 and 7.3, need to be discussed to do a thorough treatment of volumes of solids of revolution. Be sure to go over Examples 3, 4 and 5 of Section 7.3 to convince your students that it is necessary to know both methods.

Arc length, Section 7.4, should be covered because this is built upon in later chapters (Chapters 11 and 13).

Note in Example 3 of Section 7.5 that the weight of the space module is given in metric tons. To convert mile-tons to foot-pounds you need to use the fact that 1 metric ton = 2204.624 pounds.

The remaining topics in this chapter should be covered as time allows. If you prefer to cover Applications of Integration (Chapter 7) before Transcendental Functions (Chapter 5), you should postpone covering the following examples and exercises:

Section 7.1 Area of a Region Between Two Curves

Tips and Tools for Problem Solving

CalcChat.com

Before attempting the exercises, some students may need to review curve sketching (Section 3.6) and how to find points of intersection (Section P.1).

Exercises 1–6 (1–6 in *Calculus* 8/e)
According to the area formula on page 449, $g(x) \leq f(x)$ for all x in $[a, b]$. But in Exercise 1, for instance, $g(x) \geq f(x)$. The data suggest that students were confused by the use of $g(x)$ and $f(x)$ in these exercises and simply plugging them into the area formula. So, we changed $g(x)$ and $f(x)$ to y_1 and y_2 in each exercise. When you go over the examples in this section, emphasize the step determining which of the graphs of the two functions lies below the other in the interval of interest.

Exercises 19–36 (17–32 in *Calculus* 8/e)
To give students more practice, we added Exercises 19 and 20. We also revised Exercises 25, 26, and 29.

Exercises 47–52 (43–48 in *Calculus* 8/e)
We reordered the exercises to improve the grading.

Capstone

Page 456, Exercise 82 You can use this exercise to review the following concept.

- The area of a region between two curves

Use Figure 7.4 on page 449 as you go over the following solution.

Solution

The integral $\int_a^b \left[f(x) - g(x) \right] dx$ gives the area of the region bounded by the graphs of f and $g \left(g(x) \leq f(x) \text{ on } [a, b] \right)$ and the vertical lines $x = a$ and $x = b$. No, the interpretation does not change.

Section 7.2 Volume: The Disk Method

Tips and Tools for Problem Solving

CalcChat.com

Although we made changes to the section exercises, no changes were made based on the data.

Capstone

Page 466, Exercise 56 You can use this exercise to review the following concepts.

- The washer method
- The disk method

Use an illustration like Figure 7.19 to show students the relationship between the graphs of $y = f(x)$ and $y = g(x)$. Then go over the disk and washer methods. It should be clear that the answer is (b).

Solution

The answer is (b). See the formula for the Washer Method, page 461.

Section 7.3   Volume: The Shell Method

Tips and Tools for Problem Solving

CalcChat.com

Exercises 1–14 (1–12 in *Calculus* 8/e)
To give students more practice, we added Exercises 11 and 12.

Exercises 23–26 (21–24 in *Calculus* 8/e)
We reordered the exercises to improve the grading.

Capstone

Page 475, Exercise 44 You can use this exercise to review or to introduce the following concepts.

- Horizontal axis of revolution
- Vertical axis of revolution

You can go over this exercise when you introduce the shell method or as you go over the exercises. The simple plane region shown below clearly illustrates the representative rectangles used for (a) a horizontal axis of revolution and (b) a vertical axis of revolution. The plane region shown is provided on a transparency.

Solution

(a) radius $= k$
     height $= b$

(b) radius $= b$
     height $= k$

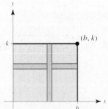

Section 7.4   Arc Length and Surfaces of Revolution

Tips and Tools for Problem Solving

CalcChat.com

We reordered many of the exercises in this section to improve the grading.

Exercises 3–16 (3–14 in *Calculus* 8/e)
To give students more practice, we added Exercises 3 and 4.

Exercise 34 (30 in *Calculus* 8/e)

Be sure students understand that the integral $4 \int_0^8 \sqrt{\dfrac{4}{x^{2/3}}} \, dx$ cannot be used to solve this problem because the integrand is not defined on $[0, 8]$. However, using symmetry, the arc length can be found by evaluating $8 \int_{2^{3/2}}^8 \sqrt{\dfrac{4}{x^{2/3}}} \, dx$. The lower limit $2^{3/2}$ is the midpoint of the curve on $[0, 8]$, where $y = x$.

Exercises 37–46 (39–44 in *Calculus* 8/e)

To give students more practice, we added Exercises 41, 42, 45, and 46.

Exercises 65–68 (33, 55, 63, and 64 in *Calculus* 8/e)

We grouped these exercises together and wrote a new direction line to set up the integral and then use a graphing utility to approximate the arc length or surface area. These exercises can be used to introduce your students to improper integrals. (There is a note saying that students will learn how to evaluate this type of integral in Section 8.8.)

Capstone

Page 487, Exercise 54 You can use this exercise to review the following concepts.

- Arc length

- Natural logarithmic and natural exponential functions

- Derivatives of natural logarithmic and natural exponential functions

- The number e

Note that both integrals fit the definition of arc length. In the solution below, note that students need to understand the definitions of natural logarithmic and natural exponential functions and also how to find their derivatives. Students will also need to understand domain, range, and exponentiating both sides of an equation to see that $y = \ln x$ is equivalent to $x = e^y$. After showing the analytical work, the result can be confirmed numerically. If time permits, graph $y = \ln x$ for $1 \le x \le e$ and $x = e^y$ for $0 \le y \le 1$. The graphs on these intervals are equivalent.

Solution

Let $y = \ln x$, $1 \le x \le e$, $y' = \dfrac{1}{x}$ and $s_1 = \displaystyle\int_1^e \sqrt{1 + \dfrac{1}{x^2}} \, dx$.

Equivalently, $x = e^y$, $0 \le y \le 1$, $\dfrac{dx}{dy} = e^y$, and $s_2 = \displaystyle\int_0^1 \sqrt{1 + e^{2y}} \, dy = \int_0^1 \sqrt{1 + e^{2x}} \, dx$.

Numerically, both integrals yield $s = 2.0035$.

Section 7.5 Work

Tips and Tools for Problem Solving

CalcChat.com

Although we made changes to the section exercises, no changes were made based on the data.

Capstone

Page 496, Exercise 36 You can use this exercise to review the following concepts.

- Force
- Work

Review the definition of work done by a variable force (see page 490). The work done equals the area under the force function. Using the graphs (see transparencies) to estimate the work done, you can then order them as shown in the solution. You can then calculate the work done to verify this order.

Solution

Because the work equals the area under the force function, you have $(c) < (d) < (a) < (b)$.

Section 7.6 Moments, Centers of Mass, and Centroids

Tips and Tools for Problem Solving

CalcChat.com

Exercises 13–26 (13–24 in *Calculus* 8/e)
To give students more practice, we added Exercises 13 and 14.

Capstone

Page 508, Exercise 58 You can use this exercise to review the following concepts.

- Centroid
- Transformations of functions

Note the use of transformations in parts (a)–(c): vertical shift up 2 units, horizontal shift right 2 units, and reflection about the x-axis. We covered these transformations in Section P.3. So, each centroid can be found by applying the transformation to the given centroid as shown below. We do not have enough information to find the centroid in part (d).

Solution

(a) Yes. $(\overline{x}, \overline{y}) = \left(\frac{5}{6}, \frac{5}{18} + 2\right) = \left(\frac{5}{6}, \frac{41}{18}\right)$

(b) Yes. $(\overline{x}, \overline{y}) = \left(\frac{5}{6} + 2, \frac{5}{18}\right) = \left(\frac{17}{6}, \frac{5}{18}\right)$

(c) Yes. $(\overline{x}, \overline{y}) = \left(\frac{5}{6}, -\frac{5}{18}\right)$

(d) No

Section 7.7 Fluid Pressure and Fluid Force

Tips and Tools for Problem Solving

CalcChat.com

Exercises 1–4 (1 and 2 in *Calculus* 8/e)
To give students more practice, we added Exercises 3 and 4.

Capstone

Page 514, Exercise 36 You can use this exercise to review the following concepts.

- Centroid

- Fluid force

You may want to use this exercise when you go over the section. Go over the definitions of centroid and fluid force. Note: In Section 7.6, Exercise 38, we found that the centroid of a semicircle bounded by the graphs of $y = \sqrt{r^2 - x^2}$ and $y = 0$ is $\left(0, \dfrac{4r}{3\pi}\right)$. You can use this to show students that the left window experiences the greater fluid force because its centroid is lower.

Solution

The left window experiences the greater fluid force because its centroid is lower.

Chapter 7 Project

Volume and Surface Area of Footballs and Basketballs

A regulation-sized football has the following dimensions.

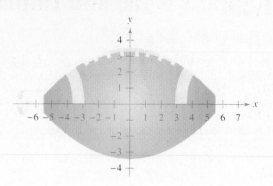

     Length: 11.00–11.25 inches

     Girth: 21.25–21.50 inches

A football can be formed by revolving the area under $f(x) = -0.0944x^2 + 3.4,\ -5.5 \le x \le 5.5$ about the x-axis.

A regulation-sized basketball is a sphere with a circumference of 29.5 inches. A basketball can be formed by revolving the area under $f(x) = \sqrt{4.7^2 - x^2},\ -4.7 \le x \le 4.7$ about the x-axis.

Exercises

1. Use the disk method to set up an integral that gives the volume of a football.

2. Evaluate the integral you wrote in Exercise 1 to approximate the volume of a football.

3. Use the shell method to set up an integral that gives the volume of a football.

4. Evaluate the integral you wrote in Exercise 3 to approximate the volume of a football. Compare this to your answer from Exercise 2.

5. Set up an integral that gives the surface area of a football.

6. Use a graphing utility to evaluate the integral you wrote in Exercise 5 to approximate the surface area of a football.

7. Approximate the volume of a basketball using the formula for the volume of a sphere.

8. Use the disk method to set up an integral that gives the volume of a basketball.

9. Evaluate the integral you wrote in Exercise 8 to approximate the volume of a basketball. Compare this with your answer from Exercise 7.

10. Use the shell method to set up an integral that gives the volume of a basketball.

11. Evaluate the integral you wrote in Exercise 10 to approximate the volume of a basketball. Compare this to your answers from Exercises 7 and 9.

12. Approximate the surface area of a basketball using the formula for the surface area of a sphere.

13. Set up an integral that gives the surface area of a basketball.

14. Use a graphing utility to evaluate the integral you wrote in Exercise 13 to approximate the surface area of a basketball. Compare this to your answer from Exercise 12.

Chapter 8 Integration Techniques, L'Hôpital's Rule, and Improper Integrals

Chapter Summary
Section Topics

8.1 **Basic Integration Rules**—Review procedures for fitting an integrand to one of the basic integration rules.

8.2 **Integration by Parts**—Find an antiderivative using integration by parts. Use a tabular method to perform integration by parts.

8.3 **Trigonometric Integrals**—Solve trigonometric integrals involving powers of sine and cosine. Solve trigonometric integrals involving powers of secant and tangent. Solve trigonometric integrals involving sine-cosine products with different angles.

8.4 **Trigonometric Substitution**—Use trigonometric substitution to solve an integral. Use integrals to model and solve real-life applications.

8.5 **Partial Fractions**—Understand the concept of a partial fraction decomposition. Use partial fraction decomposition with linear factors to integrate rational functions. Use partial fraction decomposition with quadratic factors to integrate rational functions.

8.6 **Integration by Tables and Other Integration Techniques**—Evaluate an indefinite integral using a table of integrals. Evaluate an indefinite integral using reduction formulas. Evaluate an indefinite integral involving rational functions of sine and cosine.

8.7 **Indeterminate Forms and L'Hôpital's Rule**—Recognize limits that produce indeterminate forms. Apply L'Hôpital's Rule to evaluate a limit.

8.8 **Improper Integrals**—Evaluate an improper integral that has an infinite limit of integration. Evaluate an improper integral that has an infinite discontinuity.

Chapter Comments

This chapter and the following one will take up a lot of time. Be prepared to use two class days for most of the sections in this chapter. The first section is a review of all of the integration covered up to this point. Your students should have memorized the list of basic integration rules found on page 522. Besides these basic rules, this section also reviews techniques necessary for integration, such as completing the square. Be sure to go over each of the examples in this section.

When you cover integration by parts in Section 8.2, be sure to do one of the integrals $\int \sec^3 x \, dx$ or $\int \csc^3 x \, dx$. It is important to point out that "parts" is the way to integrate $\int \sec^m x \, dx$, where m is positive and odd.

Sections 8.3 and 8.4 will give many of your students trouble because they do not have their trigonometry memorized. Insist that they learn it and deduct points when the trigonometry is not correct. In Section 8.4, do some problems converting the limits of integration when a new variable is introduced into the problem, such as Example 4 on page 548.

Section 8.5 will take 2 days to cover because most students will need help reviewing how to find partial fractions and how to solve simultaneous equations. Choose your in-class examples carefully in order to review these techniques. Spend the first day on linear factors and the second day working with the quadratic factors.

Besides Integration by Tables, Section 8.6 also covers the technique for integrating rational functions of sine and cosine (page 566). This technique is interesting and worth doing, but do not dwell on it.

When you cover indeterminate forms and L'Hôpital's Rule in Section 8.7, be sure to do Example 5 on page 573 because that limit turns out to be the number e. Some books use this limit as a definition of e and your students need to recognize it, as it comes up in problems later on.

Section 8.8 incorporates the ideas of the previous section.

Section 8.1   Basic Integration Rules

Tips and Tools for Problem Solving

CalcChat.com

Exercises 15–52 (15–50 in *Calculus* 8/e)
To give students more practice, we added Exercises 50 and 52.

Students had trouble with Exercise 35. Be sure to go over Example 4 on page 522 and the technique discussed in the note after Example 4.

Students also had trouble with Exercises 23, 37, and 39. Be sure to go over the procedures for fitting integrands to basic rules on page 523. Of course, your students should memorize the list of basic integration rules on page 522.

Exercises 59–64 (57–60 in *Calculus* 8/e)
To give students more practice, we added Exercises 60 and 61.

Capstone

Page 526, Exercise 90   You can use this exercise to review the following concepts.

* Verifying that two forms of an antiderivative are equivalent

* Using properties of exponents to rewrite an expression

* Using trigonometric identities to rewrite an expression

Use the solution below. Part (a) uses a property of exponents $\left(a^m a^n = a^{m+n}\right)$. Be sure students understand that e^{C_1} is a constant. Part (b) uses the trigonometric identity $\sec^2 x = \tan^2 x + 1$. Be sure students understand that $1 + C_1 = C$.

Solution

(a) They are equivalent because $e^{x+C_1} = e^x \cdot e^{C_1} = Ce^x, C = e^{C_1}$.

(b) They differ by a constant.

$$\sec^2 x + C_1 = \left(\tan^2 x + 1\right) + C_1 = \tan^2 x + C$$

Section 8.2   Integration by Parts

Tips and Tools for Problem Solving

CalcChat.com

Exercises 7–10 (New)
Exercises 1–6 give students practice *identifying* u and dv for finding the integral using integration by parts, but students do not have to evaluate the integral. We added Exercises 7–10 to give students practice in *applying* integration by parts with u and dv given.

To give students more practice, we added Exercises 36 and 37.

Exercises 67–74 (65–70 in *Calculus* 8/e)

To give students more practice, we added Exercises 68 and 71.

Capstone

Page 534, Exercise 78 You can use this exercise to review the following concepts.

- Integration by parts
- *u*-substitution
- Summary of common integrals using integration by parts

Use integration by parts to evaluate each integral in (b), (c), and (e). Note in part (e) that substitution also works.

For the integrals in (a), (d), and (f), use substitution as follows.

(a) Use substitution by letting $u = \ln x$ and $du = \dfrac{1}{x}\,dx$.

(d) Use substitution by letting $u = x^2$ and $du = 2x\,dx$.

(f) Use substitution by letting $u = x^2 + 1$ and $du = 2x\,dx$.

Solution

(a) No
   Substitution

(b) Yes
   $u = \ln x,\ dv = x\,dx$

(c) Yes
   $u = x^2,\ dv = e^{-3x}\,dx$

(d) No
   Substitution

(e) Yes
   $u = x,\ dv = \dfrac{1}{\sqrt{x+1}}\,dx$

   $\left(\text{Substitution also works. Let } u = \sqrt{x+1}.\right)$

(f) No
   Substitution

Section 8.3   Trigonometric Integrals

Tips and Tools for Problem Solving

CalcChat.com

Students have trouble in this section and the next section because they do not have their trigonometry memorized. We give the product-to-sum identities on page 541. We also note the importance of the half-angle formulas in part 3 of the guidelines on page 536 (see the study tip on page 531). A longer list of identities is given on page C19 in Appendix C.3.

To give students more practice, we added Exercises 53 and 56.

Capstone

Page 543, Exercise 88 You can use this exercise to review or to introduce the following concepts.

- Integrals involving powers of sine and cosine
- Integrals involving powers of secant and tangent

In part (a), the first integral can be integrated by letting $u = \sin x$ and $du = \cos x\, dx$. Then apply the Power Rule and integrate as shown below. The second integral would require you to use a half-angle identity and then convert the integrand to odd powers of cosine. So, the first integral is easier to evaluate than the second one.

In part (b), the first integral can be integrated by letting $u = \tan x$ and $du = \sec^2 x\, dx$. Then apply the Power Rule and integrate as shown below. The second integral is more difficult to evaluate because it doesn't fit any of the guidelines for evaluating integrals involving powers of secant and tangent, and it is difficult to try to convert to sines and cosines.

Solution

(a) The second one is more difficult.
The first one is easy:

$$\int \sin^{372} x \cos x\, dx = \frac{\sin^{373} x}{373} + C$$

(b) The second one is more difficult.
The first one is easy:

$$\int \tan^{400} x \sec^2 x\, dx = \frac{\tan^{401} x}{401} + C$$

Section 8.4   Trigonometric Substitution

Tips and Tools for Problem Solving

CalcChat.com

Students have trouble in this section because they do not have their trigonometry memorized. See the note at the beginning of Section 8.3 for more details.

Exercises 1–4 (New)
We added these exercises to give students practice in identifying the trigonometric substitution to use to find an integral without integrating. This allows students to focus on applying the new concept.

Capstone

Page 552, Exercise 62 You can use this exercise to review the following concepts.

- Trigonometric substitution
- *u*-substitution
- Partial fraction decomposition and integrals (previews next section)

The graphs shown on the next page in parts (a) and (c) are provided on transparencies. Note that the identity used in part (c) is the partial fraction decomposition of the rational function given in the integrand. If you have time to go over this, you can use it to preview Section 8.5 without doing the partial fraction decomposition or using the terminology.

Solution

(a) $u = x^2 + 9$, $du = 2x\,dx$

$$\int \frac{x}{x^2 + 9}\,dx = \frac{1}{2}\int \frac{du}{u} = \frac{1}{2}\ln|u| + C = \frac{1}{2}\ln(x^2 + 9) + C$$

Let $x = 3\tan\theta$, $x^2 + 9 = 9\sec^2\theta$, $dx = 3\sec^2\theta\,d\theta$.

$$\int \frac{x}{x^2 + 9}\,dx = \int \frac{3\tan\theta}{9\sec^2\theta}3\sec^2\theta\,d\theta$$

$$= \int \tan\theta\,d\theta$$

$$= -\ln|\cos\theta| + C_1$$

$$= -\ln\left|\frac{3}{\sqrt{x^2 + 9}}\right| + C_1$$

$$= -\ln 3 + \ln\sqrt{x^2 + 9} + C_1 = \frac{1}{2}\ln(x^2 + 9) + C_2$$

The answers are equivalent.

(b) $\displaystyle\int \frac{x^2}{x^2 + 9}\,dx = \int \frac{x^2 + 9 - 9}{x^2 + 9}\,dx = \int\left(1 - \frac{9}{x^2 + 9}\right)dx = x - 3\arctan\left(\frac{x}{3}\right) + C$

Let $x = 3\tan\theta$, $x^2 + 9 = 9\sec^2\theta$, $dx = 3\sec^2\theta\,d\theta$.

$$\int \frac{x^2}{x^2 + 9}\,dx = \int \frac{9\tan^2\theta}{9\sec^2\theta}3\sec^2\theta\,d\theta$$

$$= 3\int \tan^2\theta\,d\theta = 3\int(\sec^2\theta - 1)\,d\theta$$

$$= 3\tan\theta - 3\theta = C_1$$

$$= x - 3\arctan\left(\frac{x}{3}\right) + C_1$$

The answers are equivalent.

(c) $x = 2\sin\theta$, $dx = 2\cos\theta\,d\theta$, $4 - x^2 = 4\cos^2\theta$

$$\int \frac{4}{4 - x^2}\,dx = \int \frac{4 \cdot 2\cos\theta}{4\cos^2\theta}\,d\theta = 2\int \sec\theta\,d\theta$$

$$= 2\ln|\sec\theta + \tan\theta| + C$$

$$= 2\ln\left|\frac{2}{\sqrt{4 - x^2}} + \frac{x}{\sqrt{4 - x^2}}\right| + C$$

$$= \ln\left|\frac{2 + x}{\sqrt{(2 + x)(2 - x)}}\right|^2 + C = \ln\left|\frac{2 + x}{2 - x}\right| + C$$

$$\int \frac{4}{4 - x^2}\,dx = \int\left(\frac{1}{x + 2} - \frac{1}{x - 2}\right)dx = \ln|x + 2| - \ln|x - 2| + C = \ln\left|\frac{x + 2}{x - 2}\right| + C$$

The answers are equivalent.

65

Section 8.5 Partial Fractions

Tips and Tools for Problem Solving

CalcChat.com

According to the data, students need help finding partial fractions and with solving simultaneous equations. In addition to going over the examples in this section, students that need more help should review Section 7.5 of *Precalculus,* 7th edition, by Larson and Hostetler.

Exercises 41–50 (41–46 in *Calculus* 8/e)
To give students more practice, we added Exercises 43, 45, 49, and 50.

Capstone

Page 562, Exercise 62 You can use this exercise to review the following concepts.

- *u*-substitution
- Completing the square
- Partial fractions
- Arctangent rule

For the integral in part (a), use substitution with $u = x^2 + 2x - 8$ and $du = (2x + 2)\,dx$. Then apply the Log Rule.

For the integral in part (b), use partial fractions to rewrite the integrand as $\dfrac{4}{x + 4} + \dfrac{3}{x - 2}$, write the integral as the sum of two integrals, and then apply the Log Rule.

For the integral in part (c), rewrite the integral as $4 \displaystyle\int \dfrac{1}{(x + 1)^2 + 4}\,dx$ and then apply the Arctangent Rule with $u = x + 1$ and $a = 2$. (Note that the denominator is rewritten by completing the square.)

Solution

(a) Substitution: $u = x^2 + 2x - 8$

(b) Partial fractions

(c) Trigonometric substitution (tan) or inverse tangent rule

Section 8.6 Integration by Tables and Other Integration Techniques

Tips and Tools for Problem Solving

CalcChat.com

Although we made changes to the section exercises, no changes were made based on the data.

Capstone

Page 568, Exercise 78 You can use this exercise to review the following concepts.

- Integration by tables
- u-substitution
- Log Rule
- Arctangent Rule
- Integration by parts

As you go over the solution, review the formula or method as much as you think is necessary. As students do more integration problems, they should be getting a better sense of what methods to use.

Solution

(a) Arctangent Formula, Formula 23, $\int \dfrac{1}{u^2 + 1}\, du$, $u = e^x$

(b) Log Rule: $\int \dfrac{1}{u}\, du$, $u = e^x + 1$

(c) Substitution: $u = x^2$, $du = 2x\, dx$

   Then Formula 81.

(d) Integration by parts

(e) Cannot be integrated

(f) Formula 16 with $u = e^{2x}$

Section 8.7 Indeterminate Forms and L'Hôpital's Rule

Tips and Tools for Problem Solving

CalcChat.com

Exercises 11–44 (11–36 in *Calculus* 8/e)
To give students more practice, we added Exercises 19, 20, and 39–44.

Capstone

Page 577, Exercise 88 You can use this exercise to review the following concept.

- L'Hôpital's Rule

Go over Theorem 8.4 and the solution below.

Solution

(a) Yes: $\dfrac{0}{0}$

(b) No: $\dfrac{0}{-1}$

(c) Yes: $\dfrac{\infty}{\infty}$

(d) Yes: $\dfrac{0}{0}$

(e) No: $\dfrac{-1}{0}$

(f) Yes: $\dfrac{0}{0}$

Section 8.8   Improper Integrals

Tips and Tools for Problem Solving

CalcChat.com

Exercises 1–8 (1–4 in *Calculus* 8/e)
To give students more practice, we added Exercises 5–8.

Exercises 37–54 (33–48 in *Calculus* 8/e)
To give students more practice, we added Exercises 51 and 52.

Exercises 59–70 (53–62 in *Calculus* 8/e)
To give students more practice, we added Exercises 67 and 69.

Capstone

Page 589, Exercise 98 You can use this exercise to review the following concepts.

- Improper integral

- Infinite discontinuity

Some students may provide answers where b is ∞. Remind students that ∞ and $-\infty$ do not denote real numbers. The symbols ∞ and $-\infty$ simply are ways to describe unbounded conditions more concisely. Note that some of the integrands have two or more infinite discontinuities, so answers other than those shown below are possible.

Solution

(a) $b = 3$ $\left(\text{infinite discontinuity at } 3\right)$

(b) $b = 4$ $\left(\text{infinite discontinuity at } 4\right)$

(c) $b = 3$ $\left(\text{or } b = 4\right)$ $\left(\text{infinite discontinuity at } 3\right)$

(d) $b = 0$ $\left(\text{infinite discontinuity at } 0\right)$

(e) $b = \pi/4$ $\left(\text{infinite discontinuity at } \pi/4\right)$

(f) $b = \pi/2$ $\left(\text{infinite discontinuity at } \pi/2\right)$

68

Chapter 8 Project

Using Derivatives to Integrate

Repeated integration by parts can be used to show that

$$\int \cos(Ax)e^{Bx}\,dx = De^{Bx}\cos(Ax) + Fe^{Bx}\sin(Ax) + C$$

and

$$\int \sin(Ax)e^{Bx}\,dx = Ge^{Bx}\sin(Ax) - Je^{Bx}\cos(Ax) + C.$$

Exercises

1. Use the given formula to rewrite $\int \cos(3x)e^{4x}\,dx$.

2. Find the derivative of the expression you wrote in Exercise 1.

3. Use $\dfrac{d}{dx}\left[\int \cos(3x)e^{4x}\,dx\right] = \cos(3x)e^{4x}$ to find the values of D and F from Exercise 1.
   What is $\int \cos(3x)e^{4x}\,dx$?

4. Integrate $\int \cos(3x)e^{4x}\,dx$ using integration by parts. Compare the result to your answer from Exercise 3.

5. Rewrite the expression you wrote in Exercise 4 in terms of A, B, and x.

6. Integrate $\int \cos(Ax)e^{Bx}\,dx$ using integration by parts. Compare the result to your answer from Exercise 5.

7. Use the given formula to rewrite $\int \sin(5x)e^{2x}\,dx$.

8. Find the derivative of the expression you wrote in Exercise 7.

9. Use $\dfrac{d}{dx}\left[\int \sin(5x)e^{2x}\,dx\right] = \sin(5x)e^{2x}$ to find the values of G and J. What is
   $\int \sin(5x)e^{2x}\,dx$?

10. Integrate $\int \sin(5x)e^{2x}\,dx$ using integration by parts. Compare the result to your answer to Exercise 9.

11. Rewrite the expression you wrote in Exercise 10 in terms of A, B, and x.

12. Integrate $\int \sin(Ax)e^{Bx}\,dx$ using integration by parts. Compare the result to your answer to Exercise 11.

Chapter 9 Infinite Series

Chapter Summary
Section Topics

9.1 **Sequences**—List the terms of a sequence. Determine whether a sequence converges or diverges. Write a formula for the nth term of a sequence. Use properties of monotonic sequences and bounded sequences.

9.2 **Series and Convergence**—Understand the definition of a convergent infinite series. Use properties of infinite geometric series. Use the nth Term Test for Divergence of an infinite series.

9.3 **The Integral Test and p-Series**—Use the Integral Test to determine whether an infinite series converges or diverges. Use properties of p-series and harmonic series.

9.4 **Comparisons of Series**—Use the Direct Comparison Test to determine whether a series converges or diverges. Use the Limit Comparison Test to determine whether a series converges or diverges.

9.5 **Alternating Series**—Use the Alternating Series Test to determine whether an infinite series converges. Use the Alternating Series Remainder to approximate the sum of an alternating series. Classify a convergent series as absolutely or conditionally convergent. Rearrange an infinite series to obtain a different sum.

9.6 **The Ratio and Root Tests**—Use the Ratio Test to determine whether a series converges or diverges. Use the Root Test to determine whether a series converges or diverges. Review the tests for convergence and divergence of an infinite series.

9.7 **Taylor Polynomials and Approximations**—Find polynomial approximations of elementary functions and compare them with the elementary functions. Find Taylor and Maclaurin polynomial approximations of elementary functions. Use the remainder of a Taylor polynomial.

9.8 **Power Series**—Understand the definition of a power series. Find the radius and interval of convergence of a power series. Determine the endpoint convergence of a power series. Differentiate and integrate a power series.

9.9 **Representation of Functions by Power Series**—Find a geometric power series that represents a function. Construct a power series using series operations.

9.10 **Taylor and Maclaurin Series**—Find a Taylor or Maclaurin series for a function. Find a binomial series. Use a basic list of Taylor series to find other Taylor series.

Chapter Comments

You may want to think of this chapter as two parts. Part I (Sections 9.1 through 9.6) covers sequences and series of constant terms and Part II (Sections 9.7 through 9.10) covers series with variable terms. Part I should be covered quickly so that most of your time in this chapter is spent in Part II.

In Sections 9.1 through 9.6 there are many different kinds of series and many different tests for convergence or divergence. Be sure to go over each of these carefully. It is a good idea to review the basic facts of each test each day before covering the new material for that day. This provides a review for the students and also allows them to see the similarities and differences among tests. The table on page 646 in Section 9.6 is a good way to compare the various tests. Be sure to go over with your students the guidelines for choosing the appropriate test found on page 645.

The nth-Term Test for Divergence, Theorem 9.9 on page 612, is frequently misunderstood. Your students need to know that it proves divergence only and that it says absolutely nothing about convergence.

Sections 9.7 through 9.10 often seem difficult for students, so allow extra time for these sections. You will need to go over the material slowly and do lots of examples. Students should be able to find the coefficients of a Taylor or Maclaurin polynomial, write a Taylor Series, derive a Taylor Series from a basic list, and find the radius of convergence and the interval of convergence. Checking the endpoints should be a matter of recalling Sections 9.2 through 9.6.

Section 9.1   Sequences

Tips and Tools for Problem Solving

CalcChat.com

Exercises 19–22 (New)
To give students more practice with recognizing the correct expression for a sequence's nth term, we added Exercises 19–22.

Exercises 45–72 (47–68 in *Calculus* 8/e)
To give students more practice, we added Exercises 45–48, 68, and 70.

Capstone

Page 606, Exercise 110 You can use this exercise to review the following concepts.

- Monotonic sequence
- Bounded sequence
- Unbounded sequence
- Theorem 9.5

Understanding these concepts is important for students so that they can successfully complete this chapter.

Review the definitions of the concepts listed above and then go over the solution. Note that examples are not unique, so students may write different sequences.

Solution

(a) $a_n = 10 - \dfrac{1}{n}$

(b) Impossible. The sequence converges by Theorem 9.5.

(c) $a_n = \dfrac{3n}{4n + 1}$

(d) Impossible. An unbounded sequence diverges.

Section 9.2   Series and Convergence

Tips and Tools for Problem Solving

CalcChat.com

Exercises 1–6 (1–6 in *Calculus* 8/e)
We rewrote the direction line to clarify that students should find the sequence of partial sums $S_1, S_2, S_3, S_4,$ and S_5.

Exercises 25–30 (23–28 in *Calculus* 8/e)
We reordered the exercises to improve the grading.

Exercises 37–44 (35–42 in *Calculus* 8/e)
We reordered the exercises to improve the grading.

Exercises 59–70 (57–66 in *Calculus* 8/e)
We reordered the exercises to improve the grading. To give students more practice, we added Exercises 64 and 66.

Capstone

Page 615, Exercise 94 You can use this exercise to review the following concepts.

- Theorem 9.8 and its converse

- Theorem 9.9

Go over Theorem 9.8 and note that its converse is not true (see note on page 612 near Theorem 9.8). In both parts (a) and (b) the given information (the expressions approaches 0 as n approach ∞) is irrelevant and Theorem 9.9 does not apply. So, neither statement is true.

Using a CAS, you can find that $\sum_{n=1}^{\infty} \frac{1}{n^4} = \frac{\pi^4}{90}$ and that $\sum_{n=1}^{\infty} \frac{1}{\sqrt[4]{n}}$ diverges. Note that each series in parts (a) and (b) is a p-series, which will be covered in the next section (see Section 9.3).

Solution

(a) False. The fact that $\frac{1}{n^4} \to 0$ is irrelevant to the convergence of $\sum_{n=1}^{\infty} \frac{1}{n^4}$. Furthermore, $\sum_{n=1}^{\infty} \frac{1}{n^4} \neq 0$.

(b) False. The fact that $\frac{1}{\sqrt[4]{n}} \to 0$ is irrelevant to the convergence of $\sum_{n=1}^{\infty} \frac{1}{\sqrt[4]{n}}$. In fact,

$\sum_{n=1}^{\infty} \frac{1}{\sqrt[4]{n}}$ diverges.

Section 9.3   The Integral Test and *p*-Series

Tips and Tools for Problem Solving

CalcChat.com

Exercises 1–24 (1–18 in *Calculus* 8/e)
We revised the direction line to instruct students to confirm that the Integral Test can be applied to the series. To give students more practice, we added Exercises 3, 4, 19, 20, 23, and 24.

Capstone

Page 624, Exercise 56 You can use this exercise to review the following concepts.

- Theorem 9.10

- *p*-series

- Theorem 9.11

Go over Theorem 9.10 and its proof. Then go over the solutions on the next page. The graphs are provided on transparencies. The solutions can be confirmed by noting that each series is a p-series and applying Theorem 9.11.

Solution

(a)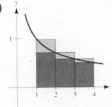

$$\sum_{n=1}^{\infty} \frac{1}{\sqrt{n}} > \int_1^{\infty} \frac{1}{\sqrt{x}}\, dx$$

The area under the rectangles is greater than the area under the curve.

Because $\int_1^{\infty} \frac{1}{\sqrt{x}}\, dx = \left[2\sqrt{x} \right]_1^{\infty} = \infty$, diverges, $\sum_{n=1}^{\infty} \frac{1}{\sqrt{n}}$ diverges.

(b)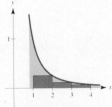

$$\sum_{n=2}^{\infty} \frac{1}{n^2} < \int_1^{\infty} \frac{1}{x^2}\, dx$$

The area under the rectangles is less than the area under the curve.

Because $\int_1^{\infty} \frac{1}{x^2}\, dx = \left[-\frac{1}{x} \right]_1^{\infty} = 1$, converges, $\sum_{n=2}^{\infty} \frac{1}{n^2}$ converges

$\left(\text{and so does } \sum_{n=1}^{\infty} \frac{1}{n^2} \right)$.

Section 9.4 Comparisons of Series

Tips and Tools for Problem Solving

CalcChat.com

Although we made changes to the section exercises, no changes were made based on the data.

Capstone

Page 631, Exercise 54 You can use this exercise to review the following concepts.

- Comparison of series
- *p*-series
- harmonic series

The main point here is that the tests in this section compare *series*, not just a few terms. Also, you can review *p*-series and harmonic series.

Solution

This is not correct. The beginning terms do not affect the convergence or divergence of a series. In fact,

$$\frac{1}{1000} + \frac{1}{1001} + \cdots = \sum_{n=1000}^{\infty} \frac{1}{n} \text{ diverges (harmonic)}$$

and $1 + \dfrac{1}{4} + \dfrac{1}{9} + \cdots = \displaystyle\sum_{n=1}^{\infty} \frac{1}{n^2}$ converges (p-series).

Section 9.5   Alternating Series

Tips and Tools for Problem Solving

CalcChat.com

Exercises 11–36 (11–32 in *Calculus* 8/e)
To give students more practice, we added Exercises 13–16.

Exercises 37–40 (33–36 in *Calculus* 8/e)
We reordered the exercises to improve the grading.

Exercises 51–70 (47–62 in *Calculus* 8/e)
To give students more practice, we added Exercises 51–54.

Capstone

Page 640, Exercise 76 You can use this exercise to review the following concepts.

- Theorem 9.16

- Absolute convergence

- Conditional convergence

Review the above concepts and then go over the solution. In part (a), ask students to classify a_n as absolutely or conditionally convergent.

Solution

(a) False. For example, let $a_n = \dfrac{(-1)^n}{n}$.

Then $\displaystyle\sum a_n = \sum \frac{(-1)^n}{n}$ converges and $\displaystyle\sum (-a_n) = \sum \frac{(-1)^{n+1}}{n}$ converges.

But, $\displaystyle\sum |a_n| = \sum \frac{1}{n}$ diverges.

(b) True. For if $\displaystyle\sum |a_n|$ converged, then so would $\displaystyle\sum a_n$ by Theorem 9.16.

Section 9.6   The Ratio and Root Tests

Tips and Tools for Problem Solving

CalcChat.com

Exercises 13–34 (13–32 in *Calculus* 8/e)
To give students more practice, we added Exercises 13 and 14.

Exercises 35–50 (37–50 in *Calculus* 8/e)
To give students more practice, we added Exercises 35 and 36.

Capstone

Page 649, Exercise 98 You can use this exercise to review the following concepts.

- Ratio Test
- Root Test

Review the Ratio and Root Tests (Theorems 9.17 and 9.18, respectively). Then apply the Ratio Test to parts (a)–(c) and the Root Test to parts (d)–(f).

Solution

(a) Converges   (Ratio Test)

(b) Inconclusive (See Ratio Test)

(c) Diverges   (Ratio Test)

(d) Diverges   (Root Test)

(e) Inconclusive (See Root Test)

(f) Diverges   (Root Test, $e > 1$)

Section 9.7   Taylor Polynomials and Approximations

Tips and Tools for Problem Solving

CalcChat.com

Although we made changes to the section exercises, no changes were made based on the data.

Capstone

Page 659, Exercise 34 You can use this exercise to review the following concepts.

- Taylor polynomials
- Natural exponential function

Go over the definition of *n*th Taylor polynomial. You can also review the natural exponential function and its derivative. The graph in part (b) is provided on a transparency. The conclusions in part (c) are also discussed in Example 2 and the *Technology* note on page 651.

Solution

(a) $f(x) = e^x$ $f(1) = e$

$f'(x) = e^x$ $f'(1) = e$

$f''(x) = f'''(x) = f^{(4)}(x) = e^x$ and $f''(1) = f'''(1) = f^{(4)}(1) = e$

$P_1(x) = e + e(x - 1)$

$P_2(x) = e + e(x - 1) + \dfrac{e}{2}(x - 1)^2$

$P_4(x) = e + e(x - 1) + \dfrac{e}{2}(x - 1)^2 + \dfrac{e}{6}(x - 1)^3 + \dfrac{e}{24}(x - 1)^4$

x	1.00	1.25	1.50	1.75	2.00
e^x	e	3.4093	4.4817	5.7546	7.3891
$P_1(x)$	e	3.3979	4.0774	4.7570	5.4366
$P_2(x)$	e	3.4828	4.4172	5.5215	6.7957
$P_4(x)$	e	3.4903	4.4809	5.7485	7.3620

(b)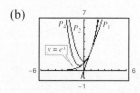

(c) As the degree increases, the accuracy increases. As the distance from x to 1 increases, the accuracy decreases.

Section 9.8   Power Series

Tips and Tools for Problem Solving

CalcChat.com

Although we made changes to the section exercises, no changes were made based on the data.

Capstone

Page 669, Exercise 62 You can use this exercise to review the following concepts.

- Power series

- Radius and interval of convergence

Review the above terms and then go over the solution. Be sure that your students understand that there are many possible answers.

Solution

Many answers possible.

(a) $\displaystyle\sum_{n=1}^{\infty} \left(\dfrac{x}{2}\right)^n$ Geometric: $\left|\dfrac{x}{2}\right| < 1 \Rightarrow |x| < 2$

(b) $\displaystyle\sum_{n=1}^{\infty} \frac{(-1)^n x^n}{n}$ converges for $-1 < x \le 1$

(c) $\displaystyle\sum_{n=1}^{\infty} (2x + 1)^n$ Geometric:

$$|2x + 1| < 1 \Rightarrow -1 < x < 0$$

(d) $\displaystyle\sum_{n=1}^{\infty} \frac{(x - 2)^n}{n4^n}$ converges for $-2 \le x < 6$

Section 9.9 Representation of Functions by Power Series

Tips and Tools for Problem Solving

CalcChat.com

Exercises 5–16 (5–16 in *Calculus* 8/e)
We reordered the exercises to improve the grading. We also revised Exercises 5–9, 11–14, and 16.

Capstone

Page 677, Exercise 64 You can use this exercise to review the following concepts.

- Operations with power series
- Interval of convergence

Review the operations with power series on page 673 and go over the solution. You can also use this exercise to review interval of convergence. Ask students to determine the interval of convergence for each series, $\displaystyle\sum_{n=0}^{\infty} x^n$ and $\displaystyle\sum_{n=0}^{\infty} \left(\frac{x}{5}\right)^n$. The intervals of convergence are $(-1, 1)$

and $(-5, 5)$, respectively. What is the interval of convergence for the sum $\displaystyle\sum_{n=0}^{\infty} x^n + \sum_{n=0}^{\infty} \left(\frac{x}{5}\right)^n$?

The answer is the intersection of the intervals of convergence of the two original series, $(-1, 1)$.

Solution

You can verify that the statement is incorrect by calculating the constant terms of each side:

$$\sum_{n=0}^{\infty} x^n + \sum_{n=0}^{\infty} \left(\frac{x}{5}\right)^n = (1 + 1) + \left(x + \frac{x}{5}\right) + \cdots$$

$$\sum_{n=0}^{\infty} \left(1 + \frac{1}{5}\right) x^n = \left(1 + \frac{1}{5}\right) + \left(1 + \frac{1}{5}\right) x + \cdots$$

The formula should be $\displaystyle\sum_{n=0}^{\infty} x^n + \sum_{n=0}^{\infty} \left(\frac{x}{5}\right)^n = \sum_{n=0}^{\infty} \left[1 + \left(\frac{1}{5}\right)^n\right] x^n$.

Section 9.10   Taylor and Maclaurin Series

Tips and Tools for Problem Solving

CalcChat.com

Exercises 1–12 (1–10 in *Calculus* 8/e)
To give students more practice, we added Exercises 5 and 6.

Exercises 17–26 (15–20 in *Calculus* 8/e)
To give students more practice, we added Exercises 18, 20, 22, and 23.

Exercises 27–40 (21–30 in *Calculus* 8/e)
To give students more practice, we added Exercises 29, 30, 32, and 34.

Exercises 63–66 (53 and 54 in *Calculus* 8/e)
To give students more practice, we added Exercises 65 and 66.

Exercises 67–74 (55–58 in *Calculus* 8/e)
We reordered the exercises to improve the grading. To give students more practice, we added Exercises 67, 70, 72, and 74.

Capstone

Page 688, Exercise 86   You can use this exercise to review the following concepts.

- Power series

- Natural exponential function

Review the power series for the natural exponential function. Then go over the solution.

Solution

(a) Replace x with $(-x)$.

(b) Replace x with $3x$.

(c) Multiply series by x.

(d) Replace x with $2x$, then replace x with $-2x$, and add the two together.

Chapter 9 Project

Chasing A Pot of Gold

You are standing at the beginning of a sidewalk, 1000 meters from a pot of gold. You walk toward the pot of gold at a rate of 1 meter per second. After each second, the sidewalk stretches uniformly and instantaneously, increasing its length by 1000 meters.

Exercises

1. What is the total length of the sidewalk after 1 second?

2. How far are you from the pot of gold after 1 second?

3. What is the total length of the sidewalk after 2 seconds?

4. How far are you from the pot of gold after 2 seconds?

In Exercises 5–11, consider the sequence $\{d_n\}$ where d_n is your distance from the pot of gold after n seconds but before the road stretches.

5. Find d_0, d_1, d_2, d_3, and d_4.

6. Find an expression for d_1 in terms of d_0. Similarly, find an expression for d_2, d_3, and d_4 in terms of d_1, d_2, and d_3, respectively.

7. Use the expressions you wrote in Exercise 6 to show that $d_1 = 1(d_0 - 1)$,
$$d_2 = 2\left(d_0 - \left(1 + \tfrac{1}{2}\right)\right), \text{ and } d_3 = 3\left[d_0 - \left(1 + \tfrac{1}{2} + \tfrac{1}{3}\right)\right].$$

8. Use the results from Exercise 7 to write an expression for d_n in terms of d_0.

9. Does the series $\displaystyle\sum_{k=1}^{\infty} \frac{1}{k}$ converge or diverge? What theorem did you use?

10. What does your answer to Exercise 9 imply about the value of d_n for large values of n? What does this mean in the context of the problem?

11. Use the integral $\displaystyle\int_{1}^{n+1} \frac{1}{x}\, dx$ to approximate how long it will take to reach the pot of gold.

In Exercises 12 and 13, suppose the sidewalk is still 1000 meters long, but you walk toward the pot of gold at a speed of 0.25 meter per second.

12. Write an expression for d_n in terms of d_0.

13. Will you reach the pot of gold? If so, approximately how long will it take?

In Exercises 14 and 15, suppose the sidewalk is 5000 meters long, you walk toward the pot of gold at a speed of 1 meter per second, and the sidewalk stretches 5000 meters after every second.

14. Write an expression for d_n in terms of d_0.

15. Will you reach the pot of gold? If so, approximately how long will it take?

16. Does the length of the sidewalk or the speed at which you walk impact whether you reach the pot of gold? Explain.

Chapter 10 Conics, Parametric Equations, and Polar Coordinates

Chapter Summary

Section Topics

10.1 **Conics and Calculus**—Understand the definition of a conic section. Analyze and write equations of parabolas using properties of parabolas. Analyze and write equations of ellipses using properties of ellipses. Analyze and write equations of hyperbolas using properties of hyperbolas.

10.2 **Plane Curves and Parametric Equations**—Sketch the graph of a curve given by a set of parametric equations. Eliminate the parameter in a set of parametric equations. Find a set of parametric equations to represent a curve. Understand two classic calculus problems: Tautochrone and brachistochrone problems.

10.3 **Parametric Equations and Calculus**—Find the slope of a tangent line to a curve given by a set of parametric equations. Find the arc length of a curve given by a set of parametric equations. Find the area of a surface of revolution (parametric form).

10.4 **Polar Coordinates and Polar Graphs**—Understand the polar coordinate system. Rewrite rectangular coordinates and equations in polar form and vice versa. Sketch the graph of an equation given in polar form. Find the slope of a tangent line to a polar graph. Identify several types of special polar graphs.

10.5 **Area and Arc Length in Polar Coordinates**—Find the area of a region bounded by a polar graph. Find the points of intersection of two polar graphs. Find the arc length of a polar graph. Find the area of a surface of revolution (polar form).

10.6 **Polar Equations of Conics and Kepler's Laws**—Analyze and write polar equations of conics. Understand and use Kepler's Laws of planetary motion.

Chapter Comments

For each of the conics (parabola, circle, ellipse, and hyperbola), your students should be able to write the equation in standard form, identify the center, radius, vertices, foci, directrix, axes, or asymptotes, and sketch the graph using these facts. Many of these concepts will be used when quadric surfaces are discussed in Section 11.6. A review of the circle can be found in Appendix C.

Eccentricity for ellipses is discussed on page 701 and for hyperbolas on page 704. For a discussion of rotation of axes and the use of the discriminant to determine which conic the general second-degree equation represents, see Appendix D.

Be sure to do some of the real life applications in Section 10.1, such as the length of a parabolic cable used for a bridge (Exercise 91 on page 708).

When you discuss parametric equations in Section 10.2, be sure to point out to your students that a parametric representation for a curve is not unique. Therefore, their answers may be correct, yet they may not agree with those provided in the back of the book. The process of writing parametric equations for a given rectangular equation should convince your students of this. The opposite process, eliminating the parameter, sometimes involves adjusting the domain, as in Example 2 of Section 10.2. When graphing in parametric form, have your students note the orientation. For example, $x = 2 \cos \theta$ and $y = 2 \sin \theta$ graphs a circle counterclockwise, but $x = 2 \sin \theta$ and $y = 2 \cos \theta$ graphs the same circle clockwise.

Parametric form of the derivative is discussed in Section 10.3. Be sure to point out to your students that the slope of the tangent line is $\dfrac{dy}{dx}$ and not $\dfrac{dy}{dt}$. Students very often have difficulty with the higher order derivatives with respect to x. For example, to find $\dfrac{d^2y}{dx^2}$, they forget to divide $\dfrac{d}{dt}\left(\dfrac{dy}{dx}\right)$ by $\dfrac{dx}{dt}$. Arc length for parametric equations of a curve is a concept that will be expanded in 3-space (Section 12.5).

Polar coordinates, discussed in Section 10.4, use only radian measure for the angle θ. Point out to your students that when plotting points in polar coordinates, it is usually easier to find the angle first and then mark off r units on the terminal side of the angle. Note, too, that contrary to rectangular coordinates, a point can be represented many ways in polar coordinates. Students should know the equations for coordinate conversion found in Theorem 10.10 on page 732.

Curve sketching in polar coordinates can be time consuming and tedious. Don't get bogged down in this. Your students should easily recognize limaçons and rose curves from the equation and be able to sketch them quickly. Use a graphing calculator and note the orientation.

Area, discussed in Section 10.5, is an important idea for a good understanding of polar coordinates. The difficulty here is in finding the limits of integration. Note that there may be points of intersection of two curves given in polar coordinates that do not show up from solving simultaneously. Therefore, it is necessary to graph the curves.

Section 10.6 on conics in polar form may be omitted if time is a problem in your course.

Section 10.1 Conics and Calculus

Tips and Tools for Problem Solving

CalcChat.com

Although we made changes to the section exercises, no changes were made based on the data.

Capstone

Page 709, Exercise 102 You can use this exercise to review the following concepts.

- Circle
- Parabola
- Ellipse
- Hyperbola

A review of the circle can be found in Appendix C. A discussion of the use of the discriminant to determine which conic the general second-degree equation represents can be found in Appendix D.

Go over the solution on the next page. You can extend the exercise by asking students to identify the center, radius, vertices, foci, directrix, axes, or asymptotes, and sketch the graph using these facts.

In part (d), you could also eliminate the x^2-term.

Solution

$$9x^2 + 4y^2 - 36x - 24y - 36 = 0$$

(a) $9(x^2 - 4x + 4) + 4(y^2 - 6y + 9) = 36 + 36 + 36$

$\quad\quad 9(x - 2)^2 + 4(y - 3)^2 = 108$

$\quad\quad \dfrac{(x - 2)^2}{12} + \dfrac{(y - 3)^2}{27} = 1$

Ellipse

(b) $9x^2 - 4y^2 - 36x - 24y - 36 = 0$

$\quad\quad 9(x^2 - 4x + 4) - 4(y^2 + 6y + 9) = 36 + 36 - 36$

$\quad\quad \dfrac{(x - 2)^2}{4} - \dfrac{(y + 3)^2}{9} = 1$

Hyperbola

(c) $4x^2 + 4y^2 - 36x - 24y - 36 = 0$

$\quad\quad 4\left(x^2 - 9x + \dfrac{81}{4}\right) + 4(y^2 - 6y + 9) = 36 + 81 + 36$

$\quad\quad \left(x - \dfrac{9}{2}\right)^2 + (y - 3)^2 = \dfrac{153}{4}$

Circle

(d) Sample answer: Eliminate the y^2-term

Section 10.2 Plane Curves and Parametric Equations

Tips and Tools for Problem Solving

CalcChat.com ⊙

Although we made changes to the section exercises, no changes were made based on the data. Be sure that your students understand that a parametric representation for a curve is not unique. So, their answers may be correct, yet they may not agree with those provided in the text.

Capstone

Page 720, Exercise 74 You can use this exercise to review the following concepts.

- Parametric equations

- Eliminating the parameter

- Transformation of a graph

- Orientation of a curve

In part (a), eliminate the parameter t to obtain a rectangular equation of the circle. Sketch a graph and note the orientation. The parametric equations in part (b) represent a horizontal shift 3 units right and a vertical shift 6 units up of the circle described in part (a). In part (c), the parametric equations are $x = 8 \sin t$ and $y = 8 \cos t$. You may need to sketch the graphs or use a table of values (see the next page) to convince students that the orientation is reversed. They can also see the orientation by using a graphing utility in *parametric mode* to graph the circles.

t	0	$\dfrac{\pi}{4}$	$\dfrac{\pi}{2}$	$\dfrac{3\pi}{4}$	π
$x = 8\cos t$	8	$4\sqrt{2}$	0	$-4\sqrt{2}$	-8
$x = 8\sin t$	0	$4\sqrt{2}$	8	$4\sqrt{2}$	0

t	0	$\dfrac{\pi}{4}$	$\dfrac{\pi}{2}$	$\dfrac{3\pi}{4}$	π
$x = 8\sin t$	0	$4\sqrt{2}$	8	$4\sqrt{2}$	0
$x = 8\cos t$	8	$4\sqrt{2}$	0	$-4\sqrt{2}$	-8

In general, the graph of the parametric equations

$x = h + r\cos\theta$ and $y = h + r\sin\theta,\ 0 \le \theta \le 2\pi$

is the circle (traced counterclockwise) given by

$(x - h)^2 + (y - k)^2 = r^2.$

In general, the graph of the parametric equations

$x = h + r\sin\theta$ and $y = h + r\cos\theta,\ 0 \le \theta \le 2\pi$

is the circle (traced clockwise) given by

$(x - h)^2 + (y - k)^2 = r^2.$

Solution

$x = 8\cos t,\ y = 8\sin t$

(a) $\left(\dfrac{x}{8}\right)^2 + \left(\dfrac{y}{8}\right)^2 = \cos^2 t + \sin^2 t = 1$

    $x^2 + y^2 = 64$ Circle radius 8,

    Center: $(0, 0)$ Oriented counterclockwise

(b) Circle of radius 8, but Center: $(3, 6)$

(c) The orientation is reversed.

Section 10.3 Parametric Equations and Calculus

Tips and Tools for Problem Solving

CalcChat.com

Exercises 15–18 (15 and 16 in *Calculus* 8/e)
To give students more practice, we added Exercises 17 and 18.

Exercises 49–56 (47–52 in *Calculus* 8/e)
To give students more practice, we added Exercises 49 and 51.

Capstone

Page 729, Exercise 82 You can use this exercise to review the following concepts.

- Graphs of parametric equations

- Derivatives of parametric equations

There are many possible answers. Sample answers are given below. Note in part (a) that
$dx/dt = 1 > 0$ and $dy/dt = -1 < 0$. In part (b), $dx/dt = -1 < 0$ and $dy/dt = -1 < 0$.

Solution

(a) One possible answer is the graph given by $x = t$, $y = -t$.

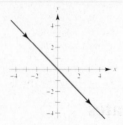

(b) One possible answer is the graph given by $x = -t$, $y = -t$.

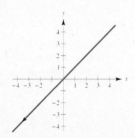

Section 10.4   Polar Coordinates and Polar Graphs

Tips and Tools for Problem Solving

CalcChat.com

Exercises 27–36 (27–34 in *Calculus* 8/e)
To give students more practice, we added Exercises 27 and 28.

Exercises 37–46 (35–42 in *Calculus* 8/e)
To give students more practice, we added Exercises 45 and 46.

Capstone

Page 739, Exercise 104 You can use this exercise to review the following concepts.

- Polar coordinates

- Theorem 10.10

- Polar-to-rectangular conversion

- Identifying the graph of a polar equation

Review the definition of polar coordinates and Theorem 10.10 (see pages 731 and 732). Then go over the solution on the next page. Have students confirm these results by using a graphing utility in *polar mode* to graph the equations.

Solution

(a) $r = 7$: Circle radius 7 centered at origin

(b) $r^2 = 7$: Circle radius $\sqrt{7}$ centered at origin

(c) $r = \dfrac{7}{\cos \theta} \Rightarrow r \cos \theta = x = 7$: Vertical line through the point $(7, 0)$

(d) $r = \dfrac{7}{\sin \theta} \Rightarrow r \sin \theta = y = 7$: Horizontal line through the point $(0, 7)$

(e) $r = 7 \cos \theta$: Circle radius $\dfrac{7}{2}$ centered at $\left(\dfrac{7}{2}, 0 \right)$

(f) $r = 7 \cos \theta$: Circle radius $\dfrac{7}{2}$ centered at $\left(0, \dfrac{7}{2} \right)$

Section 10.5   Area and Arc Length in Polar Coordinates

Tips and Tools for Problem Solving

CalcChat.com

Exercises 5–16 (7–12 in *Calculus* 8/e)
To give students more practice, we added Exercises 5, 6, and 13–16.

Exercises 17–24 (13–16 in *Calculus* 8/e)
To give students more practice, we added Exercises 18, 19, 23, and 24.

Exercises 39–46 (31–36 in Calculus 8/e)
To give students more practice, we added Exercises 44 and 45.

Exercises 55–60 (45–48 in *Calculus* 8/e)
To give students more practice, we added Exercises 55 and 57.

Capstone

Page 749, Exercise 76 You can use this exercise to review the following concepts.

- Sketching the graph of a polar equation
- Finding the area of a region bounded by a polar graph using a geometric formula
- Finding the area of a region bounded by a polar graph using Theorem 10.13

Sketch the graph and determine the interval that traces the graph only once. In both cases the interval is $0 \leq \theta < \pi$. You may need to demonstrate this using a table of values or showing how the graph is traced out on a graphing utility in *polar mode*. The geometric formula for area of a circle is $A = \pi r^2$. Because the radius in part (a) is 5, the area is 25π. Because the radius in part (b) is $5/2$, the area is $25\pi/4$. To use integration to find the area, apply Theorem 10.13 as follows.

(a) $A = 2\left(\dfrac{1}{2}\right)\displaystyle\int_0^{\pi/2}\left[10\cos\theta\right]^2 d\theta$

$\quad = 100\displaystyle\int_0^{\pi/2}\cos^2\theta\, d\theta$

$\quad = 50\displaystyle\int_0^{\pi/2}\left(1 + \cos 2\theta\right) d\theta$

$\quad = 50\left[\theta + \dfrac{\sin 2\theta}{2}\right]_0^{\pi/2}$

$\quad = 25\pi$

(b) $A = 2\left(\dfrac{1}{2}\right)\displaystyle\int_0^{\pi/2}\left[5\sin\theta\right]^2 d\theta$

$\quad = 25\displaystyle\int_0^{\pi/2}\sin^2\theta\, d\theta$

$\quad = \dfrac{25}{2}\displaystyle\int_0^{\pi/2}\left(1 - \cos 2\theta\right) d\theta$

$\quad = \dfrac{25}{2}\left[\theta - \dfrac{\sin 2\theta}{2}\right]_0^{\pi/2}$

$\quad = \dfrac{25\pi}{4}$

Solution

(a) $r = 10\cos\theta,\ 0 \le \theta < \pi$

   Circle of radius 5

   Area $= 25\pi$

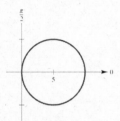

(b) $r = 5\sin\theta,\ 0 \le \theta < \pi$

   Circle of radius 5/2

   Area $= \dfrac{25}{4}\pi$

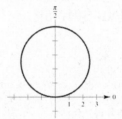

Section 10.6   Polar Equations of Conics and Kepler's Laws

Tips and Tools for Problem Solving

CalcChat.com

Exercises 13–26 (13–22 in *Calculus* 8/e)
To give students more practice, we added Exercises 13, 14, 25, and 26.

Exercises 27–30 (23–26 in *Calculus* 8/e)
We rewrote the direction line to ask students to find the eccentricity of the graph.

Exercises 61–64 (55 and 56 in *Calculus* 8/e)
To give students more practice, we added Exercises 62 and 64.

Capstone

Page 756, Exercise 54 You can use this exercise to review the following concepts.

- Parabolas

- Polar equations of parabolas

- Theorems 10.16 and 10.17

Go over Theorems 10.16 and 10.17, and then the solution given on the next page. Have students confirm these results by using a graphing utility in *polar mode* to graph the equations.

Solution

$r = \dfrac{4}{1 + \sin\theta}$ is a parabola with horizontal directrix above the pole.

(a) Parabola with vertical directrix to left of pole.

(b) Parabola with horizontal directrix below pole.

(c) Parabola with vertical directrix to right of pole.

(d) Parabola (b) rotated counterclockwise $\pi/4$.

87

Chapter 10 Project

Path of a Baseball

A baseball is hit 3 feet above home plate at a $45°$ angle with the horizontal. Its initial speed is 100 feet per second. The path of the baseball at any time t (in seconds) is given by the parametric equations

$$x = 100(\cos 45°)t \text{ and } y = 3 + 100(\sin 45°)t - 16t^2.$$

Exercises

1. Find $\dfrac{dy}{dx}$.

2. At what time is the ball at its maximum height?

3. What is the maximum height of the ball?

4. When the ball is at its maximum height, what is its vertical velocity?

5. When the ball is at its maximum height, what is its horizontal velocity?

6. How long is the ball in the air?

7. How far is the ball from home plate when it hits the ground?

8. Find the value of $\dfrac{dy}{dx}$ at the instant the ball hits the ground. What does this mean in the context of the problem?

9. What is the vertical velocity of the ball at impact?

10. What is the horizontal velocity of the ball at impact?

11. A 14-foot fence is located 300 feet from home plate. Will the ball clear the fence? Explain.

12. Set up a definite integral to determine the total length of the path traveled by the ball.

13. Use a graphing utility to evaluate the integral you wrote in Exercise 12. Compare this to your answer from Exercise 7.

14. Find a rectangular equation for the position of the ball by eliminating the parameter t.

15. Find the derivative of the function you wrote in Exercise 14.

16. According to the rectangular equation, for what value of x is the ball at its maximum height?

17. Use your answer from Exercise 16 and the equation $x = 100(\cos 45°)t$ to find when the ball is at its maximum height. Compare this to your answer from Exercise 2.

18. Why is it beneficial to express the path of the baseball with parametric equations rather than a rectangular equation? Explain.

Chapter 11   Vectors and the Geometry of Space

Chapter Summary

Section Topics

11.1   **Vectors in the Plane**—Write the component form of a vector. Perform vector operations and interpret the results geometrically. Write a vector as a linear combination of standard unit vectors. Use vectors to solve problems involving force or velocity.

11.2   **Space Coordinates and Vectors in Space**—Understand the three-dimensional rectangular coordinate system. Analyze vectors in space. Use three-dimensional vectors to solve real-life problems.

11.3   **The Dot Product of Two Vectors**—Use properties of the dot product of two vectors. Find the angle between two vectors using the dot product. Find the direction cosines of a vector in space. Find the projection of a vector onto another vector. Use vectors to find the work done by a constant force.

11.4   **The Cross Product of Two Vectors in Space**—Find the cross product of two vectors in space. Use the triple scalar product of three vectors in space.

11.5   **Lines and Planes in Space**—Write a set of parametric equations for a line in space. Write a linear equation to represent a plane in space. Sketch the plane given by a linear equation. Find the distances between points, planes, and lines in space.

11.6   **Surfaces in Space**—Recognize and write equations of cylindrical surfaces. Recognize and write equations of quadric surfaces. Recognize and write equations of surfaces of revolution.

11.7   **Cylindrical and Spherical Coordinates**—Use cylindrical coordinates to represent surfaces in space. Use spherical coordinates to represent surfaces in space.

Chapter Comments

All of the ideas in this chapter need to be discussed in order for your students to have a good understanding of vectors. Point out to your students that vectors are not little pointed arrows, but that a directed line segment is just our way of representing a vector geometrically. Also note that this geometric representation of a vector does not have location. It does have direction and magnitude. On page 785 in the text is a Note about the words perpendicular, orthogonal, and normal. This is worth discussing with your students because sometimes it seems that these words are used interchangeably.

The dot product of two vectors is sometimes referred to as scalar multiplication and the cross product as vector multiplication. The reason for this is because the dot product is a *scalar* and the cross product is a *vector*. Point out this distinction to your students. The way to find a cross product is to use a 3 by 3 determinant. You will probably have to show your students how to calculate this.

When discussing lines and planes in space, Section 11.5, point out to your students that direction numbers are not unique. If a, b, c is a set of direction numbers for a line or a plane, then ka, kb, kc where $k \in R$, $k \neq 0$, is also a set of direction numbers for that line or plane.

The distance formulas in Section 11.5 between a point and a plane and between a point and a line need not be memorized. However, go over these so that the students know where they are when they need to look them up.

It is important for your students to be familiar with the surfaces in space discussed in Section 11.6. The concepts in Chapters 14 and 15 will be much easier if the student immediately recognizes from the given equation which of the six surfaces on pages 814 and 815 is under discussion.

Two alternate coordinate systems are discussed in Section 11.7. The cylindrical coordinate system should be familiar to your students because it is an extension of the polar coordinate system in the plane. However, the spherical coordinate system will probably be new to your students. Time spent here understanding this system will be rewarded in Chapters 14 and 15 when you are performing multiple integrations.

Section 11.1   Vectors in the Plane

Tips and Tools for Problem Solving

CalcChat.com

Exercises 9–16 (9–16 in *Calculus* 8/e)
We rewrote the direction line to include a new part (c) that asks students to write the vector as the linear combination of the standard unit vectors **i** and **j** (see Example 5).

Exercises 31–36 (31–36 in *Calculus* 8/e)
We reordered the exercises to improve the grading.

Exercises 47–50 (47–50 in *Calculus* 8/e)
We reordered the exercises to improve the grading.

Exercises 69–74 (69–74 in *Calculus* 8/e)
We rewrote the direction line, replacing "normal" with "perpendicular," because we have not defined normal.

Capstone

Page 773, Exercise 78 You can use this exercise to review the following concepts.

- Writing the component form of a vector

- Writing a vector as a linear combination of standard unit vectors

- Sketching a vector

- Finding the magnitude of a vector

Go over the above concepts and the solution below.

Solution

(a) $\mathbf{v} = \langle 9 - 3, 1 - (-4) \rangle = \langle 6, 5 \rangle$

(b) $\mathbf{v} = 6\mathbf{i} + 5\mathbf{j}$

(c)

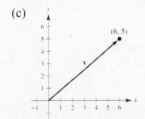

(d) $\|\mathbf{v}\| = \sqrt{6^2 + 5^2} = \sqrt{61}$

Section 11.2   Space Coordinates and Vectors in Space

Tips and Tools for Problem Solving

CalcChat.com

Exercises 1–6 (1–6 in *Calculus* 8/e)
We reordered the exercises to improve the grading.

Exercises 49–52 (49–52 in *Calculus* 8/e)
We rewrote the direction line to include a new part (b) asking students to write the vector using standard unit vector notation (see Example 6).

Exercises 57 and 58 (57 and 58 in *Calculus* 8/e)
We rewrote the direction line to include a new part (c) asking students to write the vector using standard unit vector notation (see Example 6).

Capstone

Page 781, Exercise 90   You can use this exercise to review the following concepts.

- Recognizing a geometric figure generated by the terminal points of three vectors
- Vector addition
- Scalar multiplication

The figure given in the solution is a sample figure and is provided on a transparency. However, the end result, the terminal points of the vectors are collinear, is the same. As you go over the solution, you can review vector operations such as addition and scalar multiplication.

Solution

The terminal points of the vectors $t\mathbf{v}$, $\mathbf{u} + t\mathbf{v}$ and $s\mathbf{u} + t\mathbf{v}$ are collinear.

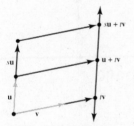

Section 11.3   The Dot Product of Two Vectors

Tips and Tools for Problem Solving

CalcChat.com

Exercises 43–50 (43–50 in *Calculus* 8/e)
These exercises used to be separate blocks. We combined them under the direction line for old 47–50. Vector $\mathbf{w}_1$ is no longer given. Also, we reordered the exercises and wrote some of the vectors using standard unit vector notation.

We also revised the example that corresponds to these exercises (Example 4 on page 787). In the example, we changed the vectors involved and redrew Figure 11.30 to show that the initial point of $\mathbf{w}_1$ is not $(4, 3)$, but $(0, 0)$.

Exercises 75 and 76 (New)
To give students more practice doing work problems, we added Exercises 75 and 76.

Exercises 81–84 (79–82 in *Calculus* 8/e)
We rewrote the direction line to include a new part (a) that asks students to find all points of intersection of the graphs of the two equations.

Capstone

Page 790, Exercise 58 You can use this exercise to review the following concepts.

- Definition of dot product

- Angle between two vectors (Theorem 11.5)

- Definition of orthogonal vectors

- Acute and obtuse angles

Go over the definition of dot product and Theorem 11.5. Then go over the solution below. You can illustrate these results using Figure 11.25 on page 785 and with the following examples.

(a) Example 2(b), page 785

(b) Exercise 15, page 789

(c) Example 2(a), page 785

Solution

(a) Orthogonal, $\theta = \dfrac{\pi}{2}$

(b) Acute, $0 < \theta < \dfrac{\pi}{2}$

(c) Obtuse, $\dfrac{\pi}{2} < \theta < \pi$

Section 11.4   The Cross Product of Two Vectors in Space

Tips and Tools for Problem Solving

CalcChat.com

Exercises 11–16 (11–16 in *Calculus* 8/e)
We reordered the exercises to improve the grading.

Exercises 17–20 (17–20 in *Calculus* 8/e)
Some students were confused by the *y*-axis tick label "4" $\left(\text{some thought if meant that } \mathbf{u} = \langle 3, 5, 4 \rangle\right)$, so we deleted the 4.

Capstone

Page 799, Exercise 54 You can use this exercise to review the following concepts.

- Definition of cross product

- Geometric properties of the cross product (Theorem 11.8)

Review the definition of cross product (see page 792) and the first geometric property of the cross product (see Theorem 11.8, page 794). Then go over the solution below. If desired, you can do an example. Let $A(0, 0, 0)$, $B(1, 2, 3)$, and $C(-3, 0, 0)$ be vertices of a triangle. The vectors for two sides of the triangle are

$$\langle 1 - 0, 2 - 0, 3 - 0 \rangle = \langle 1, 2, 3 \rangle \text{ and } \langle -3 - 0, 0 - 0, 0 - 0 \rangle = \langle -3, 0, 0 \rangle.$$

The cross product is

$$\langle 1, 2, 3 \rangle \times \langle -3, 0, 0 \rangle = \langle 0, -9, 6 \rangle.$$

So, the vector $\langle 0, -9, 6 \rangle$ is perpendicular to triangle ABC.

Solution

Form the vectors for two sides of the triangle, and compute their cross product.

$$\langle x_2 - x_1, y_2 - y_1, z_2 - z_1 \rangle \times \langle x_3 - x_1, y_3 - y_1, z_3 - z_1 \rangle$$

Section 11.5 Lines and Planes in Space

Tips and Tools for Problem Solving

CalcChat.com

Exercises 3 and 4 (New)
To give students more practice with lines and points in space, we added Exercises 3 and 4.

Exercises 27–30 (25 and 26 in *Calculus* 8/e)
To give students more practice, we added Exercises 28 and 30.

Exercises 39 and 40 (New)
To give students more practice with planes and points in space, we added Exercises 39 and 40.

Exercises 83–86 (75 and 76 in *Calculus* 8/e)
To give students more practice, we added Exercises 83 and 84.

Exercises 91 and 92 (81 and 82 in *Calculus* 8/e)
We rewrote the direction line to include a new part (a) that asks students to find the angle between the two planes.

Capstone

Page 810, Exercise 118 You can use this exercise to review the following concepts.

- Parametric equations of a line (Theorem 11.11)
- Symmetric equations of a line
- Standard equation of a plane in space (Theorem 11.12)
- General form of an equation of a plane in space

Go over the definitions of each concept listed above (see pages 800 and 801). Then note which equation or set of equations matches the correct choice.

Solution

(a) Matches (iii)

(b) Matches (i)

(c) Matches (iv)

(d) Matches (ii)

Section 11.6   Surfaces in Space

Tips and Tools for Problem Solving

CalcChat.com

Exercises 19–32 (19–30 in *Calculus* 8/e)
To give students more practice, we added Exercises 22 and 23.

Capstone

Page 821, Exercise 58   You can use this exercise to review the following concepts.

- Recognizing the generating curve for a cylinder

- Recognizing equations for cylindrical surfaces

Go over the definition of a cylinder and equations of cylinders on page 812. Then go over the solution. A graph of the cylinder is shown below and is provided on a transparency. The generating curve is a parabola in the *xz*-plane. The rulings of the cylinder are parallel to the *y*-axis.

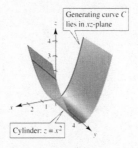

Solution

In the *xz*-plane, $z = x^2$ is a parabola.

In the three-space, $z = x^2$ is a cylinder.

11.7 Cylindrical and Spherical Coordinates

Tips and Tools for Problem Solving

CalcChat.com

Exercises 7–12 (7–12 in *Calculus* 8/e)
We reordered the exercises to improve the grading.

Exercises 21–28 (21–28 in *Calculus* 8/e)
We reordered the exercises to improve the grading.

Capstone

Page 828, Exercise 98   You can use this exercise to review the following concepts.

- Cylindrical coordinates and surfaces in space

- Spherical coordinates and surfaces in space

Go over the cylindrical coordinate system (see page 822). As you go over part (a), refer to Figures 11.69 and 11.70. Then go over the spherical coordinate system (see page 825). As you go over part (b), refer to Figure 11.76.

Solution

(a) $r = a$ Cylinder with z-axis symmetry

    $\theta = b$ Plane perpendicular to xy-plane

    $z = c$ Plane parallel to xy-plane

(b) $\rho = a$ Sphere

    $\theta = b$ Vertical half-plane

    $\phi = c$ Half-cone

Chapter 11 Project

Bond Angles

The study of the properties of molecules involves determining a molecule's three-dimensional, geometrical arrangement or molecular structure. Molecular structure is described in terms of bond distances and bond angles. A bond distance is defined as the distance of the straight line connecting the nuclei of two bonded atoms. A bond angle is the angle between any two bonded distances that include a common atom.

Exercises

Use the figure at the right as a representation of a methane molecule, CH_4. The hydrogen atoms are located at $(0, 0, 0)$, $(1, 1, 0)$, $(1, 0, 1)$, and $(0, 1, 1)$, and the carbon atom is located at $\left(\dfrac{1}{2}, \dfrac{1}{2}, \dfrac{1}{2} \right)$.

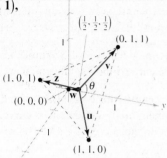

1. Find the component form of **u**.

2. Find $\|\mathbf{u}\|$.

3. Find the component form of **v**.

4. Find $\|\mathbf{v}\|$.

5. Find $\mathbf{u} \cdot \mathbf{v}$.

6. Use your answers from Exercises 1–5 to determine the bond angle between the hydrogen atoms located at $(1, 1, 0)$ and $(0, 1, 1)$.

7. Determine the bond distance between the hydrogen atoms located at $(1, 1, 0)$ and $(0, 1, 1)$.

8. Find $\|\mathbf{w}\|$ and $\|\mathbf{z}\|$.

In Exercises 9–13, determine the bond angle and the distance between the hydrogen atoms located at the given points.

9. $(0, 0, 0)$ and $(1, 1, 0)$

10. $(1, 0, 1)$ and $(1, 1, 0)$

11. $(0, 1, 1)$ and $(0, 0, 0)$

12. $(0, 1, 1)$ and $(1, 0, 1)$

13. $(0, 0, 0)$ and $(1, 0, 1)$

14. Classify the triangles formed by connecting the nuclei of two hydrogen atoms and the carbon atom of a methane molecule. Explain.

Chapter 12   Vector-Valued Functions

Chapter Summary
Section Topics

12.1   **Vector-Valued Functions**—Analyze and sketch a space curve given by a vector-valued function. Extend the concepts of limits and continuity to vector-valued functions.

12.2   **Differentiation and Integration of Vector-Valued Functions**—Differentiate a vector-valued function. Integrate a vector-valued function.

12.3   **Velocity and Acceleration**—Describe the velocity and acceleration associated with a vector-valued function. Use a vector-valued function to analyze projectile motion.

12.4   **Tangent Vectors and Normal Vectors**—Find a unit tangent vector at a point on a space curve. Find the tangential and normal components of acceleration.

12.5   **Arc Length and Curvature**—Find the arc length of a space curve. Use the arc length parameter to describe a plane curve or space curve. Find the curvature of a curve at a point on the curve. Use a vector-valued function to find frictional force.

Chapter Comments

In discussing vector-valued functions with your students, be sure to distinguish them from real-valued functions. A vector-valued function is a vector, whereas a real-valued function is a real number. Remind your students that the parameterization of a curve is not unique. As discussed on page 836 at the end of Example 3, the choice of a parameter determines the orientation of the curve.

Sections 12.1 and 12.2 of this chapter discuss the domain, limit, continuity, differentiation and integration of vector-valued functions. Go over all of this carefully because it is the basis for the applications discussed in Sections 12.3, 12.4 and 12.5. Be sure to point out that when integrating a vector-valued function, the constant of integration is a vector, not a real number.

Go over all of the ideas presented in Sections 12.3, 12.4 and 12.5. Some, such as arc length, will be familiar to your students. Choose your assignments carefully in these sections as the problems are lengthy. Be sure to assign problems with a mix of functions, transcendental as well as algebraic.

If you are pressed for time, it is not necessary to cover every formula for curvature. However, do not omit this idea entirely.

Section 12.1   Vector-Valued Functions

Tips and Tools for Problem Solving

CalcChat.com

Exercises 1–8, 27–42 (1–8, 23–38 in *Calculus* 8/e)
Be sure to go over finding the domain of a vector-valued function. Some students find this difficult. We revised Example 4 to include a discussion on the domain of $\mathbf{r}(t)$.

Exercises 69–74 (69–74 in *Calculus* 8/e)
We revised Exercises 69, 70, and 72, and reordered the exercises to improve the grading. We also rewrote the direction line to find the limit *if* it exists.

Capstone

Page 841, Exercise 84 You can use this exercise to review the following concepts.

- Vector-valued functions
- Analyzing a space curve given by a vector-valued function

Go over the definition of a vector-valued function on page 834. Then write the parametric equations and the rectangular equations as shown in the solution. Note that the curve represented by each vector-valued function is an ellipse.

Solution

(a) $x = -3 \cos t + 1$, $y = 5 \sin t + 2$, $z = 4$

$$\frac{(x - 1)^2}{9} + \frac{(y - 2)^2}{25} = 1, z = 4$$

(b) $x = 4$, $y = -3 \cos t + 1$, $z = 5 \sin t + 2$

$$\frac{(y - 1)^2}{9} + \frac{(z - 2)^2}{25} = 1, x = 4$$

(c) $x = 3 \cos t - 1$, $y = -5 \sin t - 2$, $z = 4$

$$\frac{(x + 1)^2}{9} + \frac{(y + 2)^2}{25} = 1, z = 4$$

(d) $x = -3 \cos 2t + 1$, $y = 5 \sin 2t + 2$, $z = 4$

$$\frac{(x - 1)^2}{9} + \frac{(y - 2)^2}{25} = 1, z = 4$$

(a) and (d) represent the same graph.

Section 12.2 Differentiation and Integration of Vector-Valued Functions

Tips and Tools for Problem Solving

CalcChat.com

Exercises 1–8 (1–6 in *Calculus* 8/e)
Because many students had difficulty with these exercises, we revised Example 1 to demonstrate the skills necessary to solve these exercises. To give students more practice, we added Exercises 6 and 8. Also, we rewrote Exercise 7 (old Exercise 6) in component form to pair it with new Exercise 8.

Exercises 11–22 (11–18 in *Calculus* 8/e)
To give students more practice, we added Exercises 11–14.

Exercise 32 (28 in *Calculus* 8/e)
We revised this exercise so that the vectors in the figure could be more easily discerned.

Exercises 45 and 46 (41 and 42 in *Calculus* 8/e)
We rewrote the direction line to clearly state that students should find the indicated derivatives in two different ways.

Exercises 77–84 (73–80 in *Calculus* 8/e)
We revised Theorem 12.2 and these exercises by replacing f with w. Previously, some students confused the f used in the properties of the derivative and these exercises with the f used in the **i**-component of $\mathbf{r}(t) = f(t)\mathbf{i} + g(t)\mathbf{j} + h(t)\mathbf{k}$.

Capstone

Page 849, Exercise 88 You can use this exercise to review the following concepts.

- Sketching a curve represented by a vector-valued function
- Differentiating a vector-valued function
- Theorem 12.1

Review the definition of the derivative of a vector-valued function (see page 842) and Theorem 12.1 (see page 843). After going over the solution, you can extend this exercise by asking students to sketch the vector $\mathbf{r}'(1)$. Students had trouble making similar sketches in Exercises 1–8.

Solution

(a) $\mathbf{r}(t) = t\mathbf{i} + \left(4 - t^2\right)\mathbf{j}$

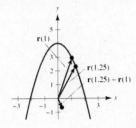

(b)
$$\mathbf{r}(1) = \mathbf{i} + 3\mathbf{j}$$
$$\mathbf{r}(1.25) = 1.25\mathbf{i} + 2.4375\mathbf{j}$$
$$\mathbf{r}(1.25) - \mathbf{r}(1) = 0.25\mathbf{i} - 0.5625\mathbf{j}$$
$$\mathbf{r}'(t) = \mathbf{i} - 2t\mathbf{j}$$
$$\mathbf{r}'(1) = \mathbf{i} - 2\mathbf{j}$$
$$\frac{\mathbf{r}(1.25) - \mathbf{r}(1)}{1.25 - 1} = \frac{0.25\mathbf{i} - 0.5625\mathbf{j}}{0.25} = \mathbf{i} - 2.25\mathbf{j}$$

This vector approximates $\mathbf{r}'(1)$.

Section 12.3 Velocity and Acceleration

Tips and Tools for Problem Solving

CalcChat.com

Exercises 1–10 (1–8 in *Calculus* 8/e)
To give students more practice, we added Exercises 4 and 6.

Exercises 11–20 (9–16 in *Calculus* 8/e)
To give students more practice, we added Exercises 18 and 20.

Exercises 23–28 (19–22 in *Calculus* 8/e)
To give students more practice, we added Exercises 26 and 28.

Capstone

Page 858, Exercise 60 You can use this exercise to review the following concepts.

- Describing the velocity associated with a vector-valued function
- Finding the speed of a particle moving on an elliptical path
- Describing the acceleration associated with a vector-valued function

Review the definitions of velocity and acceleration on page 851. Then go over the solution below.

Solution

$\mathbf{r}(t) = a \cos \omega t \mathbf{i} + b \sin \omega t \mathbf{j}$

(a) $\mathbf{r}'(t) = \mathbf{v}(t) = -a\omega \sin \omega t \mathbf{i} + b\omega \cos \omega t \mathbf{j}$

Speed $= \|\mathbf{v}(t)\| = \sqrt{a^2\omega^2 \sin^2 \omega t + b^2\omega^2 \cos^2 \omega t}$

(b) $\mathbf{a}(t) + \mathbf{v}'(t) = -a\omega^2 \cos \omega t \mathbf{i} + b\omega^2 \sin \omega t \mathbf{j}$

$= \omega^2(-a \cos \omega t \mathbf{i} - b \sin \omega t \mathbf{j})$

$= -\omega^2 \mathbf{r}(t)$

Section 12.4 Tangent Vectors and Normal Vectors

Tips and Tools for Problem Solving

CalcChat.com

Exercises 49–54 (49–52 in *Calculus* 8/e)
To give students more practice, we added Exercises 51 and 52.

Exercises 55–62 (53–56 in *Calculus* 8/e)
To give students more practice, we added Exercises 57, 58, 60, and 62.

Exercises 63–66 (57 and 58 in *Calculus* 8/e)
To give students more practice, we added Exercises 64 and 66.

Capstone

Page 867, Exercise 70 You can use this exercise to review the following concepts.

- Describing the velocity and acceleration associated with a vector-valued function
- Finding a unit tangent vector
- Finding a principal unit normal vector (if it exists)

If necessary, review velocity and acceleration in Section 12.3. Go over the definitions of the unit tangent vector (see page 859) and the principal unit normal vector (see page 860). Then go over the solution on the next page.

Solution

$$\mathbf{r}(t) = 3t\mathbf{i} + 4t\mathbf{j}$$

$$\mathbf{v}(t) = \mathbf{r}'(t) = 3\mathbf{i} + 4\mathbf{j}, \|\mathbf{v}(t)\| = \sqrt{9 + 16} = 5$$

$$\mathbf{a}(t) = \mathbf{v}'(t) = 0$$

$$\mathbf{T}(t) = \frac{\mathbf{v}(t)}{\|\mathbf{v}(t)\|} = \frac{3}{5}\mathbf{i} + \frac{4}{5}\mathbf{j}$$

$\mathbf{T}'(t) = 0 \Rightarrow \mathbf{N}(t)$ does not exist.

The path is a line. The speed is constant (5).

Section 12.5   Arc Length and Curvature

Tips and Tools for Problem Solving

CalcChat.com

Exercises 41–44 (New)
To give students practice finding the curvature of a curve at a point, we added Exercises 41–44.

Exercises 45–54 (41–46 in *Calculus* 8/e)
To give students more practice, we added Exercises 49, 50, 53, and 54.

Exercises 63–70 (55–60 in *Calculus* 8/e)
To give students more practice, we added Exercises 69 and 70.

Capstone

Page 879, Exercise 78 You can use this exercise to review the following concepts.

- Finding the arc length of a space curve

- Theorem 12.6

- Finding the curvature of a plane curve at a point on the curve

- Theorem 12.9

- Analyzing the curvature of a curve

Go over Theorem 12.6 and part (a). If you wish to skip the integration steps, show your students how to set up the integral and then use a graphing utility or CAS to find the result. Then go over the definition of curvature (see page 872) and Theorem 12.9 (see page 874). Note in part (b) that we use the rectangular equations that correspond to the given vector-valued function.

Solution

$$\mathbf{r}(t) = t\mathbf{i} + t^2\mathbf{j}$$

(a) $\dfrac{dx}{dt} = 1, \dfrac{dy}{dt} = 2t$

$$s = \int_0^2 \sqrt{1 + 4t^2}\, dt = \frac{1}{2}\int_0^2 \sqrt{1 + 4t^2}\, (2t)\, dt \, (u = 2t)$$

$$= \frac{1}{2}\cdot\frac{1}{2}\Big[2t\sqrt{1 + 4t^2} + \ln\Big|2t + \sqrt{1 + 4t^2}\Big|\Big]_0^2 \quad \text{(Theorem 8.2)}$$

$$= \frac{1}{4}\Big[4\sqrt{17} + \ln\Big|4 + \sqrt{17}\Big|\Big] \approx 4.647$$

(b) Let $y = x^2$, $y' = 2x$, $y'' = 2$

At $t = 0$, $x = 0$, $y = 0$, $y' = 0$, $y'' = 2$, $K = 2$

$[1 + 0]^{3/2} = 2$

At $t = 1$, $x = 1$, $y = 1$, $y' = 2$, $y'' = 2$

$$K = \frac{2}{\left[1 + (2)^2\right]^{3/2}} = \frac{2}{5^{3/2}} \approx 0.179$$

At $t = 2$, $x = 2$, $y = 4$, $y' = 4$, $y'' = 2$

$$K = \frac{2}{[1 + 16]^{3/2}} = \frac{2}{17^{3/2}} \approx 0.0285$$

(c) As t changes from 0 to 2, the curvature decreases.

Chapter 12 Project

Throwing a Shot-Put

The path of a shot-put thrown at an angle θ is $\mathbf{r}(t) = (v_0 \cos \theta)t\,\mathbf{i} + \left[h + (v_0 \sin \theta)t - \frac{1}{2}gt^2 \right]\mathbf{j}$

where v_0 is the initial speed, h is the initial height, t is the time in seconds and $g \approx 32$ feet per second per second is the acceleration due to gravity. (This formula neglects air resistance.)

Exercises

In Exercises 1–5, a shot-put is thrown from an initial height of 6 feet with an initial velocity of 40 feet per second and an initial angle of 35°.

1. Find the vector-valued function $\mathbf{r}(t)$ that gives the position of the shot-put.

2. At what time is the shot-put at its maximum height?

3. What is the maximum height of the shot-put?

4. How long is the shot-put in the air?

5. What is the horizontal distance traveled by the shot-put?

In Exercises 6–10, a shot-put is thrown from an initial height of 6 feet with an initial velocity of 40 feet per second and an initial angle of 45°.

6. Find the vector-valued function $\mathbf{r}(t)$ that gives the position of the shot-put.

7. At what time is the shot-put at its maximum height?

8. What is the maximum height of the shot-put?

9. How long is the shot-put in the air?

10. What is the horizontal distance traveled by the shot-put?

11. Write an equation for t, the time when a shot-put thrown from an initial height h with an initial velocity of v_0 and an initial angle of θ hits the ground.

12. Write an equation for the horizontal distance traveled by a shot-put thrown from an initial height h with an initial velocity of v_0 and an initial angle of θ.

In Exercises 13 and 14, a shot-put is thrown from an initial height of 6 feet with an initial velocity of 40 feet per second.

13. Write an equation for the time t when the shot-put hits the ground in terms of θ, the angle at which it is thrown.

14. Write an equation for the horizontal distance traveled by the shot-put in terms of θ.

15. Use a graphing utility to graph the equation you wrote in Exercise 14. Where does the maximum occur? What does this mean in the context of the problem?

Chapter 13   Functions of Several Variables

Chapter Summary

Section Topics

13.1 **Introduction to Functions of Several Variables**—Understand the notation for a function of several variables. Sketch the graph of a function of two variables. Sketch level curves for a function of two variables. Sketch level surfaces for a function of three variables. Use computer graphics to sketch the graph of a function of two variables.

13.2 **Limits and Continuity**—Understand the definition of a neighborhood in the plane. Understand and use the definition of the limit of a function of two variables. Extend the concept of continuity to a function of two variables. Extend the concept of continuity to a function of three variables.

13.3 **Partial Derivatives**—Find and use partial derivatives of a function of two variables. Find and use partial derivatives of a function of three or more variables. Find higher-order partial derivatives of a function of two or three variables.

13.4 **Differentials**—Understand the concepts of increments and differentials. Extend the concept of differentiability to a function of two variables. Use a differential as an approximation.

13.5 **Chain Rules for Functions of Several Variables**—Use the Chain Rules for functions of several variables. Find partial derivatives implicitly.

13.6 **Directional Derivatives and Gradients**—Find and use directional derivatives of a function of two variables. Find the gradient of a function of two variables. Use the gradient of a function of two variables in applications. Find directional derivatives and gradients of functions of three variables.

13.7 **Tangent Planes and Normal Lines**—Find equations of tangent planes and normal lines to surfaces. Find the angle of inclination of a plane in space. Compare the gradients $\nabla f(x, y)$ and $\nabla F(x, y, z)$.

13.8 **Extrema of Functions of Two Variables**—Find absolute and relative extrema of a function of two variables. Use the Second Partials Test to find relative extrema of a function of two variables.

13.9 **Applications of Extrema of Functions of Two Variables**—Solve optimization problems involving functions of several variables. Use the method of least squares.

13.10 **Lagrange Multipliers**—Understand the Method of Lagrange Multipliers. Use Lagrange multipliers to solve constrained optimization problems. Use the Method of Lagrange Multipliers with two constraints.

Chapter Comments

The terminology used for functions of several variables parallels functions of one variable. So, a discussion of domain, independent and dependent variables, composite functions, and polynomial and rational functions should move quickly. Graphing functions of several variables is difficult for most students, so be sure to note the comment after Example 2 on using traces in planes parallel to the coordinate planes on page 888.

Discussion of level curves and contour maps as on pages 889 and 890 is often meaningful to your students since many have seen a topographic map depicting high mountains or deep oceans.

Unless you are taking a very theoretic approach to the course, don't get bogged down in the ε-δ definition of the limit of a function of two variables in Section 13.2. Point out that limits of functions of several variables have the same properties regarding sums, differences, products and quotients as do limits of functions of one variable. Go over Example 4 on page 901 with your students and be sure to point out that in order for a limit of a function of several variables to exist, the limit must be the same along *all* possible approaches.

A discussion of continuity for functions of several variables should parallel your discussion of continuity from Chapter 1.

Be sure to have your students memorize the definitions of partial derivatives for a function of several variables. Otherwise, a partial derivative won't mean anything to them. If possible, show a video depicting a geometric interpretation of a partial derivative when applied to a function of two independent variables.

Hopefully, your students already understand that for a function of a single variable, a differential is an approximation for a change in the function value. This concept is generalized in Section 13.4. Examples, such as 3 and 4 on pages 920 and 921, showing how the total differential is used to approximate a change in the function value, are important.

Be careful of notation when discussing the Chain Rules in Section 13.5. Many students are careless about the notation and easily mix up dy/dx and $\partial y/\partial x$. Implicit differentiation seems confusing to many students. You may want to go slowly and carefully over this idea.

Sections 13.6 through 13.10 consider some applications of the partial derivative. As you begin Section 13.6 with the discussion of the directional derivative and the gradient, be sure that your students understand that a gradient is a vector; hence, the boldface print, ∇f. It is important for your students to understand the difference between $\nabla f(x, y)$, a vector in the xy-plane, and $\nabla F(x, y, z)$, a vector in space. For a function of two independent variables, the gradient is normal to the level curves in the same plane as the curves, whereas for a function of three independent variables, the gradient, ∇F, is normal to the surface $F(x, y, z) = 0$. This concept is brought out in Section 13.7 with the discussion of tangent planes and normal lines to a surface.

Section 13.8 examines extrema in space. The ideas and terminology again parallel what was done in the plane. Be sure to note that critical points occur where *one* partial derivative is undefined or when *both* partials are zero. The idea of a saddle point may be new to your students. The Second Partials Test for extrema is great when it works. However, point out to your students that like the Second Derivative Test for functions of one variable, it can fail. Example 4 on page 958 demonstrates this.

The method of least squares, discussed in Section 13.9 could be skipped if time is a problem. In order to solve extrema problems using LaGrange multipliers, Section 13.10, your students need to solve simultaneous equations. Encourage them to be creative in this regard.

Section 13.1   Introduction to Functions of Several Variables

Tips and Tools for Problem Solving

CalcChat.com

Exercises 1 and 2 (New)
To give students more practice at determining whether z is a function of x and y, we added Exercises 1 and 2.

Exercises 19–30 (17–28 in *Calculus* 8/e)
We reordered the exercises to improve the grading.

Capstone

Page 895, Exercise 64 You can use this exercise to review the following concepts.

- Definition of a function of two variables
- Sketching the graph of a function of two variables
- Transformations of the graph of a function of two variables

Go over the definition of a function of two variables on page 886 and the graph of a function of two variables on page 888. Students will need to know this material in the remaining chapters. Sketch the graph of the function. You may want to show students how to use a graphing utility or a computer algebra system to graph the function. Parts (b)–(d) involve transformations of the graph of a function of two variables, similar to a function of a single variable (see Section P.3). In part (e), note that the value of y for $z = f(x, x)$ is restricted to x. So, the graph of $z = f(x, x)$ is the intersection of the plane $y = x$ and $f(x, y) = xy$ for $x \geq 0$ and $y \geq 0$ (see transparency).

Solution

$f(x, y) = xy,\ x \geq 0,\ y \geq 0$

(a)

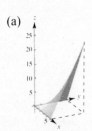

(b) g is a vertical translation of f three units downward.

(c) g is a reflection of f in the xy-plane.

(d) The graph of g is lower than the graph of f. If $z = f(x, y)$ is on the graph of f, then $\frac{1}{2}z$ is on the graph of g.

(e)

106

Section 13.2   Limits and Continuity

Tips and Tools for Problem Solving

CalcChat.com

Exercises 9–22 (9–18 in *Calculus* 8/e)
We reordered the exercises to improve the grading. To give students more practice, we added Exercises 12, 13, 18, and 19.

Exercises 23–36 (19–24 in *Calculus* 8/e)
We reordered the exercises to improve the grading. To give students more practice, we added Exercises 25–30, 33, and 34.

Exercises 43–46 (33 and 34 in *Calculus* 8/e)
To give students more practice, we added Exercises 43 and 44.

Exercises 53–62 (41–48 in *Calculus* 8/e)
We split these exercises into two groups and added Exercises 57 and 58. The new second group has a direction line instructing students to use polar coordinates and L'Hôpital's Rule to find the limit.

Exercises 73–78 (59–62 in *Calculus* 8/e)
To give students more practice, we added Exercises 75 and 76.

Capstone

Page 907, Exercise 94 You can use this exercise to review the following concepts.

- The definition of the limit of a function of two variables
- Using the definition of the limit of a function of two variables

Note that this exercise is similar to the *Capstone* in Section 1.2, except there we used a function of one variable. The existence or nonexistence of $f(x, y)$ at $(x, y) = (c_1, c_2)$ has no bearing on the existence of the limit of $f(x, y)$ as (x, y) approaches (c_1, c_2).

In addition to the solution given below, you could ask students for an example where the limit exists but the function does not, and an example where the limit and the function both exist. Example 3 is a case where the limit exists but the function does not, and Example 2 is a case where the limit and the function both exist.

Solution

(a) No. The existence of $f(2, 3)$ has no bearing on the existence of the limit as $(x, y) \to (2, 3)$.

(b) No. $f(2, 3)$ can equal any number, or not even be defined.

Section 13.3   Partial Derivatives

Tips and Tools for Problem Solving

CalcChat.com

We reordered many of the exercises in this section to improve the grading.

Exercises 9–40 (5–28 in *Calculus* 8/e)
To give students more practice, we added Exercises 11, 12, 17, 18, 31, 32, 37, and 38.

Exercises 45–52 (33–36 in *Calculus* 8/e)
To give students more practice, we added Exercises 45–48.

We reordered the exercises to improve the grading. To give students more practice, we added Exercises 65 and 67.

Exercises 81–88 (45–48 in *Calculus* 8/e)
To give students more practice, we added Exercises 81, 82, 84, and 87.

Capstone

Page 916, Exercise 116 You can use this exercise to review the following concepts.

- Finding partial derivatives of a function of two variables

- Finding higher-order partial derivatives of a function of two variables

- Theorem 13.3

Go over as much as you feel is necessary, such as the definition of partial derivatives of a function of two variables, notation for first partial derivatives, higher-order partial derivatives, and Theorem 13.3. Keep in mind that understanding this material is key for students to succeed in the remaining chapters.

Solution

$$f(x, y) = \sin(x - 2y)$$

$$f_x(x, y) = \cos(x - 2y)$$

$$f_{xx}(x, y) = -\sin(x - 2y)$$

$$f_{xy}(x, y) = 2\sin(x - 2y)$$

$$f_y(x, y) = -2\cos(x - 2y)$$

$$f_{yy}(x, y) = -4\sin(x - 2y)$$

$$f_{yx}(x, y) = 2\sin(x - 2y)$$

So, $f_{xy}(x, y) = f_{yx}(x, y)$.

Section 13.4   Differentials

Tips and Tools for Problem Solving

CalcChat.com

Although we made changes to the section exercises, no changes were made based on the data.

Capstone

Page 924, Exercise 48 You can use this exercise to review the following concepts.

- Finding the increment of z, Δz

- Finding the total differential for a function, dz

Go over increments and differentials on page 918 and approximation by differentials on page 920. Then go over the solution on the next page.

Solution

$$f(x, y) = \sqrt{x^2 + y^2}$$

(a) $f(3, 1) = \sqrt{9 + 1} = \sqrt{10} \approx 3.1623$

$\quad\quad f(3.05, 1.1) = \sqrt{3.05^2 + 1.1^2} \approx 3.2423$

(b) $\Delta z = f(3.05, 1.1) - f(3, 1) \approx 0.0800$

(c) $\quad dz = \dfrac{x}{\sqrt{x^2 + y^2}}\, dx + \dfrac{y}{\sqrt{x^2 + y^2}}\, dy$

$$= \dfrac{3}{\sqrt{10}}(0.05) + \dfrac{1}{\sqrt{10}}(0.1) \approx 0.0791$$

$\quad\quad \Delta z \approx dz$

Section 13.5   Chain Rules for Functions of Several Variables

Tips and Tools for Problem Solving

CalcChat.com

We reordered many of the exercises in this section to improve the grading.

Exercises 15–26, 31–38 (15–26, 31–38 in *Calculus* 8/e)
We reordered the exercises to improve the grading.

Exercises 43–46 (43–46 in *Calculus* 8/e)
We rewrote the direction line to include a new part (a) asking students to show that the function is homogeneous and determine its degree.

Exercises 55–65 (53–64 in *Calculus* 8/e)
We reordered the exercises to improve the grading and deleted an exercise (57 in *Calculus* 8/e).

Capstone

Page 932, Exercise 52 You can use this exercise to review the following concepts.

- Chain Rules for functions of several variables

- Product Rule for differentiation

Review Theorem 13.6 and note that it can be extended to any number of variables (see page 926). So you can write the Chain Rule shown in part (a) of the solution. Be careful of notation in this section, as many students easily mix up dy/dx and $\partial y/\partial x$. After rewriting f in part (b), you can use single-variable techniques to find df/dt. (If needed, review the Product Rule in Section 2.3.) Note that the results are the same because the two methods for calculating the derivative are equivalent.

Solution

$$f(x, y, z) = xyz, \ x = t^2, \ y = 2t, \ z = e^{-t}$$

(a) $\dfrac{df}{dt} = \dfrac{\partial f}{\partial x}\dfrac{dx}{dt} + \dfrac{\partial f}{\partial y}\dfrac{dy}{dt} + \dfrac{\partial f}{\partial z}\dfrac{dz}{dt}$

$\quad\quad = yz(2t) + xz(2) + xy(-e^{-t})$

$\quad\quad = 4t^2 e^{-t} + 2t^2 e^{-t} - 2t^3 e^{-t} = 2t^2 e^{-t}(3 - t)$

(b) $f = t^2(2t)(e^{-t}) = 2t^3 e^{-t}$

$\dfrac{df}{dt} = -2t^3 e^{-t} + 6t^2 e^{-t} = 2t^2 e^{-t}(3-t)$

The results are the same.

Section 13.6 Directional Derivatives and Gradients

Tips and Tools for Problem Solving

CalcChat.com

Exercises 1–12, 17–26 (1–12, 17–26 in *Calculus* 8/e)
We reordered the exercises to improve the grading.

Exercises 31–40 (31–38 in *Calculus* 8/e)
We reordered the exercises to improve the grading. To give students more practice, we added Exercises 31 and 32.

Exercises 55–58 (59–62 in *Calculus* 8/e)
We rewrote the direction line, which now has four parts. We now ask students to find the gradient, a unit normal vector, and the tangent line at a point P. Then we ask students to sketch the level curve, the unit normal vector, and the tangent line in the xy-plane.

Capstone

Page 943, Exercise 64 You can use this exercise to review the following concepts.

- Sketching the graph of a function of two variables

- Finding the directional derivative of a function (Theorem 13.9)

- Finding the gradient of a function

- Discussing properties of the gradient

If needed, you can review sketching the graph of a function of two variables in Section 13.1. Use the transparency to show the graph in part (a). Go over Theorem 13.9 and find the directional derivatives in part (b) and, if time permits, part (c). Go over the definition of the gradient of a function of two variables (see page 936) and be sure that your students understand that a gradient is a vector. In part (d), note that $f_x(x, y) = -2x$ and $f_y(x, y) = -2y$. When discussing the geometric meaning of the result in part (e), note that ∇f is the direction of greatest rate of change of f. So, in a direction orthogonal to ∇f, the rate of change of f is 0.

Solution

$f(x, y) = 9 - x^2 - y^2$ and

$D_\theta f(x, y) = -2x \cos \theta - 2y \sin \theta$

$\qquad\qquad = -2(x \cos \theta + y \sin \theta)$

(a) $f(x, y) = 9 - x^2 - y^2$

(b) $D_{-\pi/4} f(1, 2) = -2\left(\dfrac{\sqrt{2}}{2} - \sqrt{2}\right) = \sqrt{2}$

(c) $D_{\pi/3} f(1, 2) = -2\left(\dfrac{1}{2} + \sqrt{3}\right) = -\left(1 + 2\sqrt{3}\right)$

(d) $\nabla f(1, 2) = -2\mathbf{i} - 4\mathbf{j}$

$\left\|\nabla f(1, 2)\right\| = \sqrt{4 + 16} = \sqrt{20} = 2\sqrt{5}$

(e) $\nabla f(1, 2) = -2\mathbf{i} - 4\mathbf{j}$

$\dfrac{\nabla f(1, 2)}{\left\|\nabla f(1, 2)\right\|} = \dfrac{1}{\sqrt{5}}(-\mathbf{i} - 2\mathbf{j})$

Therefore, $\mathbf{u} = \left(1/\sqrt{5}\right)(-2\mathbf{i} + \mathbf{j})$ and

$D_{\mathbf{u}} f(1, 2) = \nabla f(1, 2) \cdot \mathbf{u} = 0$

Section 13.7 Tangent Planes and Normal Lines

Tips and Tools for Problem Solving

CalcChat.com

We reordered many of the exercises in this section to improve the grading.

Exercises 5–16 (5–14 in *Calculus* 8/e)
To give students more practice, we added Exercises 5 and 12.

Exercises 17–30 (15–28 in *Calculus* 8/e)
We reordered the exercises to improve the grading.

Exercises 31–40 (29–34 in *Calculus* 8/e)
We reordered the exercises to improve the grading. To give students more practice, we added Exercises 31, 34, 35, 38, and 40.

Capstone

Page 952, Exercise 66 You can use this exercise to review the following concepts.

- Finding an equation of a tangent plane to a surface

- Theorem 13.13

- Finding an equation of a normal line to a surface

Go over the definitions of tangent plane and normal line and Theorem 13.13 on page 946. Then go over the solution.

Solution

(a) $x^2 - y^2 + z^2 = 0, (5, 13, -12)$

$F(x, y, z) = x^2 - y^2 + z^2$

$\quad F_x(x, y, z) = 2x \qquad F_y(x, y, z) = -2y \qquad F_z(x, y, z) = 2z$

$F_x(5, 13, -12) = 10 \qquad F_y(5, 13, -12) = -26 \qquad F_z(x, y, z) = -24$

Direction numbers: $5, -13, -12$

Plane: $5(x - 5) - 13(y - 13) - 12(z + 12) = 0$

$\qquad\qquad 5x - 13y - 12z = 0$

(b) Line: $\dfrac{x - 5}{5} = \dfrac{y - 13}{-13} = \dfrac{z + 12}{-12}$

Section 13.8   Extrema of Functions of Two Variables

Tips and Tools for Problem Solving

CalcChat.com

We reordered many of the exercises in this section to improve the grading.

Exercises 7–16, 21–28 (7–16, 21–28 in *Calculus* 8/e)
We reordered the exercises to improve the grading.

Exercises 37–42 (45–50 in *Calculus* 8/e)
We rewrote the direction line, which now has four parts. Parts (a)–(c) are the previous directions, and part (d) is new. In part (d), we ask students to use a computer algebra system to graph the function.

Capstone

Page 961, Exercise 60   You can use this exercise to review the following concepts.

- Showing that a function has a critical point

- Analyzing the behavior of a function at a critical point

- Theorems 13.15–13.17

- Definition of relative extrema

- Saddle point

Note that the ideas and terminology parallel what was done in the plane. Go over the definition of critical point (see page 955). After doing part (a), review the definition of relative extrema and Theorems 13.15–13.17. Go over part (b) and use the following figures given on the transparencies to reinforce the results. The idea of a saddle point may be new to your students.

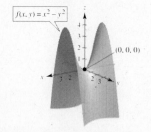

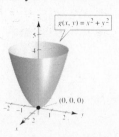

Solution

$f(x, y) = x^2 - y^2$, $g(x, y) = x^2 + y^2$

(a) $f_x = 2x = 0$, $f_y = -2y = 0 \Rightarrow (0, 0)$ is a critical point.

$g_x = 2x = 0$, $g_y = 2y = 0 \Rightarrow (0, 0)$ is a critical point.

(b) $f_{xx} = 2$, $f_{yy} = -2$, $f_{xy} = 0$

$d = 2(-2) - 0 < 0 \Rightarrow (0, 0)$ is a saddle point.

$g_{xx} = 2$, $g_{yy} = 2$, $g_{xy} = 0$

$d = 2(2) - 0 > 0 \Rightarrow (0, 0)$ is a relative minimum.

Section 13.9 Applications of Extrema of Functions of Two Variables

Tips and Tools for Problem Solving

CalcChat.com

Although we made changes to the section exercises, no changes were made based on the data.

Capstone

Page 968, Exercise 38 You can use this exercise to review the following concept.

- Solving an optimization problem

Use the following figure given on the transparency to illustrate girth.

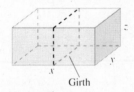
Girth

Solution

Let x, y, and z be the length, width, and height, respectively. Then the sum of the length and girth is given by $x + (2y + 2z) = 108$ or $x = 108 - 2y - 2z$. The volume is given by

$V = xyz = 108zy - 2zy^2 - 2yz^2$

$V_y = 108z - 4yz - 2z^2 = z(108 - 4y - 2z) = 0$

$V_z = 108y - 2y^2 - 4yz = y(108 - 2y - 4z) = 0$.

Solving the system $4y + 2z = 108$ and $2y + 4z = 108$, we obtain the solution $x = 36$ inches, $y = 18$ inches, and $z = 18$ inches.

Section 13.10   Lagrange Multipliers

Tips and Tools for Problem Solving

CalcChat.com

We reordered many of the exercises in this section to improve the grading. In order to solve extrema problems using Lagrange multipliers, students need to solve simultaneous equations. Students may benefit from a quick review of Sections 7.2 and 7.3 of *Precalculus*, 7th edition, by Larson and Hostetler.

Exercises 19–28 (23–26 in *Calculus* 8/e)
To give students more practice, we added Exercises 19 and 21–25.

Exercises 33–42 (New)
To give students more practice using Lagrange multipliers, we added Exercises 33–42. This will also allow students to compare the methods used in Sections 13.9 and 13.10.

Capstone

Page 977, Exercise 44 You can use this exercise to review the following concepts.

- Lagrange multipliers

- Theorem 13.19

- Method of Lagrange Multipliers

Go over the concepts listed above and then the solution. Note that the dimensions are the same as those found in Exercise 38, Section 13.9.

Solution

(a) Yes. Lagrange multipliers can be used.

(b) Maximize $V(x, y, z) = xyz$ subject to the constraint $x + 2y + 2z = 108$.

$$\left. \begin{array}{l} yz = \lambda \\ xz = 2\lambda \\ xy = 2\lambda \end{array} \right\} y = z \text{ and } x = 2y$$

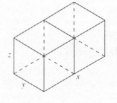

$$x + 2y + 2z = 108 \Rightarrow 6y = 108,\ y = 18$$
$$x = 36,\ y = z = 18$$

Volume is maximum when the dimensions are $36 \times 18 \times 18$ inches.

Chapter 13 Project

Satellite Receiving Dish

Some satellite receiving dishes have the shape of a circular paraboloid. This shape allows the dish to receive signals whose strength is only a few billionths of a watt. To model a circular paraboloid, you can modify the elliptic paraboloid formula described in Section 11.6.

$$z = \frac{x^2}{a^2} + \frac{y^2}{a^2} \qquad \text{Circular paraboloid}$$

For this model, the paraboloid opens up and has its vertex at the origin. For a satellite dish, the axis of the paraboloid should pass through the satellite so that all incoming signals are parallel to the paraboloid's axis. When incoming rays strike the surface of the paraboloid at a point P, they reflect at the same angle as they would if they were reflecting off a plane that was tangent to the surface at point P, as shown in the left-hand figure below. All parabolas have a special reflective property. One way to describe the property is to say that *all incoming rays that are parallel to the axis of the parabola reflect directly through the focus of the parabola*, as shown in the right-hand figure below.

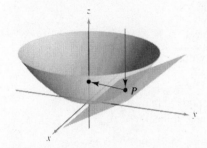
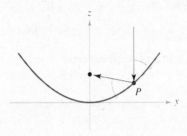

Exercises

1. You are designing a satellite receiving dish. At what point should you place the receiver? Explain your reasoning.

2. Other than satellite receiving dishes, what other common objects use the reflective property of parabolas in their design?

3. Consider the circular paraboloid given by

   $$z = x^2 + y^2$$

   and the point $P(1, 1, 2)$ on this surface. You can characterize the tangent plane to the surface at this point by saying that it is the only plane whose intersection with the paraboloid consists of the single point P. Find an equation for this tangent plane. Explain your strategy.

4. Does it make sense to talk about the "slope" of the tangent plane in Exercise 3? If so, what is the slope of this plane? How might you use differentiation to discover the slope of this plane?

5. Determine an equation of the form

   $$z = \frac{x^2}{a^2} + \frac{y^2}{a^2}$$

   for a satellite dish that has a radius of 10 feet and a depth of 3.5 feet. What is the domain and range of the equation?

Chapter 14 Multiple Integration

Chapter Summary

Section Topics

14.1 **Iterated Integrals and Area in the Plane**—Evaluate an iterated integral. Use an iterated integral to find the area of a plane region.

14.2 **Double Integrals and Volume**—Use a double integral to represent the volume of a solid region. Use properties of double integrals. Evaluate a double integral as an iterated integral. Find the average value of a function over a region.

14.3 **Change of Variables: Polar Coordinates**—Write and evaluate double integrals in polar coordinates.

14.4 **Center of Mass and Moments of Inertia**—Find the mass of a planar lamina using a double integral. Find the center of mass of a planar lamina using double integrals. Find moments of inertia using double integrals.

14.5 **Surface Area**—Use a double integral to find the area of a surface.

14.6 **Triple Integrals and Applications**—Use a triple integral to find the volume of a solid region. Find the center of mass and moments of inertia of a solid region.

14.7 **Triple Integrals in Cylindrical and Spherical Coordinates**—Write and evaluate a triple integral in cylindrical coordinates. Write and evaluate a triple integral in spherical coordinates.

14.8 **Change of Variables: Jacobians**—Understand the concept of a Jacobian. Use a Jacobian to change variables in a double integral.

Chapter Comments

The most difficult part of multiple integration for students is often setting up the limits. Go slowly and carefully over this *every time*. Point out that the variable of integration cannot appear in either limit of integration and that the outside limits must be constant with respect to *all* variables. It is important to stress early that the order of integration does not affect the value of the integral (Example 5 on page 988). However, very often it does affect the difficulty of the problem (Example 4 on page 998). Sketching the region is a necessary part of making the decision on the order of integration.

Because polar coordinates were already covered in Chapter 10, Section 14.3 should be easy for your students, so move quickly through it.

You may have to choose which of the applications in Sections 14.4 and 14.5 that you want to discuss because you probably will not have enough time for all of them. Surface area problems are often easier when done in polar coordinates.

The problems on triple integrals in Section 14.6 are lengthy. However, take the time to carefully set these up and work them out in detail. Encourage your students to consider the different orders of integration, looking for the simplest method of solving the problem.

Cylindrical and spherical coordinates, Section 14.7, are worth discussing well since many multiple integral problems are far easier done in these coordinate systems rather than in rectangular coordinates.

The Jacobian is discussed in Section 14.8. Example 1 shows why the extra factor appears when area is calculated in polar coordinates. Be sure to assign Exercise 39 which asks for the Jacobian for the change of variables from rectangular coordinates to spherical coordinates.

Section 14.1 Iterated Integrals and Area in the Plane

Tips and Tools for Problem Solving

CalcChat.com

Every time you do an example of multiple integration, be sure that your students understand how to set up the limits.

Exercises 11–30 (11–24 in *Calculus* 8/e)
To give students more practice, we added Exercises 14–16, 21, 26, and 28.

Exercises 67–72 (61–64 in *Calculus* 8/e)
To give students more practice, we added Exercises 68 and 69. We also rewrote the direction line to ask students to sketch the region of integration. This should help them to see why it is necessary to switch the order of integration and to determine the limits of integration.

Capstone

Page 991, Exercise 66 You can use this exercise to review the following concepts.

- Evaluating an iterated integral

- Finding the area of a plane region

- Comparing different orders of integration

Review as much of the section material as necessary. Complete the integrals by determining the limits of integration as shown in the solution. Determining these limits can be the most difficult part of multiple integration for students, so go over this part carefully. This exercise also gives you the opportunity to stress that the order of integration does not affect the value of the integral (see also Example 5 on page 988).

Solution

(a) $A = \int_0^2 \int_{y^2}^{2y} dx\, dy = \int_0^2 [x]_{y^2}^{2y}\, dy = \int_0^2 \left(2y - y^2\right) dy = \left[y^2 - \frac{y^3}{3}\right]_0^2 = 4 - \frac{8}{3} = \frac{4}{3}$

(b) $A = \int_0^4 \int_{x/2}^{\sqrt{x}} dy\, dx = \int_0^4 [y]_{x/2}^{\sqrt{x}}\, dx = \int_0^4 \left(\sqrt{x} - \frac{x}{2}\right) dx$

$= \left[\frac{2}{3}x^{3/2} - \frac{x^2}{4}\right]_0^4 = \frac{16}{3} - 4 = \frac{4}{3}$

Integrals (a) and (b) are the same.

Section 14.2 Double Integrals and Volume

Tips and Tools for Problem Solving

CalcChat.com

Exercises 41–46 (41 and 42 in *Calculus* 8/e)
To give students more practice, we added Exercises 41, 42, 45, and 46.

Exercises 53–58 (49–52 in *Calculus* 8/e)

To give students more practice, we added Exercises 55 and 56. We also rewrote the direction line to ask students to sketch the region of integration and then to evaluate the iterated integral, switching the order of integration if necessary.

Exercises 59–64 (53–56 in *Calculus* 8/e)

To give students more practice, we added Exercises 62 and 64.

Exercise 66 (New)

To give students more practice, we added Exercise 66.

Capstone

Page 1003, Exercise 72 You can use this exercise to review the following concepts.

- Comparing different orders of integration

- Determining which order of integration is more convenient

While some double integrals can be solved with either order of integration with comparable difficulty, others cannot. This exercise presents a case where one of the integrals does not have an elementary antiderivation (see solution). You can extend this exercise by asking students to evaluate both integrals numerically using a computer algebra system. (The answer is approximately equal to 1.6536.)

Solution

The second is integrable. The first contains

$\int \sin y^2 \, dy$ which does not have an elementary antiderivation.

Section 14.3   Change of Variables: Polar Coordinates

Tips and Tools for Problem Solving

CalcChat.com

Exercises 9–16 (9–14 in *Calculus* 8/e)
To give students more practice, we added Exercises 9 and 10.

Exercises 17–26 (15–20 in *Calculus* 8/e)
To give students more practice, we added Exercises 19, 20, 25, and 26.

Exercises 49–54 (New)
We added these exercises to give students practice in finding the area of a region where the region is bounded by two polar graphs.

Capstone

Page 1010, Exercise 60 You can use this exercise to review the following concepts.

- Writing double integrals in polar coordinates

- Theorem 14.3

Review Theorem 14.3. Note that the polar boundaries are $0 \le r \le 4$ and $0 \le \theta \le 2\pi$, as shown in the figure below.

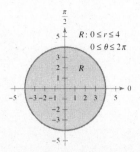

Furthermore, $x^2 + y^2 = r^2$. So, choose (c). If you choose to evaluate the integral, the answer is 128π.

Solution

$0 \le r \le 4, 0 \le \theta \le 2\pi, x^2 + y^2 = r^2$

Answer (c)

Section 14.4   Center of Mass and Moments of Inertia

Tips and Tools for Problem Solving

CalcChat.com

Exercises 11–22 (11–22 in *Calculus* 8/e)
We reordered and revised these exercises to improve the grading.

Capstone

Page 1019, Exercise 50 You can use this exercise to review the following concepts.

- Center of mass of a planar lamina

- Analyzing the center of mass of a planar lamina of nonconstant density

Review as much of the terminology as you feel is necessary.

In part (a), $\rho(x, y) = ky$, so $\bar{x}$ stays the same. The density of the lamina increases from its lower portion to its upper portion. So, $\bar{y}$ increases.

The lamina is symmetric with respect to the line $x = 2$, and in part (b) the density is also symmetric with respect to the line $x = 2$. So, $\bar{x}$ stays the same. Note that the density function increases as you move to the left or to the right of the line $x = 2$ and is at its greatest when $x = 0$ and $x = 4$. Because there is more of the lamina below the line $y = 8/5$ than above it, the change in density in the lower portion has a greater effect on the center of mass. So, $\bar{y}$ decreases.

In part (c), the density of the lamina increases as x increases and as y increases. So, the center of mass moves to the right and up.

In part (d), the density of the lamina decreases as x increases and as y increases. So, the center of mass moves to the left and down.

If you choose to do the calculations, the centers of mass are (a) $(2, 16/7)$, (b) $(2, 4/3)$, (c) $(16/7, 16/7)$, and (d) $(32/21, 8/7)$.

Solution

(a) $\rho(x, y) = ky$

$\overline{y}$ will increase.

(b) $\rho(x, y) = k|2 - x|$

$\overline{y}$ will decrease.

(c) $\rho(x, y) = kxy$

Both $\overline{x}$ and $\overline{y}$ will increase.

(d) $\rho(x, y) = k(4 - x)(4 - y)$

Both $\overline{x}$ and $\overline{y}$ will decrease.

Section 14.5   Surface Area

Tips and Tools for Problem Solving

CalcChat.com

Although we made changes to the section exercises, no changes were made based on the data.

Capstone

Page 1026, Exercise 38 You can use this exercise to review the following concepts.

- Definition of surface area

- Analyzing the surface area of a function

- Comparing the surface area of a function to the area of the region of integration R

Review pages 1020 and 1021. Then go over the solution. Note from the formula for surface area on page 1021 that the least that the radical can be is 1. In this case, the surface area is the area of R.

Solution

(a) Yes. For example, let R be the square given by

$0 \le x \le 1, 0 \le y \le 1,$

and S the square parallel to R given by

$0 \le x \le 1, 0 \le y \le 1, z = 1.$

(b) Yes. Let R be the region on part (a) and S the surface given by $f(x, y) = xy.$

(c) No.

Section 14.6   Triple Integrals and Applications

Tips and Tools for Problem Solving

CalcChat.com

Exercises 13–18 (13–16 in *Calculus* 8/e)
To give students more practice, we added Exercises 16 and 18.

Exercises 23–26 (21 and 22 in *Calculus* 8/e)
We revised Exercises 23 and 24 (21 and 22 in *Calculus* 8/e) by removing the figures. To give students more practice, we added Exercises 25 and 26.

To give students more practice, we added Exercises 27 and 28.

Capstone

Page 1037, Exercise 68 You can use this exercise to review the following concepts.

- Definition of triple integral

- Comparing different orders of integration and determining which ones are equal

Go over the definition of triple integral on page 1027. Note that the region of integration is a cube. The only integral that has the same region of integration as the given integral is (b). Drawing the region of integration for (a) and (c) may help students see the difference.

Solution

The region of integration is a cube.

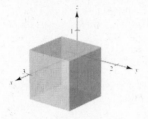

Answer: (b)

Section 14.7   Triple Integrals in Cylindrical and Spherical Coordinates

Tips and Tools for Problem Solving

CalcChat.com

Exercises 17–22 (17–20 in *Calculus* 8/e)
To give students more practice, we added Exercises 19 and 20.

Exercises 33–36 (31 and 32 in *Calculus* 8/e)
To give students more practice, we added Exercises 33 and 34.

Capstone

Page 1044, Exercise 48 You can use this exercise to review the following concepts.

- Writing a triple integral in cylindrical coordinates

- Writing a triple integral in spherical coordinates

Many multiple integral problems are far easier done in cylindrical or spherical coordinates rather than rectangular coordinates. Go over the method of converting from rectangular coordinates to cylindrical and spherical coordinates. Then go over the solution. Note that the integral in spherical coordinates appears to be easier to evaluate because the limits are all constants.

Solution

(a) $\displaystyle\int_0^{\pi/2}\int_0^a\int_0^{\sqrt{a^2-r^2}}\sqrt{r^2+z^2}\;r\;dz\;dr\;d\theta$

(b) $\displaystyle\int_0^{\pi/2}\int_0^{\pi/2}\int_0^a \rho^3\,\sin\phi\;d\rho\;d\phi\;d\theta$

Integral (b) appears easier. The limits of integration are all constants.

Section 14.8   Change of Variables: Jacobians

Tips and Tools for Problem Solving

CalcChat.com

Exercises 9–12 (9 and 10 in *Calculus* 8/e)
To give students more practice, we added Exercises 11 and 12. Also, we revised Example 2 to show more information about the transformation *T*. Hopefully, this will help students write correct transformations while doing the exercises.

Exercises 13 and 14 (New)
Students are asked to use previously learned techniques to verify the results of Examples 3 and 4.

Exercises 19 and 20 (15 and 16 in *Calculus* 8/e)
We added figures to these exercises to show the region *R*.

Exercises 21–28 (17–22 in *Calculus* 8/e)
To give students more practice, we added Exercises 21 and 22.

Exercises 35–40 (27–30 in *Calculus* 8/e)
To give students more practice, we added Exercises 37 and 38.

Capstone

Page 1051, Exercise 30 You can use this exercise to review the following concept.

* Finding a change of variables to simplify a region

Follow the solution given on the next page.

Solution

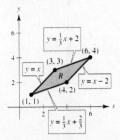

$$y - x = 0, \qquad 3y - x = 6$$
$$y - x = -2, \qquad 3y - x = 2$$

Let $u = y - x$ and $v = 3y - x$.

Then $x = \frac{1}{2}(v - 3u)$ and $y = \frac{1}{2}(v - u)$.

So, $T(u, v) = (x, y) = \left(\frac{1}{2}(v - 3u), \frac{1}{2}(v - u)\right)$.

Note that:

(x, y)	(u, v)
$(1, 1)$	$(0, 2)$
$(4, 2)$	$(-2, 2)$
$(6, 4)$	$(-2, 6)$
$(3, 3)$	$(0, 6)$

123

Chapter 14 Project

Hyperthermia Treatment for Tumors

Heating malignant tumors to a temperature of about $45°C$ can cause the tumors to regress. This treatment, known as hyperthermia, uses microwaves (or another method) to heat the tumors.

The tumor temperature during treatment is highest at the center and gradually decreases toward the edges. Regions of tissue having the same temperature, called equitherms, can be visualized as closed surfaces that are nested one inside of the other. One of the difficulties in effectively applying the hyperthermia treatment is determining the portion of the tumor heated to an effective temperature.

When normal tissue is heated, it is cooled by the dilation of blood vessels. A tumor has very few interior blood vessels and therefore is unable to take advantage of this cooling process. The problem of determining the portion of the tumor that has been heated to an effective temperature reduces to finding the ratio V_T/V, where V is the volume of the entire tumor and V_T is the volume of the portion of the tumor that is heated above temperature T.

Exercises

1. When treating a spherical tumor, a technician uses a probe to determine that the temperature has reached an appropriate level to about half the radius of the tumor. What is the ratio V_T/V? Is it $\frac{1}{2}$? Explain your reasoning.

2. Consider an ellipsoidal tumor that can be modeled by the equation

   $$\frac{x^2}{2.5} + \frac{y^2}{6.5} + \frac{z^2}{2.5} = 1.$$

   Consider a sequence of five ellipsoidal equitherms whose major and minor axes increase linearly until the fifth equitherm is the entire tumor (see figure). Write an equation for each of the five equitherms. Then find the ratio V_T/V for each of the five equitherms.

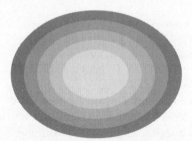

3. A certain tumor can be modeled by the wrinkled sphere given by the equation

   $$\rho = 0.5 + 0.345 \sin 8\theta \sin \phi, \ 0 \le \theta \le 2\pi, 0 \le \phi \le \pi.$$

   (a) Explain a strategy for estimating the volume of the wrinkled sphere without using integration. Use your strategy to calculate an estimate.

   (b) Find the volume of the tumor using integration and compare the result to part (a).

4. A certain tumor can be modeled by the bumpy sphere given by the equation

   $$\rho = 0.75 + 0.35 \sin 8\theta \sin 4\phi, \ 0 \le \theta \le 2\pi, 0 \le \phi \le \pi.$$

   Find the volume of the tumor using integration.

Chapter 15　Vector Analysis

Chapter Summary

Section Topics

15.1　**Vector Fields**—Understand the concept of a vector field. Determine whether a vector field is conservative. Find the curl of a vector field. Find the divergence of a vector field.

15.2　**Line Integrals**—Understand and use the concept of a piecewise smooth curve. Write and evaluate a line integral. Write and evaluate a line integral of a vector field. Write and evaluate a line integral in differential form.

15.3　**Conservative Vector Fields and Independence of Path**—Understand and use the Fundamental Theorem of Line Integrals. Understand the concept of independence of path. Understand the concept of conservation of energy.

15.4　**Green's Theorem**—Use Green's Theorem to evaluate a line integral. Use alternative forms of Green's Theorem.

15.5　**Parametric Surfaces**—Understand the definition of a parametric surface, and sketch the surface. Find a set of parametric equations to represent a surface. Find a normal vector and a tangent plane to a parametric surface. Find the area of a parametric surface.

15.6　**Surface Integrals**—Evaluate a surface integral as a double integral. Evaluate a surface integral for a parametric surface. Determine the orientation of a surface. Understand the concept of a flux integral.

15.7　**Divergence Theorem**—Understand and use the Divergence Theorem. Use the Divergence Theorem to calculate flux.

15.8　**Stokes's Theorem**—Understand and use Stokes's Theorem. Use curl to analyze the motion of a rotating liquid.

Chapter Comments

Chapter 15 is divided into two parts. Sections 15.1 through 15.4 consider situations in which the integration is done over a plane region bounded by curves. Sections 15.5 through 15.8 consider integrals over regions in space bounded by surfaces. Most students find this material difficult, so go over these topics slowly and carefully. Section 15.1 contains a lot of new ideas and terminology. Take two days if necessary to get your students familiar with these ideas. Be sure to make it clear that the divergence of a vector field **F** is a *scalar* while **curl F** is a *vector*.

When using parametric forms of line integrals, be sure that the parameters are chosen with *increasing* parameter values that keep the specified direction along the curve. Confusion often arises when the direction of the path is not considered (Example 7 on page 1076). Students need to understand that a line integral is independent of the parameterization of a curve C provided C is given the same orientation by all sets of parametric equations defining C. The discussion of work in Section 15.2 is an application of line integrals. Be sure to include it.

Conservative vector fields and potential functions, discussed in Section 15.3, are ideas that your students will see again in differential equations. It is important that your students know the conditions necessary for the Fundamental Theorem of Line Integrals and for path independence (Example 1 on page 1083).

Green's Theorem, in Section 15.4, is used to integrate line integrals over closed curves. Using this theorem should be fairly easy for your students if they are able to calculate the area between two curves. Be sure to note the alternative forms of Green's Theorem on pages 1098 and 1099.

Surface integrals, like other multiple integrals, are tedious and time consuming. However, they should be worked out in detail. Both the Divergence Theorem and Stokes's Theorem are higher dimension analogues of Green's Theorem.

Section 15.1 Vector Fields

Tips and Tools for Problem Solving

CalcChat.com

Exercises 21–30 (21–26 in *Calculus* 8/e)
We rewrote the direction line to more clearly state what is required of students to do these exercises. To give students more practice, we added Exercises 21, 22, 25, and 26.

Exercises 35–38 (31–34 in *Calculus* 8/e)
We revised Exercises 35, 37, and 38. We also reordered the exercises to improve the grading.

Exercises 39–48 (35–42 in *Calculus* 8/e)
To give students more practice, we added Exercises 39 and 43. We also reordered the exercises to improve the grading.

Exercises 57–62 (51–56 in *Calculus* 8/e)
We revised Exercises 57 and 59–61. We also reordered the exercises to improve the grading.

Capstone

Page 1068, Exercise 94 You can use this exercise to review the following concepts.

- Vector fields
- Sketching several representative vectors in a vector field

Go over the definition of a vector field on page 1058. Because vector fields consist of infinitely many vectors, it is not possible to create a sketch of the entire field. So, be sure students understand this and that when they are asked to sketch a vector field, their goal is to sketch representative vectors that will help them visualize the field. Then go over the solution below. The graphs are provided on transparencies.

Solution

(a) $\mathbf{F}(x, y) = \dfrac{x\mathbf{i} + y\mathbf{j}}{\sqrt{x^2 + y^2}}$

(b) $\mathbf{G}(x, y) = \dfrac{x\mathbf{i} + y\mathbf{j}}{\sqrt{x^2 + y^2}}$

(c) All the vectors are unit vectors. Those of **F** point away from origin. Answers will vary.

Section 15.2 Line Integrals

Tips and Tools for Problem Solving

CalcChat.com

Exercises 1–6 (1–6 in *Calculus* 8/e)
We reordered the exercises to improve the grading. We also added a note to the direction line that there is more than one correct answer.

Exercises 11–20 (11–20 in *Calculus* 8/e)
For each block of exercises, we added part (a) asking students to find a parameterization of the path C.

Capstone

Page 1082, Exercise 82 You can use this exercise to review the following concepts.

- Analyzing the work done in moving an object
- Analyzing a force field

Use the graph given on the transparency and the solution below. Note in part (a) that the work done moving from $(-3, -3)$ to $(0, 0)$ is negative (against the force field) and the work done moving from $(0, 0)$ to $(3, 3)$ is positive (with the force field). Total work done is 0 (equal distances).

Solution

(a) Work $= 0$

(b) Work is negative, because against force field.

(c) Work is positive, because with force field.

Section 15.3 Conservative Vector Fields and Independence of Path

Tips and Tools for Problem Solving

CalcChat.com

Although we made changes to the section exercises, no changes were made based on the data.

Capstone

Page 1092, Exercise 44 You can use this exercise to review the following concepts.

- Conservative vector fields
- The Fundamental Theorem of Line Integrals (Theorem 15.5)

Review conservative vector fields (see page 1061) and Theorem 15.5 (see page 1084). These are concepts that your students will see again in differential equations. The graph in this exercise is provided on a transparency.

Solution

(a) The direct path along the line segment joining $(-4, 0)$ to $(3, 4)$ requires less work than the path going from $(-4, 0)$ to $(-4, 4)$ and then to $(3, 4)$.

(b) The closed curve given by the line segments joining $(-4, 0)$, $(-4, 4)$, $(3, 4)$, and $(-4, 0)$ satisfies $\int_C \mathbf{F} \cdot d\mathbf{r} \neq 0$.

Section 15.4 Green's Theorem

Tips and Tools for Problem Solving

CalcChat.com

Although we made changes to the section exercises, no changes were made based on the data.

Capstone

Page 1101, Exercise 42 You can use this exercise to review the following concepts.

- Green's Theorem

- Verifying Green's Theorem for a given path

Review Green's Theorem (Theorem 15.8). Be sure to note the alternative forms of Green's Theorem on pages 1098 and 1099. Then go over the solution. Because students have difficulty setting up the limits of integration, go over the solution slowly and carefully. You may want to leave the evaluation of the integrals to your students. If you are pressed for time, only do part (a).

Solution

(a) $\mathbf{r}(t) = \begin{cases} t\mathbf{i}, & 0 \le t \le 4 \\ 4\mathbf{i} + (t-4)\mathbf{j}, & 4 \le t \le 8 \\ (12-t)\mathbf{i} + (12-t)\mathbf{j}, & 8 \le t \le 12 \end{cases}$

$$\int_C y^2\,dx + x^2\,dy = \int_0^4 \left[0\,dt + t^2(0)\right] + \int_4^8 \left[(t-4)^2(0) + 16\,dt\right] + \int_8^{12}\left[(12-t)^2(-dt) + (12-t)^2(-dt)\right]$$

$$= 0 + 64 - \frac{128}{3} = \frac{64}{3}$$

By Green's Theorem,

$$\int_R \int \left(\frac{\partial N}{\partial x} - \frac{\partial M}{\partial y}\right) dA = \int_0^4 \int_0^x (2x - 2y)\,dy\,dx = \int_0^4 x^2\,dx = \frac{64}{3}.$$

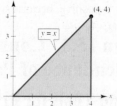

(b) $\mathbf{r}(t) = \cos t\,\mathbf{i} + \sin t\,\mathbf{j},\ 0 \le t \le 2\pi$

$$\int_C y^2\,dx + x^2\,dy = \int_0^{2\pi}\left[\sin^2 t(-\sin t\,dt) + \cos^2 t(\cos t\,dt)\right] = \int_0^{2\pi}\left(\cos^3 t - \sin^3 t\right) dt$$

$$= \int_0^{2\pi}\left[\cos t(1 - \sin^2 t) - \sin t(1 - \cos^2 t)\right] dt = \left[\sin t - \frac{\sin^3 t}{3} + \cos t - \frac{\cos^3 t}{3}\right]_0^{2\pi} = 0$$

By Green's Theorem,

$$\int_R \int \left(\frac{\partial N}{\partial x} - \frac{\partial M}{\partial y}\right) dA = \int_{-1}^{1} \int_{-\sqrt{1-x^2}}^{\sqrt{1-x^2}} (2x - 2y)\,dy\,dx$$

$$= \int_0^{2\pi}\int_0^1 (2r\cos\theta - 2r\sin\theta)r\,dr\,d\theta$$

$$= \frac{2}{3}\int_0^{2\pi}(\cos\theta - \sin\theta)\,d\theta = \frac{2}{3}(0) = 0.$$

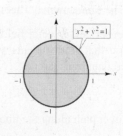

Section 15.5   Parametric Surfaces

Tips and Tools for Problem Solving

CalcChat.com

Exercises 1–6 (1–4 in *Calculus* 8/e)
To give students more practice, we added Exercises 3 and 4.

Exercises 21–30 (19–26 in *Calculus* 8/e)
To give students more practice, we added Exercises 23 and 24.

Capstone

Page 1110, Exercise 50 You can use this exercise to review the following concepts.

- Definition of parametric surfaces
- Determining the point in space from which a surface is viewed

Review the definition of a parametric surface on page 1102. Then go over the solution. If you have access to a computer algebra system, you can show students how to verify the answers. Graph the surface and the four points. Then orient the graph so that you can view the surface from one of the points.

Solution

(a) From $(-10, 10, 0)$

(b) From $(10, 10, 10)$

(c) From $(0, 10, 0)$

(d) From $(10, 0, 0)$

Section 15.6   Surface Integrals

Tips and Tools for Problem Solving

CalcChat.com

Although we made changes to the section exercises, no changes were made based on the data.

Capstone

Page 1123, Exercise 44 You can use this exercise to review the following concepts.

- Identifying a normal vector to a surface
- Explaining how to find the normal component of **F** to a surface
- Evaluating a flux integral

Review Theorems 15.10 and 15.11. To save time, you can show students how to set up the solution to each part and leave it to them to verify the answers.

Solution

(a) $\mathbf{r}_u = \mathbf{i} + \mathbf{j} + 2u\mathbf{k}$

$\mathbf{r}_v = 2v\mathbf{i} - \mathbf{j}$

$$\mathbf{r}_u \times \mathbf{r}_v = \begin{vmatrix} \mathbf{i} & \mathbf{j} & \mathbf{k} \\ 1 & 1 & 2u \\ 2v & -1 & 0 \end{vmatrix} = 2u\mathbf{i} + 4uv\mathbf{j} - (1 + 2v)\mathbf{k}$$

$\mathbf{r}_u \times \mathbf{r}_v$ is a normal vector to the surface.

(b) $\mathbf{F}(u, v) = u^2\mathbf{i} + (u + v^2)\mathbf{j} + (u - v)\mathbf{k}$

$\mathbf{F} \cdot (\mathbf{r}_u \times \mathbf{r}_v) = 2u^3 + 4uv(u + v^2) - (u - v)(1 + 2v)$

$\qquad\qquad = 2u^3 + 4u^2v + 4uv^3 + v - u + 2v^2 - 2uv$

(c) $\left.\begin{array}{l} x = 3 = u + v^2 \\ y = 1 = u - v \\ z = 4 = u^2 \end{array}\right\}$ $\begin{array}{l} u = 2 \ (u = -2 \text{ not in domain}) \\ v = 1 \end{array}$

(d) Calculate $\mathbf{F} \cdot \dfrac{\mathbf{r}_u \times \mathbf{r}_v}{\|\mathbf{r}_u \times \mathbf{r}_v\|}$ at P.

$\mathbf{F}(3, 1, 4) = 4\mathbf{i} + 3\mathbf{j} + \mathbf{k}$

$(\mathbf{r}_u \times \mathbf{r}_v)(2, 1) = 4\mathbf{i} + 8\mathbf{j} - 3\mathbf{k}$

$\|\mathbf{r}_u \times \mathbf{r}_v\| = \sqrt{89}$

$\mathbf{F} \cdot \dfrac{\mathbf{r}_u \times \mathbf{r}_v}{\|\mathbf{r}_u \times \mathbf{r}_v\|} = \dfrac{1}{\sqrt{89}}(16 + 24 - 3) = \dfrac{37}{\sqrt{89}} = \dfrac{37\sqrt{89}}{89}$

(e) $\displaystyle\int_S\int \mathbf{F} \cdot \mathbf{N}\, dS = \int_R\int \mathbf{F} \cdot (\mathbf{r}_u \times \mathbf{r}_v)\, dA$

$\qquad = \displaystyle\int_{-1}^{1}\int_{0}^{2} (2u^3 + 4u^2v + 4uv^3 + v - u + 2v^2 - 2uv)\, du\, dv$

$\qquad = \displaystyle\int_{-1}^{1}\left(8v^3 + 4v^2 + \dfrac{26v}{3} + 6\right) dv = \dfrac{44}{3}$

Section 15.7   Divergence Theorem

Tips and Tools for Problem Solving

CalcChat.com

Exercises 1–6 (1–4 in *Calculus* 8/e)
To give students more practice, we added Exercises 5 and 6.

Capstone

Page 1131, Exercise 24 You can use this exercise to review the following concepts.

- Divergence Theorem

- Using a surface integral and a triple integral to verify the Divergence Theorem for a given problem

Go over the Divergence Theorem (Theorem 15.12). You may also want to review evaluating a surface integral (Theorem 15.10) and evaluating a triple integral (Section 14.6).

Solution

$\mathbf{F}(x, y, z) = x\mathbf{i} + y\mathbf{j} + z\mathbf{k}$

Divergence Theorem: div $\mathbf{F} = 1 + 1 + 1 = 3$

$\iiint\limits_{Q} 3\, dV = 3\,(\text{Volume of cube}) = 3$

Surface Integral: There are six surfaces.

$x = 0: \quad \mathbf{N} = -\mathbf{i}, \quad \mathbf{F} \cdot \mathbf{N} = -x, \quad \int_{S_1}\int 0\, dS = 0$

$x = 1: \quad \mathbf{N} = \mathbf{i}, \quad \mathbf{F} \cdot \mathbf{N} = x, \quad \int_{S_2}\int 1\, dS = 1$

$y = 0: \quad \mathbf{N} = -\mathbf{j}, \quad \mathbf{F} \cdot \mathbf{N} = -y, \quad \int_{S_3}\int 0\, dS = 0$

$y = 1: \quad \mathbf{N} = \mathbf{j}, \quad \mathbf{F} \cdot \mathbf{N} = y, \quad \int_{S_4}\int 1\, dS = 1$

$z = 0: \quad \mathbf{N} = -\mathbf{k}, \quad \mathbf{F} \cdot \mathbf{N} = -z, \quad \int_{S_5}\int 0\, dS = 0$

$z = 1: \quad \mathbf{N} = \mathbf{k}, \quad \mathbf{F} \cdot \mathbf{N} = z, \quad \int_{S_6}\int 1\, dS = 1$

So, $\int_{S}\int \mathbf{F} \cdot \mathbf{N}\, dS = 1 + 1 + 1 = 3.$

Section 15.8 Stokes's Theorem

Tips and Tools for Problem Solving

CalcChat.com

Although we made changes to the section exercises, no changes were made based on the data.

Capstone

Page 1137, Exercise 28 You can use this exercise to review the following concept.

- Stokes's Theorem

Review Stokes's Theorem (Theorem 15.13). Because students have difficulty setting up the limits of integration, go over the solution slowly and carefully. You may want to leave the evaluation of the integrals to your students. If you are pressed for time, only do part (a). The graphs are provided on transparencies.

Solution

(a) $\mathbf{F}(x, y, z) = e^{y+z}\mathbf{i}$

From the figure you have

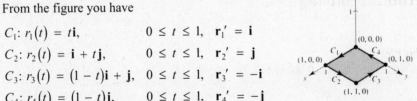

$C_1: r_1(t) = t\mathbf{i}, \qquad 0 \le t \le 1, \quad \mathbf{r}_1' = \mathbf{i}$

$C_2: r_2(t) = \mathbf{i} + t\mathbf{j}, \qquad 0 \le t \le 1, \quad \mathbf{r}_2' = \mathbf{j}$

$C_3: r_3(t) = (1-t)\mathbf{i} + \mathbf{j}, \quad 0 \le t \le 1, \quad \mathbf{r}_3' = -\mathbf{i}$

$C_4: r_4(t) = (1-t)\mathbf{j}, \qquad 0 \le t \le 1, \quad \mathbf{r}_4' = -\mathbf{j}$

$\int_C \mathbf{F} \cdot d\mathbf{r} = \int_{C_1} \mathbf{F} \cdot \mathbf{r}_1'\, dt + \int_{C_2} \mathbf{F} \cdot \mathbf{r}_2'\, dt + \int_{C_3} \mathbf{F} \cdot \mathbf{r}_3'\, dt + \int_{C_4} \mathbf{F} \cdot \mathbf{r}_4'\, dt$

$= \int_0^1 e^0\, dt + 0 + \int_0^1 -e^{1+0}\, dt + 0 = 1 - e$

Double Integral: curl $\mathbf{F} = e^{y+z}\mathbf{j} - e^{y+z}\mathbf{k}$

$G(x, y) = z = 0, \mathbf{N} = \mathbf{k}$

$\int_S \int \text{curl } \mathbf{F} \cdot \mathbf{N}\, dS = \int_R \int -e^y\, dA = \int_0^1 \int_0^1 -e^y\, dx\, dy = \int_0^1 -e^y\, dy = \left[-e^y\right]_0^1 = 1 - e$

131

(b) $\mathbf{F}(x, y, z) = z^2\mathbf{i} + x^2\mathbf{j} + y^2\mathbf{k}$

From the figure you have

$C: \mathbf{r}(t) = 2\cos t\,\mathbf{i} + 2\sin t\,\mathbf{j} + 4\mathbf{k}, \quad 0 \le t \le 2\pi.$

$$\int_C \mathbf{F} \cdot d\mathbf{r} = \int_C M\,dx + N\,dy + P\,dz = \int_0^{2\pi}\left[16(-2\sin t) + (4\cos^2 t)(2\cos t) + 0\right]dt$$

$$= \int_0^{2\pi}\left[-32\sin t + 8\cos^3 t\right]dt = 0$$

Double Integral: $\operatorname{curl}\mathbf{F} = 2y\mathbf{i} + 2z\mathbf{j} + 2x\mathbf{k}$

$z = g(x, y) = x^2 + y^2,\ g_x = 2x,\ g_y = 2y$

$$\int_S \int \operatorname{curl}\mathbf{F} \cdot \mathbf{N}\,dS = \int_R \int (2y\mathbf{i} + 2z\mathbf{j} + 2x\mathbf{k}) \cdot (-2x\mathbf{i} - 2y\mathbf{j} + \mathbf{k})\,dA$$

$$= \int_R \int \left[-4xy - 4y(x^2 + y^2) + 2x\right]dA$$

$$= \int_0^{2\pi}\int_0^2 \left[-4r\sin\theta\, r\cos\theta - 4r\sin\theta(r^2) - 2r\cos\theta\right]r\,dr\,d\theta$$

$$= \int_0^{2\pi}\left[\left[-16\sin\theta - \tfrac{16}{3}\right]\cos\theta - \tfrac{128}{5}\sin\theta\right]d\theta = 0$$

Chapter 15 Project

Mathematical Sculpture

Whether mathematics is seen as a science or as an art depends on one's perspective. One mathematician-sculptor, Helaman Ferguson, combines both viewpoints in a unique way. Ferguson's sculptures, which bear such names as *Cosine Wild Sphere* and *Esker Trefoil Torus*, are the concrete embodiments of mathematical concepts that incorporate ideas such as series expansions and vector fields into their creation. Some of the basic images of his work are tori and double tori, Möbius strips, and trefoil knots. One of his techniques is to use three-dimensional computer graphics to model his intended sculptures. The coordinates on the computer screen can then be used to direct the sculpting.

One example of Helaman Ferguson's work, *Umbilic Torus NC*, is shown below. This form can be written as a parametric surface using the following set of parametric equations.

$$x = \sin u \left[7 + \cos\left(\frac{u}{3} - 2v\right) + 2 \cos\left(\frac{u}{3} + v\right) \right]$$

$$y = \cos u \left[7 + \cos\left(\frac{u}{3} - 2v\right) + 2 \cos\left(\frac{u}{3} + v\right) \right]$$

$$z = \sin\left(\frac{u}{3} - 2v\right) + 2 \sin\left(\frac{u}{3} + v\right)$$

$$-\pi \le u \le \pi, \quad -\pi \le v \le \pi$$

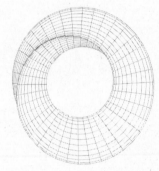

Generated by Mathematica

Mathematica rendition of *Umbilic Torus NC*

Exercises

1. Explain how the umbilic torus shown above is similar to a Möbius strip like the one shown below.

2. Use a three-dimensional computer algebra system to graph the torus. You will have to use the *parametric surface* graphing mode.

3. When viewed head-on (along the z-axis), the torus appears nearly circular. Is it possible to alter this appearance so that the shape of the torus is more like that of an elongated ellipse? If so, use a computer algebra system to sketch an "elliptical" torus.

Project Answers

Chapter P

1. (a) $x^2 + y^2 = 2500$

(b)

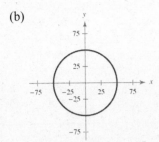

(c) y is not a function of x.

(d) *Sample answer:* For any given horizontal position x, a car could be at one of two vertical positions y. For instance, if the horizontal position of a car is 30 units, its vertical position could be ± 40 units.

2. (a) $h = 50 + 50 \sin 8\pi t$

(b)

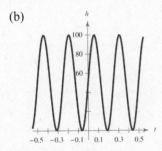

(c) h is a function of t.

(d) For any given time t, a car can be in only one position h.

3. $h = 50 + 50 \sin\left(8\pi t - \dfrac{\pi}{2}\right)$; $h(0) = 50 + 50 \sin\left(0 - \dfrac{\pi}{2}\right) = 50 - 50 = 0$

Chapter 1

1. 12 mL, 9mL, 6.75 mL, 5.0625 mL

2. $a(n) = \left(\dfrac{3}{4}\right)^n (16)$

3. There is no value of n for which $a(n)$ equals zero. The only way a fraction can equal zero is when the numerator equals zero.

4. 28 mL

5. 37 mL, 43.75 mL; Increasing

6.

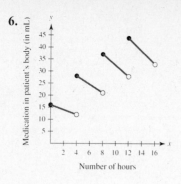

7. (a) 12

(b) 28

(c) 27.75

(d) 43.75

8. The function has a nonremovable discontinuity at $x = 4n$, where n is a nonnegative integer. Discontinuities occur when the patient takes an additional dose of medication, causing the amount of medication in the patient's body to suddenly increase.

9. $\frac{1}{4} \cdot y = 16$; 64 mL

Chapter 2

1. $s(t) = kt$

2. $k = \frac{15}{4}t - \frac{5}{12}t^2$

3. $v(t) = \frac{15}{2}t - \frac{5}{4}t^2$

4. 4.5 sec

5. $k = 8.4375$ m/sec

6.

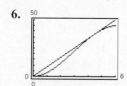

7. (4.5, 37.96875); The chase car catches you 4.5 seconds after you pass the 10-mile mark. When the car catches you, you are both 37.96875 meters past the 10-mile mark.

8. At (4.5, 37.96875), the graph of your position function is tangent to the graph of the chase car's position function. So, at this point, both velocities are equal, which makes the handoff easy.

9. (a)

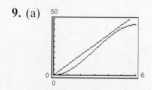

(b) 0

(c) No. In this scenario, the chase car will never catch you.

10. (a)

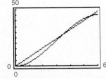

(b) 2

(c) Even though they will be in the same position twice, they will not be traveling at the same velocity at those times. This will make it very difficult to handoff the cup of water.

Chapter 3

1. $y' = 0.45\pi \sin^2\left(\dfrac{\pi}{12}x - \dfrac{\pi}{2}\right) \cos\left(\dfrac{\pi}{12}x - \dfrac{\pi}{2}\right)$

2. $x = 0, 6, 12, 18, 24$

3. 12 P.M.; 12 A.M.; The First Derivative Test

4.

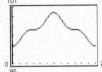

The graph has points of inflection when $x = 6$ and $x = 18$. Although a body's temperature increases from 12 A.M. to 12 P.M., the rate of increase slows and then picks back up at 6 A.M. Similarly, although a body's temperature decreases from 12 P.M. to 12 A.M., the rate of decrease slows and then picks back up at 6 P.M.

5. $y = 1.8 \sin^3\left(\dfrac{\pi}{12}x - \dfrac{3\pi}{2}\right) + 98.6$

6. $x = 0, 6, 12, 18, 24$

7. 12 A.M.; 12 P.M.

8.

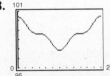

This graph also has points of inflection when $x = 6$ and $x = 18$. However, for the third shift worker, the rate of decrease slows and then picks back up at 6 A.M. and the rate of increase slows and then picks back up at 6 P.M.

9. $y = 1.8 \sin^3\left(\dfrac{\pi}{12}x - \pi\right) + 98.6$

10. $x = 0, 6, 12, 18, 24$

11. 6 P.M.; 6 A.M.

Chapter 4

1. (a) $y = \sqrt{100 - x^2}$

   (b) $A = 50\pi$ ft^2 ≈ 157.08 ft^2

   (c) $2\int_0^{10} \sqrt{100 - x^2}\, dx$

   (d) About 157.08 ft^2; Approximately equal

2. $A = 2314.16$ ft^2

3. (a)

   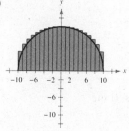

   It is important to use an upper sum to ensure no pieces will be too short.

   (b)

Dimensions of board	Number of pieces
1 ft by 20 ft	60
1 ft by 30 ft	20
1 ft by 29 ft	4
1 ft by 28 ft	8
1 ft by 26 ft	4
1 ft by 25 ft	4

   (c) 2344 ft^2

   (d) 29.84 ft^2

   (e) If the width of the siding increases, the amount of wasted wood increases. If the width of the siding decreases, the amount of wasted wood decreases.

4. (a)

   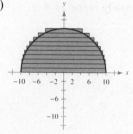

Dimensions of board	Number of pieces
1 ft by 30 ft	40
1 ft by 20 ft	48
1 ft by 19 ft	2
1 ft by 18 ft	2
1 ft by 16 ft	2
1 ft by 15 ft	2
1 ft by 12 ft	2
1 ft by 9 ft	2

(c) 2338 ft^2

(d) 23.84 ft^2

(e) If the width of the siding increases, the amount of wasted wood increases. If the width of the siding decreases, the amount of wasted wood decreases.

5. *Sample answer:* Siding horizontally decreases the amount of wasted wood. Using a narrower siding might also be advisable since it would decrease the amount of waste. However, this would also increase the amount of work.

Chapter 5

1. (a) $42.575 million

   (b) About $1798 million = $1.798 billion

   (c) 1993

2. $y = \log_{1.707}\left(\dfrac{x}{42.575}\right)$; The inverse function gives the year y corresponding to the revenue x.

3. 1993; Same

4. $y' = 22.766(1.707)^x$

5. $22.766 million per year; about $113.24 million per year

6. Because the revenue function is exponential, the derivative is an increasing function. That is, the rate of change will continue to increase over time. This means that not only is the revenue increasing, but it is increasing more rapidly.

7. $\displaystyle\int_0^8 42.575(1.707)^x\ dx$

8. About $5660 million = $5.66 billion

9. About $58.958 million

10. About $13.606 million

11. About $1.938 million

12. About $3,206,701.98 million $\approx$ $3.2 trillion

13. It is unlikely that the revenue continues to follow the model because $3.2 trillion is a very large amount for revenue in 2006.

14. $56 billion

15. It appears that the revenue does not continue to follow the growth model. Although the revenue appears to continue to increase, it is increasing much more slowly than the model indicated.

Chapter 6

1. $s''(t) = -32$, $s'(0) = 0$, $s(3) = 0$

2. $v(t) = -32t$

3. $s(t) = -16t^2 + 144$

4. 144 ft

5. $s''(t) = -32$, $s'(0) = 2$, $s(3) = 0$

6. $v(t) = -32t + 2$

7. $s(t) = -16t^2 + 2t + 138$

8. 138 ft

9. $s''(t) = -32$, $s'(0) = -3$, $s(3) = 0$

10. $v(t) = -32t - 3$

11. $s(t) = -16t^2 - 3t + 153$

12. 153 ft

13. The height of the building

14. If the building is 144 feet tall, the man most likely fell off the roof accidentally. So, the detective should not suspect foul play.

15. To travel more than 144 feet in 3 seconds, the man must have had a negative initial velocity. So, he was most likely pushed off the roof.

16. To travel less than 144 feet in 3 seconds, the man must have had a positive initial velocity. So, he most likely jumped off the roof.

17. Because the man fell 160 feet in 3 seconds, he must have been pushed off the building.

Chapter 7

1. $V = \pi \int_{-5.5}^{5.5} \left(-0.0944x^2 + 3.4\right)^2 dx$

2. $V \approx 232.2 \text{ in.}^3$

3. $V = \dfrac{4\pi}{\sqrt{0.0944}} \int_0^{3.4} y\sqrt{3.4 - y}\, dy$

4. $V \approx 232.5$ in.^{3}; Approximately equal

5. $S = 2\pi \int_{-5.5}^{5.5} \left(-0.0944x^2 + 3.4\right)\sqrt{1 + \left(-0.1888x\right)^2} \, dx$

6. $S \approx 188.1$ in.^{2}

7. $V \approx 434.9$ in.^{3}

8. $V = \pi \int_{-4.7}^{4.7} \left(4.7^2 - x^2\right) dx$

9. $V \approx 434.9$ in.^{3}; Equal

10. $V = 4\pi \int_{0}^{4.7} y\sqrt{4.7^2 - y^2} \, dy$

11. $V \approx 434.9$ in.^{3}; Equal

12. $S \approx 277.6$ in.^{2}

13. $S = 2\pi \int_{-4.7}^{4.7} 4.7 \, dx$

14. $S \approx 277.6$ in.^{2}; Equal

Chapter 8

1. $De^{4x} \cos(3x) + Fe^{4x} \sin(3x) + C$

2. $\left(4D + 3F\right)e^{4x} \cos(3x) + \left(4F - 3D\right)e^{4x} \sin(3x)$

3. $D = \frac{4}{25}$, $F = \frac{3}{25}$; $\frac{4}{25}e^{4x} \cos(3x) + \frac{3}{25}e^{4x} \sin(3x) + C$

4. $\frac{4}{25}e^{4x} \cos(3x) + \frac{3}{25}e^{4x} \sin(3x) + C$; Same

5. $\dfrac{B}{A^2 + B^2}e^{Bx} \cos(Ax) + \dfrac{A}{A^2 + B^2}e^{Bx} \sin(Ax) + C$

6. $\dfrac{B}{A^2 + B^2}e^{Bx} \cos(Ax) + \dfrac{A}{A^2 + B^2}e^{Bx} \sin(Ax) + C$; Same

7. $Ge^{2x} \sin(5x) - Je^{2x} \cos(5x) + C$

8. $\left(5G - 2J\right)e^{2x} \cos(5x) + \left(2G + 5J\right)e^{2x} \sin(5x)$

9. $G = \frac{2}{29}$, $J = \frac{5}{29}$, $\frac{2}{29}e^{2x} \sin(5x) - \frac{5}{29}e^{2x} \cos(5x) + C$

10. $\frac{2}{29}e^{2x} \sin(5x) - \frac{5}{29}e^{2x} \cos(5x) + C$; Same

11. $\dfrac{B}{A^2 + B^2}e^{Bx} \sin(Ax) - \dfrac{A}{A^2 + B^2}e^{Bx} \cos(Ax) + C$

12. $\dfrac{B}{A^2 + B^2}e^{Bx} \sin(Ax) - \dfrac{A}{A^2 + B^2}e^{Bx} \cos(Ax) + C$; Same

Chapter 9

1. 2000 m

2. 1998 m

3. 3000 m

4. 2995.5 m

5. $d_0 = 1000$, $d_1 = 999$, $d_2 = 1997$, $d_3 = 2994.5$, $d_4 = 3991.\overline{6}$

6. $d_1 = 1 \cdot d_0 - 1$, $d_2 = 2 \cdot d_1 - 1$, $d_3 = \frac{3}{2} \cdot d_2 - 1$, $d_4 = \frac{4}{3} \cdot d_3 - 1$

7. $d_1 = 1 \cdot d_0 - 1 = 1(d_0 - 1)$

   $d_2 = 2 \cdot d_1 - 1 = 2\left(d_1 - \frac{1}{2}\right) = 2\left[(d_0 - 1) - \frac{1}{2}\right] = 2\left[d_0 - \left(1 + \frac{1}{2}\right)\right]$

   $d_3 = \frac{3}{2} \cdot d_2 - 1 = \frac{3}{2} \cdot 2\left[d_0 - \left(1 + \frac{1}{2}\right)\right] - 1 = 3\left(\left[d_0 - \left(1 + \frac{1}{2}\right)\right] - \frac{1}{3}\right) = 3\left[d_0 - \left(1 + \frac{1}{2} + \frac{1}{3}\right)\right]$

8. $d_n = n\left(d_0 - \sum_{k=1}^{n} \frac{1}{k}\right)$

9. Divergent harmonic series; Theorem 9.11

10. Because $\sum_{k=1}^{n} \frac{1}{k}$ gets infinitely large as n gets large, d_n approaches 0. You will reach the pot of gold.

11. $e^{1000} - 1$ seconds

12. $d_n = n\left(d_0 - \frac{1}{4}\sum_{k=1}^{n} \frac{1}{k}\right)$

13. Yes; $e^{4000} - 1$ seconds

14. $d_n = n\left(d_0 - \sum_{k=1}^{n} \frac{1}{k}\right)$

15. Yes; $e^{5000} - 1$ seconds

16. No. You will always reach the pot of gold. The length of the sidewalk and the speed at which you walk affect only the time it takes you to reach the pot of gold.

Chapter 10

1. $\dfrac{dy}{dx} = 1 - \dfrac{8\sqrt{2}t}{25}$

2. About 2.2 sec

3. About 81 ft

4. 0 ft/sec

5. About 70.7 ft/sec

142

6. About 4.5 sec

7. About 318 ft

8. About -1.04; The ball is falling approximately 1.04 feet for every 1 foot it moves horizontally.

9. About -73.3 ft/sec

10. About 70.7 ft/sec

11. Yes; The ball is 300 feet from home plate after $\dfrac{300}{100(\cos 45°)} \approx 4.2$ seconds. At this time, the ball will have a vertical position of 15 feet. It will just clear the fence.

12. $\displaystyle\int_0^{4.5} \sqrt{\left[100(\cos 45°)\right]^2 + \left[100(\sin 45°) - 32t\right]^2}\, dt$

13. About 366.8 ft; 366.8 ft $>$ 318 ft

14. $y = 3 + x - \dfrac{2x^2}{625}$

15. $y' = 1 - \dfrac{4x}{625}$

16. $x = 156.25$ ft

17. About 2.2 sec; Equal

18. A rectangular equation only tells you *where* the baseball has been. Expressing the path of the baseball parametrically enables you to determine *when* the baseball was at a given point.

Chapter 11

1. $\left\langle \dfrac{1}{2}, \dfrac{1}{2}, -\dfrac{1}{2} \right\rangle$

2. $\dfrac{\sqrt{3}}{2}$

3. $\left\langle -\dfrac{1}{2}, \dfrac{1}{2}, \dfrac{1}{2} \right\rangle$

4. $\dfrac{\sqrt{3}}{2}$

5. $-\dfrac{1}{4}$

6. $\theta \approx 1.91$ radians $\approx 109.5°$

7. $\sqrt{2}$

8. $\dfrac{\sqrt{3}}{2}; \dfrac{\sqrt{3}}{2}$

9–13. $\theta \approx 1.91$ radians $\approx 109.5°; \sqrt{2}$

143

14. The triangles formed by connecting the nuclei of two hydrogen atoms and the carbon atom of a methane molecule are isosceles triangles with side measures of $\frac{\sqrt{3}}{2}$, $\frac{\sqrt{3}}{2}$, and $\sqrt{2}$, and angle measures of 109.5°, 35.25°, and 35.25°.

Chapter 12

1. $\mathbf{r}(t) = (40 \cos 35°)t\mathbf{i} + \left[6 + (40 \sin 35°)t - 16t^2 \right]\mathbf{j}$

2. About 0.72 sec

3. About 14.22 ft

4. About 1.66 sec

5. About 54.39 ft

6. $\mathbf{r}(t) = (40 \cos 45°)t\mathbf{i} + \left[6 + (40 \sin 45°)t - 16t^2 \right]\mathbf{j}$

7. About 0.88 sec

8. 18.5 ft

9. About 1.96 sec

10. About 55.41 ft

11. $t = \dfrac{v_0 \sin \theta + \sqrt{v_0^2 \sin^2 \theta + 2gh}}{g}$

12. $x(\theta) = v_0 \cos \theta \left(\dfrac{v_0 \sin \theta + \sqrt{v_0^2 \sin^2 \theta + 2gh}}{g} \right)$

13. $t = \dfrac{40 \sin \theta + \sqrt{1600 \sin^2 \theta + 384}}{32}$

14. $x(\theta) = 40 \cos \theta \left(\dfrac{40 \sin \theta + \sqrt{1600 \sin^2 \theta + 384}}{32} \right)$

15.

(41.92, 55.68); The shot-put will travel a maximum distance of 55.68 ft when thrown at an angle of 41.92 degrees.

Chapter 13

1. The receiver should be located at the focus of the circular paraboloid. When the dish is pointed at a satellite, the incoming signals will be reflected to the receiver so that signal strength will increase.

2. Answers will vary. *Sample answer:* Headlights, movie projectors, flashbulbs, and some telescopes use parabolic reflectors.

3. Suppose that the tangent plane has an equation of the form $ax + by + cz + d = 0$. Because the plane is not vertical, $c \neq 0$ and we may assume that $c = -1$. Because $(1, 1, 2)$ is a point on the plane, $a + b - 2 + d = 0$. Thus, the plane has the equation $z = a(x - 1) + b(y - 1) + 2$.

The vertical plane $y = 1$ intersects both the paraboloid and the tangent plane giving a parabola and one of its tangent lines. The parabola is also the intersection of the cylinder $z = x^2 + 1$ with the plane $y = 1$. Similarly, the tangent line is the intersection of the plane $z = a(x - 1) + 2$ and the plane $y = 1$.

In the xz-plane $(y = 0)$, the line $z = a(x - 1) + 2$ must be tangent to the parabola $z = x^2 + 1$ at the point $(1, 2)$. Also in the xz-plane, methods of single variable calculus show that the tangent line has the equation $z = 2x$. Thus, $a = 2$.

By symmetry (interchanging the roles of x and y), $b = 2$. Thus, the tangent plane has the equation $z = 2(x - 1) + 2(y - 1) + 2$.

4. You may talk about the normal vector for a plane, but it does not make sense to talk about the slope of a plane. Nonetheless, the tangent plane has a "slope on the x-direction" of $a = 2$ as derived (using differentiation) in the answer to Exercise 3. Likewise, the "slope in the y-direction" is $b = 2$. These pieces of slope information are combined with $c = -1$ to give the normal vector for the plane: $a\mathbf{i} + b\mathbf{j} + c\mathbf{k} = 2\mathbf{i} + 2\mathbf{j} - \mathbf{k}$.

5. $z = \dfrac{7x^2}{200} + \dfrac{7y^2}{200}$

The domain of the equation is the set of all points such that

$$0 \leq \frac{7x^2}{200} + \frac{7y^2}{200} \leq 3.5.$$

The range is $0 \leq z \leq 3.5$.

Chapter 14

1. Doubling the radius of a sphere increases its volume eightfold. Hence, $\dfrac{V_T}{V} = \dfrac{1}{8}$.

2. The method of Example 2 in Section 14.6 can be used to verify that $\dfrac{4}{3}\pi abc$ is the volume enclosed by the ellipsoid $\dfrac{x^2}{a^2} + \dfrac{y^2}{b^2} + \dfrac{z^2}{c^2} = 1$, where a, b, and c are positive.

Equitherm	$\dfrac{V_T}{V}$
$\dfrac{x^2}{0.1} + \dfrac{y^2}{0.26} + \dfrac{z^2}{0.1} = 1$	$\dfrac{1}{125}$
$\dfrac{x^2}{0.4} + \dfrac{y^2}{1.04} + \dfrac{z^2}{0.4} = 1$	$\dfrac{8}{125}$
$\dfrac{x^2}{0.9} + \dfrac{y^2}{2.34} + \dfrac{z^2}{0.9} = 1$	$\dfrac{27}{125}$
$\dfrac{x^2}{1.6} + \dfrac{y^2}{4.16} + \dfrac{z^2}{1.6} = 1$	$\dfrac{64}{125}$
$\dfrac{x^2}{2.5} + \dfrac{y^2}{6.50} + \dfrac{z^2}{2.5} = 1$	1

3. (a) The volume can be estimated by finding the volume of the spheres that inscribe and circumscribe the wrinkled sphere. The inscribed sphere has a radius of $r = 0.155$ and the circumscribed sphere has a radius of $r = 0.845$. Thus, the radius of the wrinkled sphere is greater than

   $\frac{4}{3}\pi(0.155)^3 \approx 0.00497\pi$ cubic units or 0.0156 cubic units

   and less than

   $\frac{4}{3}\pi(0.845)^3 \approx 0.80447\pi$ cubic units or 2.5273 cubic units.

   (b) 0.7736 cubic units; This value falls within the range found in part (a).

4. 2.0609 cubic units

Chapter 15

1. Imagine a long flexible solid with a uniform cross section in the shape of an equilateral triangle. When the solid is straightened out, it has three identical sides, each lying in a distinct plane. Twist one end by $120°$ (one-third of a complete revolution). Then bring the twisted end around and butt it against the untwisted end. The alignment will be perfect and you will have made a torus with only one side. This is similar to the Möbius strip, which has only one side even though each small segment appears to have two sides. The umbilic torus is also similar to the twisted solid we described, but the cross sections of the umbilic torus are more interesting than equilateral triangles. In summary, the umbilic torus has only one side, but short segments seem to have three sides.

2. Use the equations given in terms of the two parameters u and v.

3. Try multiplying the formula for y by 4.

Dear Colleagues-

Over the past 15 years, I have taught calculus to hundreds of students. It hasn't been easy but over the course of time, I have discovered some strategies that have helped me be successful. I am grateful for the opportunity to share with you some teaching tips I have found to be useful.

Tip #1: Do the work you assign your students

I started teaching Calculus during my college years as a student teacher. My first teaching position was at a private school in Tennessee. I had four preps with one of them being Calculus I. I was scared to death! I spent every day working on calculus. Every problem I gave the students, I did. I found myself only staying ahead of the students by a few days. I spent weekends doing every problem I could get my hands on. It was stressful, but I think I learned the most that first year. I had no one else to rely on. I had to be ready for any question that students would ask. As I did the problems, I found myself thinking about the areas where the students would struggle. I would spend extra time on these areas in class. As I have continued to implement this practice, I have found that my predictions about where students need help are always right on. By spending the extra time teaching the areas needed, I avoid students' confusion later on.

Tip #2: Allow the students to guide the lesson

After teaching at the private school for three years, I moved to Arizona. I have been teaching at Chandler High School since that time. My first position was teaching Calculus II (Calculus BC). Since at the private school I only taught Calculus I (Calculus AB), I had to study like I did when I first taught Calculus I. Again, I spent every day doing Calculus II problems. The nice thing about teaching Calculus II at the high school level is the class sizes. Not as many students take Calculus II in high school so the classes are small. In fact, one year I had only four students. On average I have 10 to 15 students in Calculus II. The smaller class size allows me to interact one-on-one with the students more often. As a result, the students play an active role in guiding the lesson. For example, I often give the students one problem and then let them discuss the problem while I just watch. These students have the discipline and the willingness to learn which allows them to be able to work either independently or as a group to solve a problem without much input from the teacher. I simply act as a facilitator to keep the discussion heading in the right direction. I used to think that if I was not in front of the class showing them every step that they could not possibly learn something new. I have since discovered students are able to learn without me giving them every detail.

Tip #3: Incorporate sample AP exam questions into your teaching

Overall, the biggest concern any calculus teacher faces is the advanced placement (AP) test. These tests are designed to give students college credit for taking calculus in high school. In general, students need to be able to pass the test with at least a score of 3 or better with 5 being the highest score. When I first started teaching, the test included questions that were straight forward such as "how do you take the derivative of a function" or "how do you integrate a function." But today the test utilizes Bloom's Taxonomy of higher level thinking skills. The test demands that students be able to evaluate, conjecture, and interpret problems. As I always tell my students, every question is "outside the box". The students need to be able to read the questions and determine what the question is asking them to do. The students always tell me that they know what to do. They just are not able to interpret the question. So in addition to teaching your students the basics of calculus (i.e. product, quotient, chain rule, etc.), incorporate AP type questions (like the ones in this guide) so that they get used to the wording and are able to interpret what is being asked. The problems on the AP exam are not difficult. Any student should be able to take the test and pass if they have the calculus basics. I would suggest that you start incorporating these AP questions as soon as possible. The College Board website is a great resource for information regarding the AP exams.

Tip #4: Use mnemonic devices to help students remember rules

I have found that mnemonic devices help students remember derivative and integration rules. Of course, I go completely through the mathematical proof of each theorem, but ultimately they need to remember how to compute a derivative. I use these devices so that they will remember. For example, for the quotient rule I use "lo d hi minus hi d lo over lo lo". During Christmas time I add a little humor by saying "ho d hi minus hi d ho over ho ho". When I first started using this, I thought it was a little ridiculous. But I have to say that the students always remember it. I actually hear them saying it throughout the year when they are computing the derivative using the quotient rule.

Tip #5: Use all available teaching resources

My last tip would be to use any and all resources you can beg, borrow, or research. There are many resources available which can help you teach your classes. I always like to use hands on activities. Students who are able to touch, feel, and evaluate problems are more likely to comprehend a concept. Many of my memories of teaching calculus are related to the activities that we complete in class. For example, when working with optimization, the students are asked to create a box out of material that is given to them. They are to create a box with maximum volume with the material given. The students then make the box and have to take it home and explain what they did to someone outside of school. They come back to school with many stories about how either their dad kept asking them too many questions or how their friend just looked at them with questioning eyes. I have run into students years after they graduated and they still talk about these projects!

I hope these tips will help you to teach calculus to your students. Ultimately the students will learn if you are excited to teach. My students comment about how much of a math geek I am because I get really excited about mathematical proofs. Be sure to never become complacent and always stay ahead of the students. Good luck.

Sincerely,

Jacqueline Hartrick
Math Department Chair
Chandler High School
Chandler, Arizona

Dear Students-

Over the past decade, I have scored thousands of free response exam questions at the AP Calculus Reading. Each year in June, several hundred calculus teachers meet together and spend seven days scoring more than one million free response questions. It is a challenging yet richly rewarding experience. Great effort is taken to make sure that the exams are graded fairly. In fact, as a Table Leader one of my roles was to train other Readers how to score the exams consistently. As a result of my experience as a Reader and Table Leader, I have gained some insights on strategies that you can use to help maximize your score on the free response portion of the exam.

Tip #1: Show your work

At the Reading, we call answers without shown work "bald answers." In many cases, bald answers receive 0 points even if the final answer is correct. As the test taker, your job is to demonstrate that you know the process necessary to obtain the correct answer. Ask yourself, "Does the work I've shown clearly demonstrate how I reached my final answer?" If the answer is "no", go back and add additional details. Another benefit of showing your work is earning partial credit. Even if your final answer is wrong due to a minor computation error, you will often be awarded several points of partial credit for demonstrating a clear understanding of the problem solving process.

Tip #2: Read and comply with the exam instructions

Each exam has very specific instructions which must be followed. Failure to follow these instructions often costs precious points. Here are some guidelines you will want to follow.

- Give final answers accurate to **three** places after the decimal.
- Clearly label all graphs, functions, tables, or other things you use to solve a problem.
- Justify answers when the problem requires it.
- Write all solutions and supporting work in the correct section of the exam booklet. If you mistakenly write part (a) of a problem in the part (b) space, draw arrows or otherwise communicate which problem is written in each section.
- Cross out any work you don't want graded

Tip #3: Use the graphing calculator appropriately

The graphing calculator is a powerful tool that can be used to help you solve problems and to check your work. In fact, some exam questions require the use of a graphing calculator to reach the solution. However, calculator syntax is not calculus. For example, although the calculator command fnInt(sin(5x^2), X, 2,3) tells the calculator to find the definite integral of $f(x) = \sin(5x^2)$ over the interval $[2,3]$, you must write $\int_{2}^{3} \sin(5x^2)\,dx$ in your exam booklet to show that you have some understanding of what the calculator is doing. But you can use your calculator to calculate the numerical value of the definite integral. Similarly, you are allowed to use your calculator to graph functions, solve equations numerically, and calculate numerical values of derivatives without showing additional work.

Tip #4: When required to justify answers, use clear and complete explanations

Frequently free response questions ask you to *justify your conclusion*. Numerical answers alone are not sufficient to show that you understand the meaning of your answers. In writing your justification, use complete sentences and explain the reasoning behind your conclusions. Your goal is to demonstrate that you understand the calculus concepts that make your answer correct. For example, consider the following justification for why a relative maximum of $f(x) = x^2 e^{-x}$ occurs at $x = 2$.

Since $f'(x) = xe^{-x}(2-x)$ equals zero at $x = 0$ and $x = 2$, f has critical values at $x = 0$ and $x = 2$. We can determine the increasing and decreasing behavior of f by evaluating the derivative at x-values in the intervals $(-\infty, 0)$, $(0, 2)$, and $(2, \infty)$. Since $f'(-1) < 0$, f is decreasing on the interval $(-\infty, 0)$. Since $f'(1) > 0$, f is increasing on the interval $(0, 2)$. Since $f'(3) < 0$, f is decreasing on the interval $(2, \infty)$. Since f is continuous and f changes from increasing to decreasing at $x = 2$, a relative maximum occurs at $x = 2$.

Tip #5: Manage your time wisely

Work the problems that you best understand first. This will help you in two ways. First, it will help to ensure that your best work makes it into the exam booklet. This will increase the likelihood of you scoring more points. Second, it will boost your confidence and reduce your anxiety. After completing two problems with relative ease, you will approach the third problem with a feeling of optimism. On the other hand, if you start with the most challenging problem and have difficulty in solving it, you may waste precious time and increase your anxiety.

I hope that each of these tips will help you do your very best on the AP Calculus exam. I'll be watching for your quality work.

Sincerely,

Frank Wilson
Chandler–Gilbert Community College
Chandler, Arizona

P.1 Homework Quiz

1. Match the equation with its

   a. $y = 1 - x^2$

   b. $y = -2x + 1$

   c. $y = -x^3 + x$

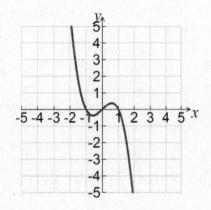

2. Sketch the graph of $y - x^2 = -4$. Identify any intercepts and test for symmetry.

3. Sketch the graph of $x = 2y^3$. Identify any intercepts and test for symmetry.

4. Find the points of intersection of the graphs of the equations.

   $y = x^2 + 1$

   $x + y = 3$

P.1 Homework Quiz Answers

1. Match the equation with its graph. (Similar to Exercise #4.)

    a. $y = 1 - x^2$

    b. $y = -2x + 1$

    c. $y = -x^3 + x$

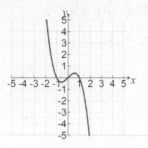

The correct answer is (c).

2. Sketch the graph of $y - x^2 = -4$. Identify any intercepts and test for symmetry. (Similar to Exercise #46.)

    x-intercepts: $(-2, 0)$, $(2, 0)$

    y-intercept: $(0, -4)$

    Symmetric with respect to y-axis.

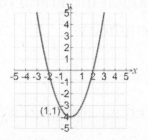

3. Sketch the graph of $x = 2y^3$. Identify any intercepts and test for symmetry. (Similar to Exercise #53.)

    x-intercept: $(0, 0)$

    y-intercept: $(0, 0)$

    Symmetric with respect to origin.

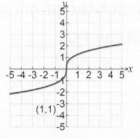

4. Find the points of intersection of the graphs of the equations.

    $y = x^2 + 1$

    $x + y = 3$

    (Similar to Exercise #65.)

$$y = (3 - y)^2 + 1 \Rightarrow y = 2 \text{ and } y = 5. \text{ The points of intersection are}$$
$$(-2, 5), (1, 2)$$

P.2 Homework Quiz

1. Find the slope of the line passing through the points $(-2,3)$ and $(6,-1)$.

2. Find the slope and y-intercept of the line $6x - 2y = 8$.

3. Find an equation of the line that passes through the points $(1,2)$ and $(3,8)$.

4. Write an equation of the line containing the point $(4,1)$ that is:
   a. parallel to $y = 2x + 3$
   b. perpendicular to $y = 2x + 3$

P.2 Homework Quiz Answers

1. Find the slope of the line passing through the points $(-2,3)$ and $(6,-1)$. (Similar to Exercise #9.)

    Using the slope formula $\dfrac{y_2 - y_1}{x_2 - x_1}$, we get $\dfrac{-1-3}{6-(-2)} = \dfrac{-4}{8} = -\dfrac{1}{2}$.

2. Find the slope and y-intercept of the line $6x - 2y = 8$. (Similar to Exercise #26.)
$$6x - 2y = 8$$
$$-2y = -6x + 8.$$
$$y = 3x - 4$$
    Therefore, the slope is 3 and the y-intercept is $(0,-4)$.

3. Find an equation of the line that passes through the points $(1,2)$ and $(3,8)$. (Similar to Exercise #38.)

    The slope is $m = \dfrac{8-2}{3-1} = 3$.
$$y = mx + b$$
$$2 = 3(1) + b$$
$$b = -1$$
    So $y = 3x - 1$.

4. Write an equation of the line containing the point $(4,1)$ that is:
    a. parallel to $y = 2x + 3$
    b. perpendicular to $y = 2x + 3$
    (Similar to Exercise #63.)

    a. Use $m = 2$. Then $1 = 2(4) + b \Rightarrow b = -7$. So $y = 2x - 7$.

    b. Use $m = -\dfrac{1}{2}$. Then $1 = -\dfrac{1}{2}(4) + b \Rightarrow b = 3$. So $y = -\dfrac{1}{2}x + 3$.

P.3 Homework Quiz

1. Find the domain of the function $f(x) = \dfrac{1}{\sqrt{x-2}}$.

2. Let $f(x) = \begin{cases} (x-2)^2 + 1, & x < 2 \\ x - 3, & x \geq 2 \end{cases}$. Evaluate $f(1)$, $f(2)$, and $f(3)$.

3. Given that $f(x) = x - 1$ and $g(x) = x^2$, find $f(g(3))$, $g(f(3))$, $f(g(x))$, and $g(f(x))$.

4. Determine whether $f(x) = x^2 + \cos x$ is even, odd, or neither.

P.3 Homework Quiz Answers

1. Find the domain of the function $f(x) = \dfrac{1}{\sqrt{x-2}}$.

   (Similar to Exercise #21.)

   Since the denominator can't be zero, set $x - 2 > 0$. Thus, $x > 2$.

2. Let $f(x) = \begin{cases} (x-2)^2 + 1, & x < 2 \\ x^2 - 3, & x \geq 2 \end{cases}$. Evaluate $f(1)$, $f(2)$, and $f(3)$.

   (Similar to Exercise #28.)

   Using the first piece, $f(1) = (1-2)^2 + 1 = 2$.

   Using the second piece, $f(2) = 2^2 - 3 = 1$.

   Using the second piece, $f(3) = 3^2 - 3 = 6$.

3. Given that $f(x) = x - 1$ and $g(x) = x^2$, find $f(g(3))$, $g(f(3))$, $f(g(x))$ and $g(f(x))$. (Similar to Exercise #59.)

   $f(g(3)) = f(9) = 8$

   $g(f(3)) = g(2) = 4$

   $f(g(x)) = f(x^2) = x^2 - 1$

   $g(f(x)) = g(x-1) = (x-1)^2$

4. Determine whether $f(x) = x^2 + \cos x$ is even, odd, or neither. (Similar to Exercise #71.)

   $$f(-x) = (-x)^2 + \cos(-x)$$
   $$= x^2 + \cos x$$
   $$= f(x)$$

   Therefore, $f(x)$ is an even function.

P.4 Homework Quiz

1. Plot the data and determine whether the data is best modeled by a linear, quadratic, or trigonometric function, or if there appears to be no relationship between x and y.

x	7	4	9	1	8	4	5
y	3	8	2	5	9	5	1

2. The ordered pairs are the student scores on two consecutive 100 point tests for a class.

$$(88, 96), (57, 62), (73, 74), (81, 89),$$
$$(66, 70), (77, 73), (90, 92), (64, 59),$$
$$(70, 76), (82, 85), (96, 99), (78, 83)$$

Plot the data. Does the graph appear to be approximately linear? If so, find a linear model for the data.

3. A company makes a profit based on the number of transmissions it sells. The table shows the number it sells, x, and the profit in thousands of dollars, P. Use the regression to find a quadratic model for the data. Then predict profit when 85 transmissions are sold.

x	20	40	60	80	100
P	9	16	21	19	13

4. The average high temperatures of Phoenix, Arizona, denoted by F and in degrees Fahrenheit, are displayed by month m, in the table below.

m	1	2	3	4	5	6	7	8	9	10	11	12
F	66	70	75	84	93	93	105	103	99	88	75	66

What model type best fits the data? Why?

P.4 Homework Quiz Answers

1. Plot the data and determine whether the data is best modeled by a linear, quadratic, or trigonometric function, or if there appears to be no relationship between x and y.

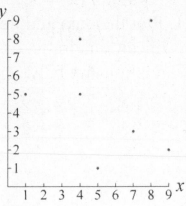

x	7	4	9	1	8	4	5
y	3	8	2	5	9	5	1

(Similar to Exercise #3.)

There appears to be no relationship between x and y.

2. The ordered pairs are the student scores on two consecutive 100 point tests for a class.
$(88, 96), (57, 62), (73, 74), (81, 89),$

$(66, 70), (77, 73), (90, 92), (64, 59),$

$(70, 76), (82, 85), (96, 99), (78, 83)$

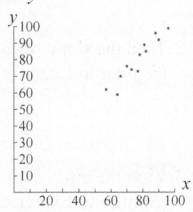

Plot the data. Does the graph appear to be approximately linear? If so, find a linear model for the data. (Similar to Exercise #6.)
The linear equation $y = 1.07x - 2.51$ best fits the data.

3. A company makes a profit based on the number of transmissions it sells. The table shows the number it sells, x, and the profit in thousands of dollars, P. Use the regression to find a quadratic model for the data. Then predict profit when 85 transmissions are sold. (Similar to Exercise #12.)

x	20	40	60	80	100
P	9	16	21	19	13

The equation $y = -0.00589x^2 + 0.762x - 4.2$ best fits the data. Based on this model, the company should make about an $18,000 profit.

4. The average high temperatures of Phoenix, Arizona, denoted by F and in degrees Fahrenheit, are displayed by month m, in the table below.

m	1	2	3	4	5	6	7	8	9	10	11	12
F	66	70	75	84	93	93	105	103	99	88	75	66

What model type best fits the data? Why? (Similar to Exercise #17.)

Since the data is periodic, a sinusoidal function will best fit the data.

158

1.1 Homework Quiz

1. Graph $f(x) = 4x - x^2$ and the secant line passing through $(1,3)$ and
   $Q(x, f(x))$ for x-values of 0, 0.5, and 1.50.   (Similar to Exercise #6.)

2. Find the slope of each secant line in Problem # 1.
   (Similar to Exercise #1.)

3. Find the area of the shaded region.
   (Similar to Exercise #5.)

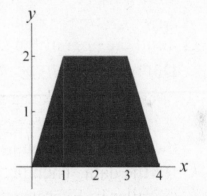

4. Use the rectangles in the graph to
   approximate the area of the region bounded

   by $y = \dfrac{8}{x}$, $y = 0$, $x = 1$, and $x = 4$.

   (Similar to Exercise #9.)

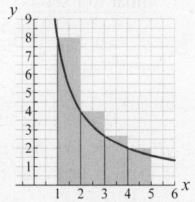

1.1 Homework Quiz Answers

1. Graph $f(x) = 4x - x^2$ and the secant line passing through $(1, 3)$ and $Q(x, f(x))$ for x-values of 0, 0.5, and 1.50.   (Similar to Exercise #6.)

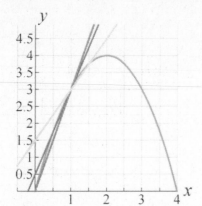

2. Find the slope of each secant line in Problem # 1. (Similar to Exercise #1.)

$$m = \frac{3 - y_1}{1 - x_1} = \frac{3 - \left(4x_1 - x_1^2\right)}{1 - x_1}$$

At $x_1 = 0$, $m = 3$.

At $x_1 = 0.5$, $m = 2.5$.

At $x_1 = 1.5$, $m = 1.5$.

3. Find the area of the shaded region. (Similar to Exercise #5.)

$$\frac{1}{2}(4 + 2)2 = 6 \text{ square units}$$

4. Use the rectangles in the graph to approximate the area of the region bounded by $y = \dfrac{8}{x}$, $y = 0$, $x = 1$, and $x = 4$. (Similar to Exercise #9.)

$$y = \left(\frac{8}{1}\right)1 + \left(\frac{8}{2}\right)1 + \left(\frac{8}{3}\right)1 = 14\frac{2}{3}$$

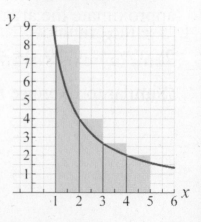

1.2 Homework Quiz

1. Complete the table and use the result to estimate the limit.

$$\lim_{x \to 1} \frac{\left(x^3 - 1\right)^2}{x - 1} .$$

x	0.9	0.99	0.999	1	1.001	1.01	1.1
y							

2. Graph the following: $f(x) = \begin{cases} x - 5 & x < 2 \\ -3 & x = 2 \\ -3x + 3 & x < 2 \end{cases}$.

3. Using the graph from Problem #2, find $\lim_{x \to 2} f(x)$. If the limit does not exist, explain why.

4. Use the graph of f to decide whether $\lim_{x \to -1} f(x)$ exists. If the limit exists, find it. If not, explain why.

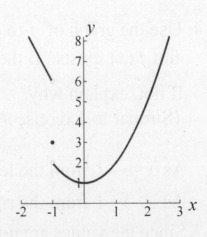

1.2 Homework Quiz Answers

1. Complete the table and use the result to estimate the limit.

$$\lim_{x \to 1} \frac{\left(x^3 - 1\right)^2}{x - 1}$$. (Similar to Exercise #8.)

x	0.9	0.99	0.999	1	1.001	1.01	1.1
y	−0.734	−0.088	−0.009	Error	0.009	0.092	1.096

$$\lim_{x \to 1} \frac{\left(x^3 - 1\right)^2}{x - 1} = 0$$

2. Graph the following: $f(x) = \begin{cases} x - 5 & x < 2 \\ -3 & x = 2 \\ -3x + 3 & x < 2 \end{cases}$

   (Similar to Exercise #29.)

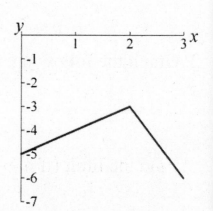

3. Using the graph from Problem #2, find $\lim_{x \to 2} f(x)$. If the limit does not exist, explain why. (Similar to Exercise #18.)

$$\lim_{x \to 2} f(x) = -3$$

4. Use the graph of f to decide whether $\lim_{x \to -1} f(x)$ exists. If the limit exists, find it. If not, explain why. (Similar to Exercise #25.)

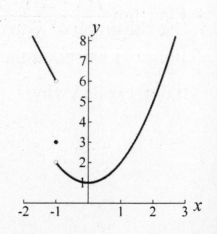

As $x \to -1$ from the left, $f(x) \to 6$.

As $x \to -1$ from the right, $f(x) \to 2$.

Since the values are not equal, the limit does not exist.

1.3 Home Quiz

1. Find the limit (if it exists). $\lim\limits_{x\to3}\dfrac{x^3+1}{x-4}$

2. Find the limit (if it exists). $\lim\limits_{x\to-2}\tan\left(\dfrac{\pi x}{8}\right)$

3. Find the limit (if it exists). $\lim\limits_{x\to6}\dfrac{x^2-3x+2}{x^2-x-30}$

4. Find $\lim\limits_{\Delta x\to0}\dfrac{f(x+\Delta x)-f(x)}{\Delta x}$ for $f(x)=x^2+3x$.

1.3 Homework Quiz Answers

1. Find the limit (if it exists). $\lim\limits_{x\to 3}\dfrac{x^3+1}{x-4}$

   (Similar to Exercise #20.)

$$\lim_{x\to 3}\frac{x^3+1}{x-4}=-28$$

2. Find the limit (if it exists). $\lim\limits_{x\to -2}\tan\left(\dfrac{\pi x}{8}\right)$

   (Similar to Exercise #35.)

$$\lim_{x\to -2}\tan\left(\frac{\pi x}{8}\right)=\tan\left(\frac{-\pi}{4}\right)$$
$$=-1$$

3. Find the limit (if it exists). $\lim\limits_{x\to 6}\dfrac{x^2-3x+2}{x^2-x-30}$

   (Similar to Exercise #54.)

$$\lim_{x\to 6}\frac{x^2-3x+2}{x^2-x-30}=\frac{20}{0}=\text{undefined}$$

The limit does not exist.

4. Find $\lim\limits_{\Delta x\to 0}\dfrac{f(x+\Delta x)-f(x)}{\Delta x}$ for $f(x)=x^2+3x$.

   (Similar to Exercise #88.)

$$\lim_{\Delta x\to 0}\frac{(x+\Delta x)^2+3(x+\Delta x)-\left(x^2+3x\right)}{\Delta x}=\lim_{\Delta x\to 0}2x+\Delta x+3$$

1.4 Homework Quiz

1. Find $\displaystyle\lim_{x \to 5} \frac{x^2 - 25}{x - 5}$.

2. Find the x-values (if any) where f is not continuous. State whether the x-value is removable or non-removable.

3. Find the constant a such that the function is continuous on the entire real line.

4. Discuss the continuity of the given function $\displaystyle f(x) = \frac{x(x-1)}{x}$.

1.4 Homework Quiz Answers

1. Find $\lim\limits_{x \to 5} \dfrac{x^2 - 25}{x - 5}$. (Similar to Exercise #9.)

$$\lim\limits_{x \to 5} \frac{x^2 - 25}{x - 5} = \lim\limits_{x \to 5} \frac{(x-5)(x+5)}{x-5} = 10$$

2. Find the x-values (if any) where f is not continuous. State whether the x-value is removable or non-removable. (Similar to Exercise #43.)

$$f(x) = \frac{x}{2x^2 - 2x} = \frac{1}{2(x-1)}$$

Hole at $x = 0$ is removable. Vertical asymptote at $x = 1$ is non-removable.

3. Find the constant a such that the function is continuous on the entire real line. (Similar to Exercise #68.)

$$g(x) = \begin{cases} \dfrac{x^2 - a^2}{x - a} & x \neq a \\ 1/2 & x = a \end{cases}$$

$$\frac{(x-a)(x+a)}{x-a} = x + a \text{ for } x \neq a$$
$$x + a = 1/2$$
$$2a = 1/2 \text{ when } x = a$$
$$a = 1/4$$

4. Discuss the continuity of the given function $f(x) = \dfrac{x(x-1)}{x}$.

There is a hole at $x = 0$.

1.5 Homework Quiz

1. Determine whether $\lim\limits_{x \to 5^+} \dfrac{3x-5}{5-x}$ approaches ∞ or $-\infty$.

2. Find the vertical asymptote(s) of $f(t) = \dfrac{t}{4t^2 - 2t - 12}$.

3. Determine whether $f(x)$ approaches ∞ or $-\infty$ as x approaches 2.

4. Determine whether the graph of $f(x) = \dfrac{x+2}{x^2 - 4}$ has a vertical asymptote or a removable discontinuity at $x = 2$.

1.5 Homework Quiz Answers

1. Determine whether $\displaystyle\lim_{x\to 5^+}\frac{3x-5}{5-x}$ approaches ∞ or $-\infty$.
   (Similar to Exercise #49.)

$$\lim_{x\to 5^+}\frac{3x-5}{5-x}=-\infty$$

2. Find the vertical asymptote(s) of $\displaystyle f(t)=\frac{t}{4t^2-2t-12}$.
   (Similar to Exercise #37.)

$$f(t)=\frac{t}{(2t+3)(2t-4)}.$$

   The function has vertical asymptotes at $t=-\dfrac{3}{2}$ and $t=2$.

3. Determine whether $f(x)$ approaches ∞ or $-\infty$ as x approaches 2.
   (Similar to Exercise #27.)

$$\lim_{x\to 2^+}\frac{3}{(x-2)^2}=+\infty \text{ and } \lim_{x\to 2^-}\frac{3}{(x-2)^2}=+\infty \text{ so } \lim_{x\to 2}\frac{3}{(x-2)^2}=\infty.$$

4. Determine whether the graph of $\displaystyle f(x)=\frac{x+2}{x^2-4}$ has a vertical
   asymptote or a removable discontinuity at $x=2$.
   (Similar to Exercise #35.)

   Vertical asymptote at $x=2$.

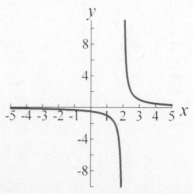

2.1 Homework Quiz

1. Find the slope of the tangent line to the graph of the function $f(x) = 4 - 9x$ at $(1, -5)$.

2. Find the derivative of $f(x) = -x^2 + 4$ by the limit process.

3. Find an equation of the tangent line to graph of $f(x) = \dfrac{1}{x}$ at $(4, 0.25)$.

4. The graph of f is a concave down parabola with vertex $(0,0)$. Which graph is the graph of f'?

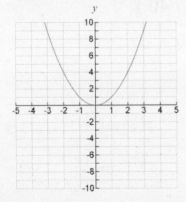 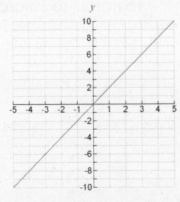 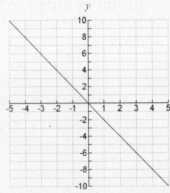

2.1 Homework Quiz Answers

1. Find the slope of the tangent line to the graph of the function $f(x) = 4 - 9x$ at $(1, -5)$. (Similar to Exercise #5.)

Since the graph of f is a line, the slope of the graph will be the same as the slope of the tangent line. The slope of the tangent line is -9.

2. Find the derivative of $f(x) = -x^2 + 4$ by the limit process. (Similar to Exercise #18.)

$$f'(x) = \lim_{\Delta x \to 0} \frac{f(x + \Delta x) - f(x)}{\Delta x} = \lim_{\Delta x \to 0} \frac{-(x + \Delta x)^2 + 4 - (-x^2 + 4)}{\Delta x}$$

$$= \lim_{\Delta x \to 0} \frac{-(x^2 + 2x\Delta x + (\Delta x))^2 + 4 - (-x^2 + 4)}{\Delta x} = \lim_{\Delta x \to 0} (-2x - \Delta x) = -2x$$

3. Find an equation of the tangent line to graph of $f(x) = \dfrac{1}{x}$ at $(4, 0.25)$. (Similar to Exercise #32.)

$$f'(x) = -\frac{1}{x^2}$$
$$f'(4) = -0.0625$$

$$y = mx + b$$
$$0.25 = -0.0625(4) + b$$
$$b = 0.50$$

$$y = -0.0625x + 0.50$$

4. The graph of f is a concave down parabola with vertex $(0, 0)$. Which graph is the graph of f'? (Similar to Exercise #40.)

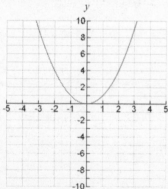
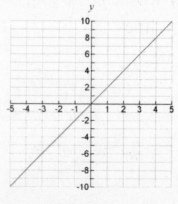
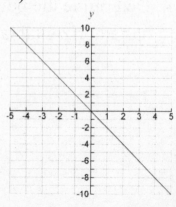

The graph on the right is the graph of f'.

170

2.2 Homework Quiz

1. Use the rules of differentiation to find the derivative of the function $g(x) = x^3 + 9x - 4$.

2. Find the slope of the graph of the function $f(t) = 3\sin t + 4t - 1$ at $(0, -1)$.

3. Find the derivative of $f(x) = 3\sqrt{x} - 7\sin x$.

4. Determine the point(s) at which the graph of the function $y = x^3 + 3x^2$ has a horizontal tangent line.

2.2 Homework Quiz Answers

1. Use the rules of differentiation to find the derivative of the function $g(x) = x^3 + 9x - 4$. (Similar to Exercise #16.)

$$g'(x) = 3x^2 + 9$$

2. Find the slope of the graph of the function $f(t) = 3\sin t + 4t - 1$ at $(0, -1)$. (Similar to Exercise #37.)

$f'(t) = 3\cos t + 4$ The slope of the graph is 7 at $(0, -1)$.

$f'(0) = 3\cos 0 + 4$

$\quad\quad = 7$

3. Find the derivative of $f(x) = 3\sqrt{x} - 7\sin x$. (Similar to Exercise #53.)

$$f(x) = 3x^{0.5} - 7\sin x$$
$$f'(x) = 1.5x^{-0.5} - 7\cos x$$

4. Determine the point(s) at which the graph of the function $y = x^3 + 3x^2$ has a horizontal tangent line. (Similar to Exercise #60.)

$$y' = 3x^2 + 6x$$
$$0 = 3x(x + 2)$$

At $x = 0$ and $x = -2$, the graph has a horizontal tangent line.

2.3 Homework Quiz

1. Use the Product Rule to differentiate $f(x) = (x^3 + 4)(4x^2 + 6)$.

2. Use the Quotient Rule to differentiate $f(x) = \dfrac{\cos x}{3x}$.

3. Find the derivative of the algebraic function $f(x) = \dfrac{4x + 5}{\sqrt{x}}$.

4. Find the derivative of the trigonometric function $y = 3x \cos x$.

2.3 Homework Quiz Answers

1. Use the Product Rule to differentiate $f(x) = (x^3 + 4)(4x^2 + 6)$.
   (Similar to Exercise #2.)

$$f'(x) = (x^3 + 4)(8x) + (4x^2 + 6)(3x^2)$$
$$= 20x^4 + 18x^2 + 32x$$

2. Use the Quotient Rule to differentiate $f(x) = \dfrac{\cos x}{3x}$.
   (Similar to Exercise #12.)

$$f'(x) = \frac{3x(-\sin x) - (\cos x)(3)}{(3x)^2} = \frac{-x \sin x - \cos x}{3x^2}$$

3. Find the derivative of the algebraic function $f(x) = \dfrac{4x + 5}{\sqrt{x}}$.
   (Similar to Exercise #29.)

$$f(x) = \frac{4x + 5}{\sqrt{x}}$$
$$= 4x^{0.5} + 5x^{-0.5}$$

$$f'(x) = 2x^{-0.5} - 2.5x^{-1.5}$$

4. Find the derivative of the trigonometric function $y = 3x \cos x$.
   (Similar to Exercise #53.)

$$y' = 3x(-\sin x) + \cos x(3)$$
$$= -3x \sin x + 3 \cos x$$

2.4 Homework Quiz

1. Given $y = f(g(x)) = \left(5x^4 + 20x\right)^3$, find $u = g(x)$ and $y = f(u)$.

2. Find the derivative of $g(t) = \left(5t^4 - 17t + 4\right)^{-3}$.

3. Find the derivative of $y = \sin(\cos x)$.

4. Evaluate the derivative of $f(x) = \dfrac{-2x + 4}{6x - 4}$ at $(0, -1)$.

2.4 Homework Quiz Answers

1. Given $y = f(g(x)) = \left(5x^4 + 20x\right)^3$, find $u = g(x)$ and $y = f(u)$.
   (Similar to Exercise #1.)

$$u = 5x^4 + 20x \text{ and } y = u^3$$

2. Find the derivative of $g(t) = \left(5t^4 - 17t + 4\right)^{-3}$.
   (Similar to Exercise #18.)

$$g'(t) = -3\left(5t^4 - 17t + 4\right)^{-4}\left(20t^3 - 17\right)$$

3. Find the derivative of $y = \sin(\cos x)$.
   (Similar to Exercise #65.)

$$y' = \cos(\cos x)(-\sin x)$$
$$= -\sin x \cos(\cos x)$$

4. Evaluate the derivative of $f(x) = \dfrac{-2x + 4}{6x - 4}$ at $(0, -1)$.
   (Similar to Exercise #72.)

$$f'(x) = \frac{(6x - 4)(-2) - (-2x + 4)(6)}{(6x - 4)^2}$$

$$f'(0) = \frac{(6(0) - 4)(-2) - (-2(0) + 4)(6)}{(6(0) - 4)^2} = -1$$

2.5 Homework Quiz

1. Find $\dfrac{dy}{dx}$ by implicit differentiation given $3x^2 y - y^2 = x$.
   (Similar to Exercise #7.)

2. Find two explicit functions for $8x^2 - y^2 = 32$ by solving the equation for y in terms of x. (Similar to Exercise #22.)

3. Find $\dfrac{d^2 y}{dx^2}$ in terms of x and y given $x^2 = y^3$.
   (Similar to Exercise #49.)

4. Differentiate $3x^2 + 4y = 10$ with respect to t.
   (Similar to Exercise #65.)

2.5 Homework Quiz Answers

1. Find $\dfrac{dy}{dx}$ by implicit differentiation given $3x^2y - y^2 = x$.
   (Similar to Exercise #7.)

$$3x^2 \frac{dy}{dx} + y(6x) - 2y \frac{dy}{dx} = 1 \qquad\qquad \frac{dy}{dx} = \frac{1 - 6xy}{3x^2 - 2y}$$

$$\left(3x^2 - 2y\right) \frac{dy}{dx} = 1 - 6xy$$

2. Find two explicit functions for $8x^2 - y^2 = 32$ by solving the equation
   for y in terms of x. (Similar to Exercise #22.)

$$8x^2 - 32 = y^2 \qquad\qquad \text{So } y = \sqrt{8x^2 - 32} \text{ or } y = -\sqrt{8x^2 - 32}$$

$$y = \pm\sqrt{8x^2 - 32}$$

3. Find $\dfrac{d^2y}{dx^2}$ in terms of x and y given $x^2 = y^3$.
   (Similar to Exercise #49.)

$$2x = 3y^2 \frac{dy}{dx} \qquad \frac{d^2y}{dx^2} = \frac{3y^2(2) - 2x\left(6y\dfrac{dy}{dx}\right)}{\left(3y^2\right)^2} \qquad = \frac{6y^2 - \left(\dfrac{8x^2}{y}\right)}{9y^4}$$

$$\frac{dy}{dx} = \frac{2x}{3y^2} \qquad\qquad = \frac{6y^2 - 12xy\left(\dfrac{2x}{3y^2}\right)}{9y^4} \qquad = \frac{6y^3 - 8x^2}{9y^5}$$

4. Differentiate $3x^2 + 4y = 10$ with respect to t.
   (Similar to Exercise #65.)

$$6x \frac{dx}{dt} + 4 \frac{dy}{dt} = 0$$

2.6 Homework Quiz

1. Given $xy = 36$ and $\dfrac{dy}{dt} = 9$, find $\dfrac{dx}{dt}$ when $y = 12$.

2. A point is moving along the graph of $y = \sin x$ such that $\dfrac{dx}{dt} = 2$ centimeters per second. Find $\dfrac{dy}{dt}$ for $x = \pi$.

3. Let V be the volume of a sphere with radius r that is changing with respect to time. If $\dfrac{dr}{dt}$ is constant, is $\dfrac{dV}{dt}$ constant? Explain.

4. A ladder 20 feet long leans against the wall of a house. The base of the ladder is pulled away at a rate of 3 feet per second. How fast is the top of the ladder moving down the wall when the base is 12 feet from the wall? (Similar to Exercise #25.)

2.6 Homework Quiz Answers

1. Given $xy = 36$ and $\dfrac{dy}{dt} = 9$, find $\dfrac{dx}{dt}$ when $y = 12$.
   (Similar to Exercise #3.)

$$x\frac{dy}{dt} + y\frac{dx}{dt} = 0 \qquad\qquad -27 = 12\frac{dx}{dt}$$

$$3(9) + 12\left(\frac{dx}{dt}\right) = 0 \qquad\qquad \frac{dx}{dt} = -\frac{9}{4}$$

2. A point is moving along the graph of $y = \sin x$ such that $\dfrac{dx}{dt} = 2$
   centimeters per second. Find $\dfrac{dy}{dt}$ for $x = \pi$. (Similar to Exercise #8.)

$$\frac{dy}{dt} = \cos x \frac{dx}{dt} \qquad\qquad \frac{dy}{dt} = -2$$

$$= \cos \pi (2)$$

3. Let V be the volume of a sphere with radius r that is changing with
   respect to time. If $\dfrac{dr}{dt}$ is constant, is $\dfrac{dV}{dt}$ constant? Explain.
   (Similar to Exercise #14.)

   We know $V = \dfrac{4}{3}\pi r^3$ and $\dfrac{dV}{dt} = 4\pi r^2 \dfrac{dr}{dt}$. Since $\dfrac{dV}{dt}$ depends on
   r (which is changing), it is not constant.

4. A ladder 20 feet long leans against the wall of a house. The base of
   the ladder is pulled away at a rate of 3 feet per second. How fast is
   the top of the ladder moving down the wall when the base is 12 feet
   from the wall? (Similar to Exercise #25.)

$$a^2 + b^2 = c^2$$

$$2a\frac{da}{dt} + 2b\frac{db}{dt} = 2c\frac{dc}{dt} \qquad 2(12)(3) + 2(16)\frac{db}{dt} = 2(20)(0)$$

$$\frac{db}{dt} = -2.25 \text{ feet per second}$$

3.1 Homework Quiz

1. Approximate the critical numbers of the function shown in the graph.

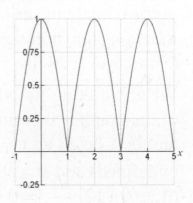

2. Find any critical numbers for the function $f(\theta) = \sin\theta - \cos^2\theta$ with $0 < \theta < 2\pi$.

3. Locate the absolute extrema of $h(t) = \dfrac{1}{t^2 + 1}$ on $[-1, 1]$.

4. Graph a function with critical number (no extremum) at $x = 0$ and absolute minimum at $x = 3$.

3.1 Homework Quiz Answers

1. Approximate the critical numbers of the function shown in the graph. (Similar to Exercise #9.)	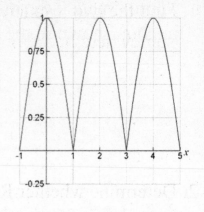
We are looking for points where the slope of the graph is 0 or undefined. Critical numbers occur at $x = -1, 1, 3, 5$ (slope undefined) and at $x = 0, 2, 4$ (slope equal to 0).	

2. Find any critical numbers for the function $f(\theta) = \sin\theta - \cos^2\theta$ with $0 < \theta < 2\pi$. (Similar to Exercise #15.)

$f'(\theta) = \cos\theta - 2\cos\theta(-\sin\theta)$ $0 = \cos\theta + 2\sin\theta\cos\theta$ $0 = \cos\theta(1 - 2\sin\theta)$ so $\cos\theta = 0$ or $1 - 2\sin\theta = 0$	$\cos\theta = 0$ at $\theta = \dfrac{\pi}{2}$ and $\dfrac{3\pi}{2}$ $\sin\theta = \dfrac{1}{2}$ at $\theta = \dfrac{\pi}{6}$ and $\dfrac{5\pi}{6}$ These are the critical numbers.

3. Locate the absolute extrema of $h(t) = \dfrac{1}{t^2 + 1}$ on $[-1, 1]$.

(Similar to Exercise #26.)

$h'(t) = -(t^2 + 1)^{-2}(2t)$ At $t = 0$, $h'(t) = 0$. This is a critical number.	$h(-1) = 0.5$ $h(0) = 1$ $h(1) = 0.5$	The absolute minima are $(\pm 1, 0.5)$ and the absolute maximum is $(0, 1)$.

4. Graph a function with critical number (no extremum) at $x = 0$ and absolute minimum at $x = 3$. (Similar to Exercise #56.)

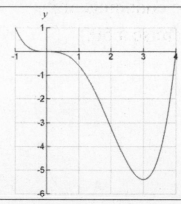

3.2 Homework Quiz

1. Find the two x-intercepts of $f(x) = x^2 - 4x$ and show that $f'(x) = 0$ somewhere between them.

2. Determine whether Rolle's Theorem can be applied to $f(x) = x^{1/3}$ on $[-4, 4]$.

3. Given $f(x) = x^3 - x$ find all values of c in the open interval $(1, 2)$ such that $f'(c) = \dfrac{f(2) - f(1)}{2 - 1}$.

4. Given the graph of $f(x) = x - \sin \pi x$ on $[0, 2]$, graph the secant line through points on the graph of f at the endpoints of the interval. (Similar to Exercise # 50.)

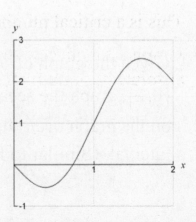

3.2 Homework Quiz Answers

1. Find the two x-intercepts of $f(x) = x^2 - 4x$ and show that $f'(x) = 0$ somewhere between them. (Similar to Exercise #5.)

$$0 = x(x - 4) \qquad\qquad f'(x) = 2x - 4$$
$$x = 0 \text{ and } x = 4 \text{ are } x\text{-intercepts} \qquad 0 = 2x - 4$$
$$x = 2$$

2. Determine whether Rolle's Theorem can be applied to $f(x) = x^{1/3}$ on $[-4, 4]$. (Similar to Exercise #15.)

$$f'(x) = \frac{1}{3}x^{-2/3}$$
$$= \frac{1}{3\sqrt[3]{x^2}}$$

Since $f'(x) > 0$ for all x, f is increasing. Thus $f(a) \neq f(b)$ for all a and b in $[-4, 4]$.

Therefore, Rolle's Theorem does not apply.

3. Given $f(x) = x^3 - x$ find all values of c in the open interval $(1, 2)$ such that $f'(c) = \dfrac{f(2) - f(1)}{2 - 1}$. (Similar to Exercise #41.)

$$f'(x) = 3x^2 - 1 \qquad \frac{f(2) - f(1)}{2 - 1} = \frac{6 - 0}{1} \qquad 3x^2 - 1 = 6$$
$$= 6 \qquad 3x^2 = 7$$
$$x = \sqrt{7/3} \approx 1.52$$

4. Given the graph of $f(x) = x - \sin \pi x$ on $[0, 2]$, graph the secant line through points on the graph of f at the endpoints of the interval. (Similar to Exercise # 50.)

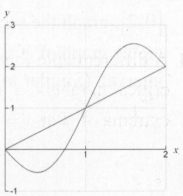

3.3 Homework Quiz

1. Identify the open intervals on which $g(x) = 2x - \dfrac{6}{x}$ is increasing or decreasing.

2. Find the open intervals on which $f(x) = \sin x - \cos x$ is increasing or decreasing.

3. The graph of f is shown. Sketch a graph of f' on the same axes.

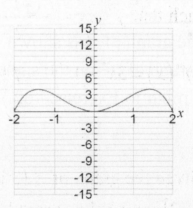

4. A differentiable function f has a critical number at $x = 2$ and no other critical numbers. $f'(1) = -3$ and $f'(3) = 5$. Identify the relative extrema of f at $x = 2$.

3.3 Homework Quiz Answers

1. Identify the open intervals on which $g(x) = 2x - \dfrac{6}{x}$ is increasing or decreasing. (Similar to Exercise #12.)

$$g'(x) = 2 + \frac{6}{x^2}$$

Since $g'(x) > 0$ for all x, g is increasing on $(-\infty, \infty)$.

2. Find the open intervals on which $f(x) = \sin x - \cos x$ is increasing or decreasing. (Similar to Exercise #45.)

$f'(x) = \cos x + \sin x$ 　　 Critical numbers are $x = \dfrac{3\pi}{4} + \pi k$.

$0 = \cos x + \sin x$

$-\cos x = \sin x$ 　　 $f'(\pi) = -1$ and $f'(2\pi) = 1$

Between $\dfrac{3\pi}{4} + 2\pi k$ and $\dfrac{7\pi}{4} + 2\pi k$, f is decreasing. Similarly, f is

increasing between $\dfrac{7\pi}{4} + 2\pi k$ and $\dfrac{11\pi}{4} + 2\pi k$.

3. The graph of f is shown. Sketch a graph of f' on the same axes. (Similar to Exercise #62.)

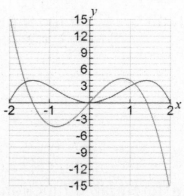

4. A differentiable function f has a critical number at $x = 2$ and no other critical numbers. $f'(1) = -3$ and $f'(3) = 5$. Identify the relative extrema of f at $x = 2$. (Similar to Exercise #78.)

Since f' changes from negative to positive at $x = 2$, f has a relative minimum at $x = 2$.

3.4 Homework Quiz

1. The graph of f is shown. State the signs of f' and f''.

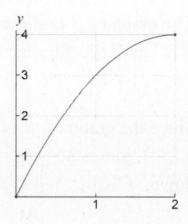

2. Find the open intervals on which $f(x) = x^4 - 4x^3 + 1$ is concave upward or downward.

3. Find the points of infection of $f(x) = \cos x - \sin x$ on $[0, 2\pi]$.

4. Use the Second Derivative test to find the relative extrema of $f(x) = 4x + \dfrac{4}{x}$.

3.4 Homework Quiz Answers

1. The graph of f is shown. State the signs of f' and f''. (Similar to Exercise #4.)

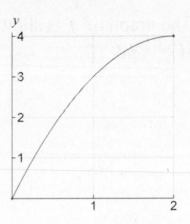

   Since the graph of f is increasing, $f' > 0$. Since the graph of f is concave down, $f'' < 0$.

2. Find the open intervals on which $f(x) = x^4 - 4x^3 + 1$ is concave upward or downward. (Similar to Exercise #8.)

   $f'(x) = 4x^3 - 12x^2$ $0 = 12x(x-2)$ $f''(-1) > 0 \Rightarrow$ up on $(-\infty, 0)$

   $f''(x) = 12x^2 - 24x$ $x = 0$ and $x = 2$ $f''(1) < 0 \Rightarrow$ down on $(0, 2)$

                                                          $f''(3) > 0 \Rightarrow$ up on $(2, \infty)$

3. Find the points of infection of $f(x) = \cos x - \sin x$ on $[0, 2\pi]$. (Similar to Exercise #34.)

   $f'(x) = -\sin x - \cos x$ $f''(0) = -1$

   $f''(x) = -\cos x + \sin x$ $f''(\pi) = 1$

   $0 = -\cos x + \sin x$ $f''(2\pi) = -1$

   $\cos x = \sin x$ f changes from concave down to up at

   $x = \dfrac{\pi}{4}, \dfrac{5\pi}{4}$ $x = \dfrac{\pi}{4}$ and from up to down at $x = \dfrac{5\pi}{4}$.

                                These are points of inflection.

4. Use the Second Derivative test to find the relative extrema of $f(x) = 4x + \dfrac{4}{x}$. (Similar to Exercise #49.)

   $f'(x) = 4 - 4x^{-2}$ f has critical numbers $x = \pm 1$.

   $f''(x) = 8x^{-3}$ $f''(1) = 8 \Rightarrow$ relative minimum

                        $f''(-1) = -8 \Rightarrow$ relative maximum

3.5 Homework Quiz

1. Find $\lim\limits_{x\to\infty} \dfrac{6x^2 - 3x + 1}{-2x^2 + 4x + 7}$, if possible.

2. Find $\lim\limits_{x\to\infty}\left(6 - \dfrac{2}{x^2}\right)$.

3. Graph the function $g(x) = \dfrac{3x + 2}{\sqrt{x^2 + 4}}$ and identify any horizontal asymptotes.

4. Given $f(x) = \dfrac{2x - 9}{x\sqrt{x}}$, complete the table.

x	1	10	10^2	10^3	10^4	10^5	10^6
$f(x)$							

189

3.5 Homework Quiz Answers

1. Find $\lim\limits_{x \to \infty} \dfrac{6x^2 - 3x + 1}{-2x^2 + 4x + 7}$, if possible.
   (Similar to Exercise #13.)

   For large values of x, $\dfrac{6x^2 - 3x + 1}{-2x^2 + 4x + 7} \approx \dfrac{6x^2}{-2x^2} = -3$.
   So the limit is equal to -3.

2. Find $\lim\limits_{x \to \infty} \left(6 - \dfrac{2}{x^2} \right)$. (Similar to Exercise #19.)

   As $x \to \infty$, $\dfrac{2}{x^2} \to 0$. So $\lim\limits_{x \to \infty} \left(6 - \dfrac{2}{x^2} \right) = 6$.

3. Graph the function $g(x) = \dfrac{3x + 2}{\sqrt{x^2 + 4}}$ and identify any horizontal

   asymptotes. (Similar to Exercise #41.)

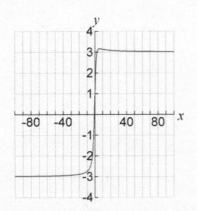

   There is a horizontal asymptote at
   $y = 3$ and at $y = -3$.

4. Given $f(x) = \dfrac{2x - 9}{x\sqrt{x}}$, complete the table. (Similar to Exercise #52.)

x	1	10	10^2	10^3	10^4	10^5	10^6
$f(x)$	-7	0.347	0.191	0.063	0.020	0.006	0.002

3.6 Homework Quiz

1. Graph $y = \dfrac{3}{x-5} + 4$. Label any intercepts, relative extrema, points of inflection, and asymptotes.

2. Graph $y = \left| x^2 - 7x + 6 \right|$. Label any intercepts, relative extrema, points of inflection, and asymptotes.

3. Graph $y = \dfrac{\sin x}{x}$ on $[-10, 10]$.

4. Create a function with vertical asymptote $x = 4$ and horizontal asymptote $y = 2$. (Similar to Exercise #67.)

3.6 Homework Quiz Answers

1. Graph $y = \dfrac{3}{x-5} + 4$. Label any intercepts, relative extrema, points of inflection, and asymptotes. (Similar to Exercise #5.)

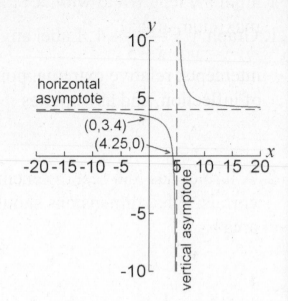

vertical asymptote: $x = 5$

horizontal asymptote: $y = 4$

y-intercept: $(0, 3.4)$

x-intercept: $(4.25, 0)$

2. Graph $y = \left| x^2 - 7x + 6 \right|$. Label any intercepts, relative extrema, points of inflection, and asymptotes. (Similar to Exercise #32.)

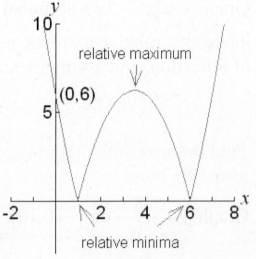

y-intercept: $(0, 6)$

x-intercepts: $(1, 0), (6, 0)$

relative maximum: $(3.5, 6.25)$

relative minima: $(1, 0), (6, 0)$

3. Graph $y = \dfrac{\sin x}{x}$ on $[-10, 10]$. (Similar to Exercise #45.)

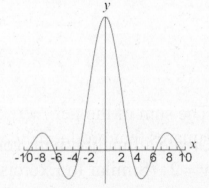

4. Create a function with vertical asymptote $x = 4$ and horizontal asymptote $y = 2$. (Similar to Exercise #67.)

$$y = \frac{2x}{x-4}$$

3.7 Homework Quiz

1. Find the length and width of a rectangle with perimeter 60 meters and maximum area.

2. A farmer has 360 feet of fencing to enclose two adjacent rectangular corrals. What dimensions should be used to maximize the enclosed area?

3. Find the area of the largest rectangle than can be created inside a circle of radius 3 feet.

4. The sum of the perimeters two squares is 24. Find the dimensions of the squares that produce the minimum total area.

3.7 Homework Quiz Answers

1. Find the length and width of a rectangle with perimeter 60 meters and maximum area. (Similar to Exercise #9.)

$$2l + 2w = 60 \qquad A = lw \qquad 0 = 30 - 2w$$

$$l + w = 30 \qquad A = (30 - w)w \qquad w = 15 \text{ meters}$$

$$l = 30 - w \qquad A = 30w - w^2$$

$$A' = 30 - 2w \qquad l = 30 - 15 = 15 \text{ meters}$$

2. A farmer has 360 feet of fencing to enclose two adjacent rectangular corrals. What dimensions should be used to maximize the enclosed area? (Similar to Exercise #22.)

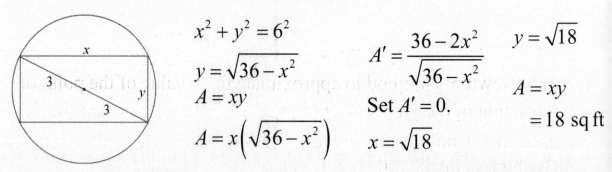

$$360 = 4x + 3y \qquad A = 2xy$$

$$4x = 360 - 3y \qquad A = 2(90 - 0.75y)y$$

$$x = 90 - 0.75y \qquad A = 180y - 1.5y^2$$

$$A' = 180 - 3y$$

$$x = 90 - 0.75(60) \qquad 0 = 180 - 3y$$

$$x = 45 \text{ feet} \qquad y = 60 \text{ feet}$$

3. Find the area of the largest rectangle than can be created inside a circle of radius 3 feet. (Similar to Exercise #30.)

$$x^2 + y^2 = 6^2 \qquad A' = \frac{36 - 2x^2}{\sqrt{36 - x^2}} \qquad y = \sqrt{18}$$

$$y = \sqrt{36 - x^2} \qquad\qquad A = xy$$

$$A = xy \qquad\qquad \text{Set } A' = 0.$$

$$A = x\left(\sqrt{36 - x^2}\right) \qquad x = \sqrt{18} \qquad = 18 \text{ sq ft}$$

4. The sum of the perimeters two squares is 24. Find the dimensions of the squares that produce the minimum total area. (Similar to Exercise #41.)

The sum of the perimeters is $4x + 4y = 24 \Rightarrow y = 6 - x$. The sum of the areas is $A = x^2 + y^2 = x^2 + (6 - x)^2 = 36 - 12x + 2x^2$. We know $A' = 4x - 12$ has critical number $x = 3$. Since the graph of A is a concave up parabola, a minimum must occur at $x = 3$. Since $y = 6 - x$, $y = 3$. Both squares are 3×3.

3.8 Homework Quiz

1. Calculate two iterations of Newton's Method to approximate a zero of $f(x) = 2x^4 - 4x$. Use $x_1 = 1.2$ as the initial guess.

2. Use Newton's Method to approximate the zeros of $f(x) = 3\sqrt{x+2} - 5x$. Continue the iterations until two successive approximations differ by less than 0.001.

3. Apply Newton's Method to $f(x) = 4x^3 - 3x + 1$ using $x_1 = -1$ as the initial guess. Explain why the method fails.

4. Apply Newton's Method to approximate the x-value of the point of intersection of the graphs of $f(x) = 3x^2 - 1$ and $g(x) = \sin x$ that is closest to 1. Continue the process until two successive approximations differ by less than 0.001. [Hint: Let $h(x) = f(x) - g(x)$.]

3.8 Homework Quiz Answers

1. Calculate two iterations of Newton's Method to approximate a zero of $f(x) = 2x^4 - 4x$. Use $x_1 = 1.2$ as the initial guess. (Similar to Exercise # 2.)

$f'(x) = 8x^3 - 4$. We know $x_{n+1} = x_n - \dfrac{2x_n^4 - 4x_n}{8x_n^3 - 4}$.

The calculations for the two iterations are shown.

n	x_n
1	1.200000
2	1.266450
3	1.259988

2. Use Newton's Method to approximate the zeros of $f(x) = 3\sqrt{x+2} - 5x$. Continue the iterations until two successive approximations differ by less than 0.001. (Similar to Exercise #12.)

From the graph of f, we see the zero is close to 1.0.

We use $x_{n+1} = x_n - \dfrac{3\sqrt{x_n + 2} - 5x_n}{\dfrac{3}{2}(x_n + 2)^{-\frac{1}{2}} - 5}$. $x \approx 1.047$

n	x_n
1	1.000000
2	1.047449
3	1.047410

3. Apply Newton's Method to $f(x) = 4x^3 - 3x + 1$ using $x_1 = -1$ as the initial guess. Explain why the method fails. (Similar to Exercise #22.)

We use $x_{n+1} = x_n - \dfrac{4x_n^3 - 3x_n + 1}{12x_n^2 - 3} = \dfrac{8x_n^3 - 1}{12x_n^2 - 3}$.

As $n \to \infty$, $x_n \to \infty$ so Newton's Method fails.

n	x_n
1	-1.00000
2	-4269.05
3	-6.2×10^{11}

4. Apply Newton's Method to approximate the x-value of the point of intersection of the graphs of $f(x) = 3x^2 - 1$ and $g(x) = \sin x$ that is closest to 1. Continue the process until two successive approximations differ by less than 0.001. [Hint: Let $h(x) = f(x) - g(x)$.] (Similar to Exercise #16.)

$x_{n+1} = x_n - \dfrac{3x_n^2 - 1 - \sin x_n}{6x_n - \cos x_n}$. The x-value of the point of intersection that is closest to $x = 1$ is $x \approx 0.748$.

n	x_n
1	1.000000
2	0.787804
3	0.749733
4	0.748444
5	0.748442

3.9 Homework Quiz

1. If $f(x) = 2x^3$, find the equation of the tangent line to the point $(1,2)$ and use this linear approximation to estimate $f(1.3)$.

2. Find the differential dy for $y = \cos^2 x$.

3. Use differentials and the graph of f to approximate $f(1.5)$.

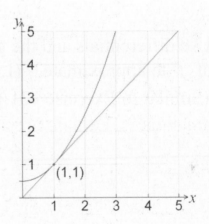

4. The measurement of one side of a cube is found to be 4 centimeters, with a possible error of 0.02 centimeters. Use differentials to approximate the maximum possible propagated error in computing the volume of the cube.

3.9 Homework Quiz Answers

1. If $f(x) = 2x^3$, find the equation of the tangent line to the point (1,2) and use this linear approximation to estimate $f(1.3)$.
   (Similar to Exercise #3.)

$y = 6x - 4$ is the equation of the tangent line.
$$f(1.3) \approx 6(1.3) - 4 = 3.8$$

2. Find the differential dy for $y = \cos^2 x$.
   (Similar to Exercise #17.)

$$dy = -2\cos x \sin x \, dx$$

3. Use differentials and the graph of f to approximate $f(1.5)$.
   (Similar to Exercise #21.)

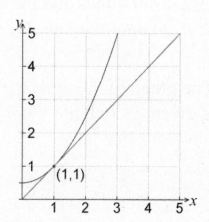

$$f(1.5) \approx 1.5$$

4. The measurement of one side of a cube is found to be 4 centimeters, with a possible error of 0.02 centimeters. Use differentials to approximate the maximum possible propagated error in computing the volume of the cube. (Similar to Exercise #30.)

$$\Delta V \approx dV = 3s^2 ds = 3(4)^2(0.02) = 0.96 \text{ square inches}$$

4.1 Homework Quiz

1. Find the indefinite integral $\int x^2 - 4x\,dx$.

2. Find the indefinite integral $\int (3\sin x - 4\cos x)\,dx$.

3. The graph of the derivative of a function is given. Sketch the graphs of two functions that have the given derivative.

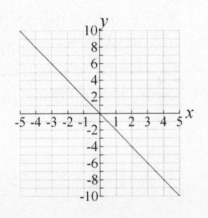

4. A ball is thrown vertically upward from a height of 5 feet with an initial velocity of 64 feet per second. How high will the ball go? (Hint: Use $a(t) = -32$ feet per second per second as the acceleration due to gravity.)

4.1 Homework Quiz Answers

1. Find the indefinite integral $\int x^2 - 4x\,dx$.
   (Similar to Exercise #19.)

$$\int x^2 - 4x\,dx = \frac{1}{3}x^3 - 2x^2 + C$$

2. Find the indefinite integral $\int (3\sin x - 4\cos x)\,dx$.
   (Similar to Exercise #35.)

$$\int (3\sin x - 4\cos x)\,dx = -3\cos x - 4\sin x + C$$

3. The graph of the derivative of a function is given. Sketch the graphs of two functions that have the given derivative.
   (Similar to Exercise #44.)

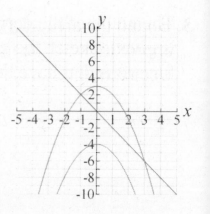

4. A ball is thrown vertically upward from a height of 5 feet with an initial velocity of 64 feet per second. How high will the ball go? (Hint: Use $a(t) = -32$ feet per second per second as the acceleration due to gravity.) (Similar to Exercise #67.)

$$v(t) = \int -32\,dt = -32t + 64 \qquad\qquad v(2) = 0 \text{ ft/sec}$$

$$s(t) = \int -32t + 64\,dt = -16t^2 + 64t + 5 \qquad s(2) = 69 \text{ ft is max height}$$

4.2 Homework Quiz

1. Use sigma notation to write the sum.

$$\frac{4+1}{2(1)}+\frac{4+2}{2(2)}+\frac{4+3}{2(3)}+\dots+\frac{4+10}{2(10)}$$

2. Use the formula $\sum_{i=1}^{n} i = \frac{n(n+1)}{2}$ in evaluating the sum $\sum_{i=1}^{20} 6i$.

3. Bound the area of the shaded region by approximating the upper and lower sums. Use rectangles of width 1.

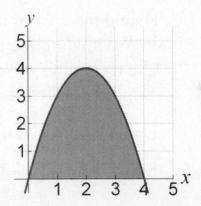

4. Find $\lim_{n \to \infty} \frac{64}{n^4}\left[\frac{n^2(n+1)^2}{16}\right]$.

4.2 Homework Quiz Answers

1. Use sigma notation to write the sum.
   $$\frac{4+1}{2(1)}+\frac{4+2}{2(2)}+\frac{4+3}{2(3)}+...+\frac{4+10}{2(10)}$$ (Similar to Exercise #7.)

   $$\sum_{k=1}^{10}\frac{4+k}{2k}$$

2. Use the formula $\sum_{i=1}^{n}i=\frac{n(n+1)}{2}$ in evaluating the sum $\sum_{i=1}^{20}6i$.
   (Similar to Exercise #15.)

   $$\sum_{i=1}^{20}6i=6\sum_{i=1}^{20}i=6\left(\frac{20(21)}{2}\right)=1260$$

3. Bound the area of the shaded region by approximating the upper and lower sums. Use rectangles of width 1.
   (Similar to Exercise #24.)

   Upper sum $=(3+4+4+3)(1)=14$

   Lower sum $=(0+3+3+0)(1)=6$

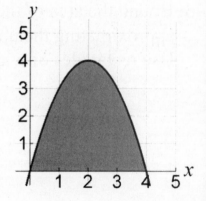

4. Find $\lim\limits_{n\to\infty}\dfrac{64}{n^4}\left[\dfrac{n^2(n+1)^2}{16}\right]$.
   (Similar to Exercise #31.)

   $$\lim_{n\to\infty}\frac{64}{n^4}\left[\frac{n^2(n+1)^2}{16}\right]=\lim_{n\to\infty}\frac{64}{16}\left[\frac{n^4+2n^3+n^2}{n^4}\right]=4$$

4.3 Homework Quiz

1. Set up a definite integral that yields the area of the region. (Do not evaluate the integral.) The function is $f(x) = -x^2 + 2x + 3$.

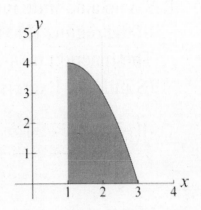

2. Sketch the region whose area is given by $\int_0^4 (-x + 4)\, dx$. Then calculate the area.

3. Given $\int_1^3 f(x)\, dx = 4$ and $\int_1^6 f(x)\, dx = -5$, evaluate $\int_3^6 f(x)\, dx = 4$.

4. Given the graph of $y = \ln x$, to which value is $\int_2^4 \ln x\, dx$ closest? (a) 1 (b) 2 (c) 4 (d) 8

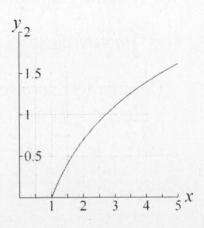

4.3 Homework Quiz Answers

1. Set up a definite integral that yields the area of the region. (Do not evaluate the integral.) The function is $f(x) = -x^2 + 2x + 3$. (Similar to Exercise #16.)

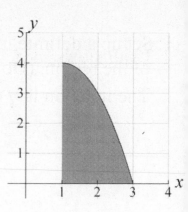

$$\int_1^3 \left(-x^2 + 2x + 3\right) dx$$

2. Sketch the region whose area is given by $\int_0^4 \left(-x + 4\right) dx$. Then calculate the area. (Similar to Exercise #27.)

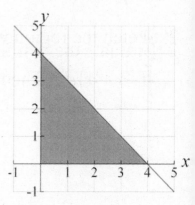

$$A = \frac{1}{2}bh = \frac{1}{2}(4)(4) = 8$$

3. Given $\int_1^3 f(x)\,dx = 4$ and $\int_1^6 f(x)\,dx = -5$, evaluate $\int_3^6 f(x)\,dx = 4$. (Similar to Exercise #44.)

$$\int_3^6 f(x)\,dx = \int_1^6 f(x)\,dx - \int_1^3 f(x)\,dx = -5 - (4) = -9$$

4. Given the graph of $y = \ln x$, to which value is $\int_2^4 \ln x\,dx$ closest? (a) 1 (b) 2 (c) 4 (d) 8 (Similar to Exercise #55.)

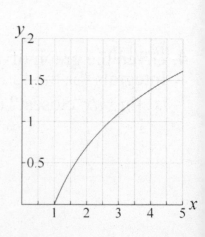

(b) 2

4.4 Homework Quiz

1. Evaluate the definite integral $\displaystyle\int_2^4 3x\,dx$.

2. Evaluate the definite integral $\displaystyle\int_0^\pi 1 - \cos x\,dx$.

3. Determine the area of the given region.
$$y = -x^2 + 4x$$

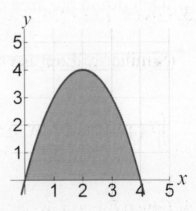

4. Find the values of c guaranteed by the Mean Value Theorem for Integrals for the function over the given interval.
$$f(x) = \frac{1}{x^2},[1,\,2]$$

4.4 Homework Quiz Answers

1. Evaluate the definite integral $\int_{2}^{4} 3x\,dx$.

   (Similar to Exercise #5.)

   $$\int_{2}^{4} 3x\,dx = \frac{3x^2}{2}\Bigg|_{2}^{4} = \frac{3(4)^2}{2} - \frac{3(2)^2}{2} = 18$$

2. Evaluate the definite integral $\int_{0}^{\pi} 1 - \cos x\,dx$.

   (Similar to Exercise #27.)

   $$\int_{0}^{\pi} 1 - \cos x\,dx = x - \sin x\Bigg|_{0}^{\pi} = (\pi - \sin\pi) - (0 - \sin 0) = \pi$$

3. Determine the area of the given region.
   $$y = -x^2 + 4x$$
   (Similar to Exercise #33.)

   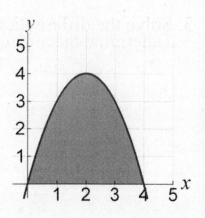

   $$\int_{0}^{4} -x^2 + 4x\,dx = -\frac{x^3}{3} + 2x^2\Bigg|_{0}^{4} = 10\tfrac{2}{3}$$

4. Find the values of c guaranteed by the Mean Value Theorem for Integrals for the function $f(x) = \dfrac{1}{x^2}$ over the interval $[1,2]$.

   (Similar to Exercise #44.)

   We find $\int_{1}^{2} f(x)\,dx = 0.5$. $0.5 = \dfrac{1}{c^2}(2-1)$

   $$c^2 = 2 \Rightarrow c = \pm\sqrt{2}$$

4.5 Homework Quiz

1. Determine whether or not it is necessary to use substitution to integrate $\int 3x \sin x^2 \, dx$.

2. Find the indefinite integral $\int x\left(4x^2 + 9\right)^4 dx$.

3. Solve the differential equation.
$$\frac{dy}{dx} = \frac{x+2}{\left(x^2 + 4x + 7\right)^2}$$

4. Find an equation for the function f that has derivative $f'(x) = \cos\frac{x}{3}$ and passes through the point $(0,4)$.

4.5 Homework Quiz Answers

1. Determine whether or not it is necessary to use substitution to integrate $\int 3x \sin x^2 \, dx$.
   (Similar to Exercise #10.)

   Since the product of $3x$ and $\sin x^2$ is not readily integrable with basic integration rules, substitution is needed. An appropriate substitution is $u = x^2$.

2. Find the indefinite integral $\int x\left(4x^2 + 9\right)^4 dx$.
   (Similar to Exercise #18.)

   $$\text{Let } u = 4x^2 + 9. \qquad \int x\left(4x^2 + 9\right)^4 dx = \tfrac{1}{8}\int u^4 \, du$$

   $$du = 8x \, dx$$

   $$\tfrac{1}{8} du = x \, dx \qquad\qquad\qquad = \tfrac{1}{40}\left(4x^2 + 9\right)^5 + C$$

3. Solve the differential equation.
   $$\frac{dy}{dx} = \frac{x+2}{\left(x^2 + 4x + 7\right)^2} \qquad \text{(Similar to Exercise #41.)}$$

   $$dy = \frac{x+2}{\left(x^2 + 4x + 7\right)^2}\, dx \Rightarrow dy = \frac{1}{u^2}\left(\frac{1}{2}\, du\right) \Rightarrow dy = \frac{1}{2}u^{-2}\, du$$

   $$\Rightarrow y = -\frac{1}{2}u^{-1} + C \Rightarrow y = -\frac{1}{2}\left(x^2 + 4x + 7\right)^{-1} + C$$

4. Find an equation for the function f that has derivative $f'(x) = \cos\dfrac{x}{3}$ and passes through the point $(0, 4)$. (Similar to Exercise #61.)

   We find $f(x) = 3\sin\dfrac{x}{3} + C$.   Thus $f(x) = 3\sin\dfrac{x}{3} + 4$.

   $f(0) = 4$ so $C = 4$

4.6 Homework Quiz

1. Use the Trapezoidal Rule to approximate the value of $\int_0^2 \left(2 + x^2\right) dx$ for $n = 4$.

2. Use the Simpson's Rule to approximate the value of $\int_0^{\sqrt{\pi}} \left(\sin\left(x^2\right)\right) dx$ for $n = 4$.

3. Find n such that the error in the approximation of $\int_1^2 \frac{1}{x} dx$ is at most 0.00001 using the Trapezoidal Rule.

4. Find n such that the error in the approximation of $\int_0^1 1 + \cos x \, dx$ is at most 0.00001 using Simpson's Rule.

4.6 Homework Quiz Answers

1. Use the Trapezoidal Rule to approximate the value of $\int_0^2 (2+x^2)\,dx$ for $n = 4$. (Similar to Exercise #8.)

$$\int_0^2 (2+x^2)\,dx \approx \frac{2-0}{2(4)}\left(f(0)+2f(0.5)+2f(1.0)+2f(1.5)+f(2)\right)$$

$$\approx 0.25\left(2+2(2.25)+2(3)+2(4.25)+6\right) = 6.75$$

2. Use the Simpson's Rule to approximate the value of $\int_0^{\sqrt{\pi}} \left(\sin(x^2)\right)dx$ for $n = 4$. (Similar to Exercise #15.)

$$\int_0^{\sqrt{\pi}} \left(\sin(x^2)\right)dx \approx \frac{\sqrt{\pi}-0}{3(4)}\left(0+4(0.195)+2(0.707)+4(0.981)+0\right)$$

$$\approx 0.148(6.118) = 0.905$$

3. Find n such that the error in the approximation of $\int_1^2 \frac{1}{x}\,dx$ is at most 0.00001 using the Trapezoidal Rule. (Similar to Exercise #29.)

$f''(x) = \dfrac{2}{x^3}$

This function is decreasing on $[1,2]$ with max value $f''(1) = 2$.

$\dfrac{(2-1)^3}{12n^2}(2) \le 0.00001$

$n^2 \ge 16666.6$

$n \ge 130\,(rounding\ up)$

4. Find n such that the error in the approximation of $\int_0^1 1 + \cos x\,dx$ is at most 0.00001 using Simpson's Rule. (Similar to Exercise #38.)

$f^{(4)}(x) = \cos x$

This function is decreasing on $[0,1]$ with max value $f^{(4)}(0) = 1$.

$\dfrac{(1-0)^5}{180n^4}(1) \le 0.00001$

$n \ge 6\,(rounding\ up\ to\ even\ integer)$

5.1 Homework Quiz

1. Use the properties of logarithms to expand the logarithmic
   expression $\ln\dfrac{y(y+2)^5}{y-1}$.

2. Write the expression $\dfrac{2}{3}\Big[\ln(x)+\ln(x^3-2)-\ln(x+4)\Big]$ as a
   logarithm of a single quantity.

3. Use logarithmic differentiation to find the derivative of
   $y=\dfrac{(2x-1)}{(3x-2)}, x>1$.

4. Find the equation of the tangent line to the graph of
   $f(x)=\cos 3x \ln x^4$ at $(1,0)$.

5.1 Homework Quiz Answers

1. Use the properties of logarithms to expand the logarithmic expression
$\ln \dfrac{y(y+2)^5}{y-1}$. (Similar to Exercise #26.)

$$\ln y(y+2)^5 - \ln(y-1) = \ln y + 5\ln(y+2) - \ln(y-1)$$

2. Write the expression $\dfrac{2}{3}\left[\ln(x) + \ln(x^3-2) - \ln(x+4)\right]$ as a logarithm of a single quantity. (Similar to Exercise #36.)

$$\frac{2}{3}\left[\ln \frac{x(x^3-2)}{x+4}\right] = \ln \frac{x^{2/3}(x^3-2)^{2/3}}{(x+4)^{2/3}}$$

3. Use logarithmic differentiation to find the derivative of
$y = \dfrac{(2x-1)}{(3x-2)}, x>1$ (Similar to Exercise #106.)

$$\ln y = \ln\left[\frac{(2x-1)}{(3x-2)}\right] \qquad y' = \left[\frac{(2x-1)}{(3x-2)}\right]\left[\frac{2}{2x-1} - \frac{3}{3x-2}\right]$$

$$= \ln(2x-1) - \ln(3x-2) \qquad = \frac{-1}{(3x-2)^2}$$

$$\frac{y'}{y} = \frac{2}{2x-1} - \frac{3}{3x-2}$$

4. Find the equation of the tangent line to the graph of
$f(x) = \cos 3x \ln x^4$ at $(1,0)$. (Similar to Exercise #80.)

$$f'(x) = -3\sin 3x \ln x^4 + \cos 3x\left(\frac{4}{x}\right)$$

$$f'(1) = 0 + 4\cos 3 \approx -3.96$$

Using $m = -3.96$ and $(1,0)$, the equation of the tangent line is
$$y - 0 = -3.96(x-1)$$
$$y = -3.96x + 3.96$$

5.2 Homework Quiz

1. Find the indefinite integral $\displaystyle\int \frac{x^3 + 2x^2 - 4}{x^2 - 2}\,dx$.

2. Solve the differential equation $\displaystyle\frac{ds}{d\theta} = \frac{2\csc^2\theta}{\cot\theta}$. Then find the particular

   solution at $\left(\dfrac{\pi}{4}, 4\right)$.

3. Evaluate the definite integral $\displaystyle\int_1^3 \frac{1 - \csc 2\theta \cot 2\theta}{2\theta + \csc 2\theta}\,d\theta$.

4. Find the average value of the function over the given interval.
   $$f(x) = \frac{3(x^2 - 2)}{x^3}, \; [1, e]$$

5.2 Homework Quiz Answers

1. Find the indefinite integral $\int \dfrac{x^3 + 2x^2 - 4}{x^2 - 2} dx$ (Similar to Exercise #20.)

$$\int \left(x + 2 + \frac{2x}{x^2 - 2} \right) dx = \frac{x^2}{2} + 2x + \ln\left|x^2 - 2\right| + C$$

2. Solve the differential equation $\dfrac{ds}{d\theta} = \dfrac{2\csc^2 \theta}{\cot \theta}$. Then find the particular

solution at $\left(\dfrac{\pi}{4}, 4 \right)$. (Similar to Exercise #46.)

$s = \int \dfrac{\csc^2 \theta}{\cot \theta} d\theta = -\ln\left|\cot \theta\right| + C$

So the particular solution is
$s = \ln\left|\cot \theta\right| + 4$.

$\text{At}\left(\dfrac{\pi}{4}, 4 \right) : 4 = -\ln\left|\cot \dfrac{\pi}{4}\right| + C \Rightarrow C = 4$

3. Evaluate the definite integral $\displaystyle\int_1^3 \dfrac{1 - \csc 2\theta \cot 2\theta}{2\theta + \csc 2\theta} d\theta$.

(Similar to Exercise #60.)

$\dfrac{1}{2} \displaystyle\int_1^3 \dfrac{2 - 2\csc 2\theta \cot 2\theta}{2\theta + \csc 2\theta} d\theta$

$= \dfrac{1}{2}\left[\ln\left|2\theta + \csc 2\theta\right| \right]_1^3$

$= \dfrac{1}{2}\left[\ln\left|6 + \csc 6\right| - \ln\left|1 + \csc 1\right| \right]$

$= \dfrac{1}{2}(0.884 - 0.173) \approx 0.356$

4. Find the average value of the function over the given interval.

$f(x) = \dfrac{3(x^2 - 2)}{x^3}, [1, e]$ (Similar to Exercise #98.)

$\dfrac{1}{e-1} \displaystyle\int_1^e \dfrac{3(x^2 - 2)}{x^3} dx$

$= \dfrac{1}{e-1} \displaystyle\int_1^e \left(x^{-1} - 2x^{-3} \right) dx$

$= \dfrac{1}{e-1}\left(\ln|x| + x^{-2} \right)\Big|_1^e$

$= \dfrac{1}{e-1}\left(\ln|e| + e^{-2} - \ln|1| - (1)^{-2} \right) \approx 0.079$

5.3 Homework Quiz

1. Show analytically that $f(x) = x^3 + 2$ and $g(x) = \sqrt[3]{x-2}$ are inverse functions.

2. Find the inverse function of $f(x) = 4 - x^2$, $x \geq 0$. Specify the domain of the inverse.

3. State the domain and range of the inverse of $f(x) = \dfrac{x}{\sqrt{x^2 + 4}}$.

4. If $f(x) = \sqrt{x-1}$ has an inverse function, use the inverse to find $(f^{-1})'(2)$.

5.3 Homework Quiz Answers

1. Show analytically that $f(x) = x^3 + 2$ and $g(x) = \sqrt[3]{x-2}$ are inverse functions. (Similar to Exercise #4.)

$$f(g(x)) = \left(\sqrt[3]{x-2}\right)^3 + 2$$

$$= x - 2 + 2$$

$$= x$$

Since $f(g(x)) = x$, f and g are inverses.

2. Find the inverse function of $f(x) = 4 - x^2$, $x \geq 0$. Specify the domain of the inverse. (Similar to Exercise #26.)

$$y = 4 - x^2$$

$$x^2 = 4 - y$$

$$x = \sqrt{4 - y}$$

$$f^{-1}(x) = \sqrt{4 - x}$$

The range of the f is the domain of f^{-1}. The graph of f is a concave down parabola with maximum value of 4. Therefore, the domain of f^{-1} is $(-\infty, 4]$.

3. State the domain and range of the inverse of $f(x) = \dfrac{x}{\sqrt{x^2 + 4}}$

(Similar to Exercise #35.)

$$\left(y\sqrt{x^2 + 4}\right)^2 = x^2$$

$$x^2 y^2 + 4y^2 = x^2$$

$$4y^2 = x^2(1 - y^2)$$

$$x^2 = \frac{4y^2}{(1 - y^2)}$$

$$f^{-1}(x) = \frac{2|x|}{\sqrt{1 - x^2}}$$

Domain: $[-1, 1]$

Range: $\mathbb{R}$

4. If $f(x) = \sqrt{x - 1}$ has an inverse function, use the inverse to find $\left(f^{-1}\right)'(2)$. (Similar to Exercise #80.)

Since f is one-to-one and $f(x) = 2$ when $x = 5$, $\left(f^{-1}\right)(2) = 5$.

$$\left(f^{-1}\right)'(2) = \frac{1}{f'(5)} = \frac{1}{(1/2)(5-1)^{-1/2}} = \frac{1}{1/4} = 4$$

5.4 Homework Quiz

1. Solve $\dfrac{2000}{2+e^{3x}} = 1$ for x accurate to 3 decimal places.

2. Find the derivative of $y = 2e^{-2x^3}$.

3. Find the equation of the tangent line to the graph of $y = 2xe^{-x} + e^{2x}$ at $(0,1)$.

4. Evaluate the definite integral $\displaystyle\int_{0}^{1/2} \dfrac{8e^{2x}}{2e^{2x}-1}\,dx$

5.4 Homework Quiz Answers

1. Solve $\dfrac{2000}{2+e^{3x}}=1$ for x accurate to 3 decimal places.

   (Similar to Exercise #10.)

$$2000 = 1\left(2+e^{3x}\right)$$

$$2000 = 2+e^{3x}$$

$$1998 = e^{3x}$$

$$\ln 1998 = 3x$$

$$x \approx 2.533$$

2. Find the derivative of $y = 2e^{-2x^3}$ (Similar to Exercise #50.)

$$\text{Let } u = -2x^3$$

$$u' = -6x^2$$

$$y' = -6x^2 \cdot 2e^{-2x^3}$$

$$y' = -12x^2 e^{-2x^3}$$

3. Find the equation of the tangent line to the graph of $y = 2xe^{-x} + e^{2x}$ at $(0,1)$. (Similar to Exercise #66.)

$$y' = 2e^{-x} - 2xe^{-x} + 2e^{2x}$$

$$\text{At } x = 0,\ y' = 2e^0 - 2(0)e^0 + 2e^{2(0)} = 4$$

$$y - 1 = 4(x-0)$$

$$y = 4x+1$$

4. Evaluate the definite integral $\displaystyle\int_0^{1/2} \dfrac{8e^{2x}}{2e^{2x}-1}\,dx$

   (Similar to Exercise #124.)

$$u = 2e^{2x}-1$$

$$du = 4e^{2x}\,dx$$

$$2du = 8e^{2x}\,dx$$

$$2\int_a^b \frac{1}{u}\,du = 2\Big[\ln\left(2e^{2x}-1\right)\Big]_0^{1/2}$$

$$= 2\left(\ln 2e - \ln 1\right)$$

$$\approx 3.386$$

5.5 Homework Quiz

1. Write the logarithmic equation $\log_4 \dfrac{1}{4^3} = -3$ as an exponential equation.

2. Solve the equation $\log_3 \sqrt{2x-1} = 1.3$ accurate to three decimal places.

3. Find the derivative of $g(x) = x^2 \log_3 \sqrt{x-1}$.

4. Evaluate the integral $\displaystyle\int (x+1)3^{(x+1)^2}\, dx$.

5.5 Homework Quiz Answers

1. Write the logarithmic equation $\log_4 \dfrac{1}{4^3} = -3$ as an exponential equation.

   (Similar to Exercise #8.)

$$4^{-3} = \frac{1}{4^3}$$

2. Solve the equation $\log_3 \sqrt{2x-1} = 1.3$ accurate to three decimal places.
   (Similar to Exercise #34.)

$$\frac{1}{2}\log_3(2x-1) = 1.3 \qquad 2x \approx 17.399 + 1$$

$$\qquad\qquad\qquad\qquad\quad x \approx 9.199$$

$$2x - 1 = 3^{2.6}$$

3. Find the derivative of $g(x) = x^2 \log_3 \sqrt{x-1}$. (Similar to Exercise #62.)

$$g(x) = \frac{1}{2}x^2 \log_3(x-1)$$

$$g'(x) = \frac{1}{2}2x\log_3(x-1) + \frac{1}{2}x^2 \frac{1}{\ln 3(x-1)}$$

$$= x\log_3(x-1) + \frac{x^2}{2(x-1)\ln 3}$$

4. Evaluate the integral $\int (x+1)3^{(x+1)^2}\,dx$. (Similar to Exercise #80.)

$$\int 3^{(x+1)^2}(x+1)\,dx$$

$$u = (x+1)^2 \Rightarrow du = 2(x+1)\,dx$$

$$\frac{1}{2}\int 3^u\,du = \frac{1}{2}\left(\frac{3^{(x+1)^2}}{\ln 3}\right) + C = \frac{3^{(x+1)^2}}{2\ln 3} + C$$

5.6 Homework Quiz

1. Evaluate $\arccos\left(-\dfrac{\sqrt{3}}{2}\right)$ without using a calculator.

   (Similar to Exercise #8.)

2. Evaluate $\cot\left(\arccos\left(-\dfrac{4}{5}\right)\right)$ without using a calculator.

   (Similar to Exercise #20.)

3. Solve the equation $\arccos\left(\dfrac{1}{2}x-3\right)=1$ for x.

   (Similar to Exercise #38.)

4. Find the derivative of $h(x)=6\,\mathrm{arc\,sec}\,\dfrac{x}{3}$. (Similar to Exercise #60.)

5.6 Homework Quiz Answers

1. Evaluate $\arccos\left(-\dfrac{\sqrt{3}}{2}\right)$ without using a calculator.

   (Similar to Exercise #8.)

   $$y = \arccos\left(-\frac{\sqrt{3}}{2}\right) \Rightarrow \cos y = -\frac{\sqrt{3}}{2}. \qquad \text{In the interval } [0,\pi] \ \ y = \frac{5\pi}{6}$$

   $$\text{So } \arccos\left(-\frac{\sqrt{3}}{2}\right) = \frac{5\pi}{6}$$

2. Evaluate $\cot\left(\arccos\left(-\dfrac{4}{5}\right)\right)$ without using a calculator.

   (Similar to Exercise #20.)

   $$\cot\left(\arccos\left(-\frac{4}{5}\right)\right) = \frac{adj}{opp} = \frac{-4}{3}$$

   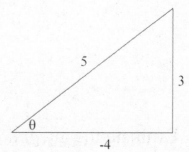

3. Solve the equation $\arccos\left(\dfrac{1}{2}x - 3\right) = 1$ for x.

   (Similar to Exercise #38.)

   $$\frac{1}{2}x - 3 = \cos(1)$$

   $$x = 2\big[\cos(1) + 3\big] \approx 7.081$$

4. Find the derivative of $h(x) = 6\,\text{arc}\sec\dfrac{x}{3}$. (Similar to Exercise #60.)

   $$\frac{dh}{dx} = 6\,\frac{1/3}{\left|\dfrac{x}{3}\right|\sqrt{\left(\dfrac{x}{3}\right)^2 - 1}} = \frac{6}{|x|\sqrt{\dfrac{x^2}{9} - 1}} = \frac{18}{|x|\sqrt{x^2 - 9}}$$

5.7 Homework Quiz

1. Find the integral $\displaystyle\int \frac{1}{4+9x^2}\,dx$

2. Evaluate the integral $\displaystyle\int_{-4/3}^{-2\sqrt{2}/3} \frac{3}{x\sqrt{9x^2-4}}\,dx$.

3. Evaluate the integral $\displaystyle\int \frac{x}{\sqrt{5-4x^2-x^4}}\,dx$ by completing the square

4. Find the area of the region $y = \dfrac{4}{x^2-2x+10}$ bounded from $x=1$ to $x=4$.

5.7 Homework Quiz Answers

1. Find the integral $\int \dfrac{1}{4+9x^2}\,dx$. (Similar to Exercise #8.)

$$\int \frac{1}{2^2+(3x)^2}\,dx = \frac{1}{2}\arctan\frac{3x}{2}+C$$

2. Evaluate the integral $\displaystyle\int_{-4/3}^{-2\sqrt{2}/3} \dfrac{3}{x\sqrt{9x^2-4}}\,dx$. (Similar to Exercise #36.)

$$u = 3x \Rightarrow du = 3dx$$

$$3\int_{-4/3}^{-2\sqrt{2}/3} \frac{1}{3x\sqrt{(3x)^2-2^2}}\,3\,dx$$

$$= \frac{3}{2}\left[\operatorname{arcsec}\frac{|3x|}{2}\right]_{-4/3}^{-2\sqrt{2}/3} = \frac{3}{2}\left[\frac{\pi}{4}-\frac{\pi}{3}\right] = -\frac{\pi}{8}$$

3. Evaluate the integral $\int \dfrac{x}{\sqrt{5-4x^2-x^4}}\,dx$ by completing the square (Similar to Exercise #50.)

$$\int \frac{x}{\sqrt{5+4-(x^4+4x^2+4)}}\,dx = \frac{1}{2}\int \frac{2x}{\sqrt{3^2-(x^2+2)^2}}\,dx$$

$$= \frac{1}{2}\arcsin\frac{(x^2+2)}{3}+C$$

4. Find the area of the region $y = \dfrac{4}{x^2-2x+10}$ bounded by $x=1$ and $x=4$. (Similar to Exercise #74.)

$$\int_1^4 \frac{4}{x^2-2x+10}\,dx = \int_1^4 \frac{4}{(x-1)^2+9}\,dx = \frac{4}{3}\left[\arctan\frac{x-1}{3}\right]_1^4 = \frac{4}{3}\left(\frac{\pi}{4}\right) = \frac{\pi}{3}$$

5.8 Homework Quiz

1. Evaluate the functions accurate to three decimal places.
   a. $\cosh^{-1} 4$
   b. $\coth(\ln 2)$

2. Find the derivative of $g(x) = \operatorname{csch}^2(2x)$.

3. Evaluate the integral $\displaystyle\int \frac{\sinh x}{4 - \cosh^2 x}\,dx$.

4. Find $\displaystyle\lim_{x \to 0} \cosh x$.

5.8 Homework Quiz Answers

1. Evaluate the functions accurate to three decimal places.
   a. $\cosh^{-1} 4$
   b. $\coth(\ln 2)$

   (Similar to Exercise #6.)

   a.
   $$\cosh^{-1} 4 = \ln\left(4 + \sqrt{15}\right)$$
   $$\approx 2.063$$

   b.
   $$\coth(\ln 2) = \frac{\cosh(\ln 2)}{\sinh(\ln 2)}$$
   $$= \frac{e^{\ln 2} + e^{-\ln 2}}{2} \cdot \frac{2}{e^{\ln 2} - e^{-\ln 2}}$$
   $$= \frac{2 + 1/2}{2 - 1/2} = \frac{5}{3}$$

2. Find the derivative of $g(x) = \operatorname{csch}^2(2x)$. (Similar to Exercise #30.)

   $$-\operatorname{csch}(2x)\coth(2x)(2)(2\operatorname{csch}2x) = -4\operatorname{csch}^2(2x)\coth(2x)$$

3. Evaluate the integral $\displaystyle\int \frac{\sinh x}{4 - \cosh^2 x}\,dx$. (Similar to Exercise #56.)

   $$u = \cosh x \Rightarrow du = \sinh x\,dx \Rightarrow \int \frac{du}{2^2 - u^2} = \frac{1}{4}\ln\left(\frac{2 + \cosh x}{2 - \cosh x}\right) + C$$

4. Find $\displaystyle\lim_{x \to 0} \cosh x$. (Similar to Exercise #80.)

   $$\lim_{x \to 0} \cosh x = 1$$

6.1 Homework Quiz

1. Verify that $y = 2e^{-x}\sin x + 4e^{-x}\cos x$ is a solution of the

   differential equation $\dfrac{y''}{2} + y' = -y$.

2. Verify that $y = C_1\ln x + 2C_2$ satisfies the differential equation
   $x^2y'' + xy' = 0$. Then find the particular solution that satisfies the
   conditions $y(1) = 2, y'(1) = 1$.

3. Use integration to find a general solution of the differential
   equation $\dfrac{dy}{dx} = x\sin x^2$.

4. Determine whether the function $y = 2xe^x + x$ is a solution of the
   differential equation $xy' - xy'' - 2x = -y$.

6.1 Homework Quiz Answers

1. Verify that $y = 2e^{-x}\sin x + 4e^{-x}\cos x$ is a solution of the differential

    equation $\dfrac{y''}{2} + y' = -y$ (Similar to Exercise #6.)

$$y' = -6e^{-x}\sin x - 2e^{-x}\cos x$$
$$y'' = 8e^{-x}\sin x - 4e^{-x}\cos x$$

$$\dfrac{y''}{2} + y' = -2e^{-x}\sin x - 4e^{-x}\cos x$$
$$= -y$$

2. Verify that $y = C_1\ln x + 2C_2$ satisfies the differential equation
    $x^2 y'' + xy' = 0$. Then find the particular solution that satisfies the
    conditions $y(1) = 2, y'(1) = 1$ (Similar to Exercise #38.)

$$y' = \dfrac{C_1}{x} \Rightarrow y'' = -\dfrac{C_1}{x^2}$$

$$x^2\left(-\dfrac{C_1}{x^2}\right) + x\left(\dfrac{C_1}{x}\right) = 0$$

$$2 = C_1\ln 1 + 2C_2$$
$$2 = 0 + 2C_2$$
$$C_2 = 1$$

$$1 = -\dfrac{C_1}{1}$$
$$C_1 = -1$$
$$y = -\ln x + 2$$

3. Use integration to find a general solution of the differential equation
    $\dfrac{dy}{dx} = x\sin x^2$ (Similar to Exercise #46.)

$$y = \int x\sin x^2\,dx$$
$$= \dfrac{1}{2}\int \sin x^2\, 2x\,dx$$

$$y = -\dfrac{1}{2}\cos x^2 + C$$

4. Determine whether the function $y = 2xe^x + x$ is a solution of the
    differential equation $xy' - xy'' - 2x = -y$.
    (Similar to Exercise # 24.)

$$y' = 2e^x + 2xe^x + 1 \quad x(2e^x + 2xe^x + 1) - x(4e^x + 2xe^x) - 2x = -2xe^x - x$$
$$y'' = 4e^x + 2xe^x$$
$$= -y$$

6.2 Homework Quiz

1. Solve the differential equation $\dfrac{dy}{dx} = 2x(y-1)$

2. If the rate of change of Q is proportional to Q and $Q = 2000$ when $t = 0$, and when $t = 2, Q = 1250$, what is the value of Q when $t = 4$?

3. The isotope ^{14}C has a half-life of 5715 years. If there is 2g after 1000 years, what was the initial quantity?

4. $15,000 is invested in a savings account that doubles every 30 years. What is the amount after 12 years?

6.2 Homework Quiz Answers

1. Solve the differential equation $\dfrac{dy}{dx} = 2x(y-1)$

   (Similar to Exercise #8.)

$$\int \frac{dy}{(y-1)} = \int 2x\,dx$$

$$\ln|y-1| = x^2 + C_1$$

$$y - 1 = \pm e^{x^2 + C}$$

$$y = Ce^{x^2} + 1$$

2. If the rate of change of Q is proportional to Q and $Q = 2000$ when $t = 0$, and when $t = 2, Q = 1250$, what is the value of Q when $t = 4$? (Similar to Exercise #24.)

$$\frac{dQ}{dt} = kQ$$

$$Q = Ce^{kt}$$

$$(0, 2000) \Rightarrow C = 2000$$

$$1250 = 2000e^{2k}$$

$$k = \frac{1}{2}\ln\frac{5}{8}$$

When $t = 4$,

$$Q = 2000e^{\frac{1}{2}\ln\frac{5}{8}(4)}$$

$$\approx 3162.28$$

3. The isotope ^{14}C has a half-life of 5715 years. If there is 2g after 1000 years, what was the initial quantity?
   (Similar to Exercise #38.)

$$0.5 = e^{k\,5715}$$

$$k = \frac{1}{5715}\ln(0.5)$$

$$2 = Ce^{\frac{1}{5715}\ln(0.5)(1000)}$$

$$C \approx 2.258$$

The initial quantity was 2.258g.

4. $15,000 is invested in a savings account that doubles every 30 years. What is the amount after 12 years? (Similar to Exercise #44.)

$$30000 = 15000e^{30r}$$

$$r = \frac{1}{30}\ln 2$$

$$r \approx 0.0231$$

$$A = 15000e^{\frac{1}{30}\ln 2(12)}$$

$$\approx 19792.62$$

After 12 years there is $19792.62.

6.3 Homework Quiz

1. What is the general solution of $(x^2 - 3)\dfrac{dy}{dx} = xy$?

2. Find the solution to $dT - k(T + 45)dt = 0$ that satisfies $T(0) = 200$.

3. Solve the homogeneous equation $4xy\,dy - (x^2 - y^2)dx = 0$.

4. Write a differential equation for the statement: The rate of change of y with respect to x is proportional to the square of the sum of x and 6.

6.3 Homework Quiz Solutions

1. What is the general solution of $(x^2 - 3)\dfrac{dy}{dx} = xy$?

   (Similar to Exercise #4.)

$$\int \frac{dy}{y} = \int \frac{xdx}{(x^2 - 3)} \qquad \ln y = \ln\left|(x^2 - 3)\right|^{\frac{1}{2}} + C_1$$

$$\ln|y| = \frac{1}{2}\ln\left|x^2 - 3\right| + C_1 \qquad y = C(x^2 - 3)^{\frac{1}{2}}$$

2. Find the solution to $dT - k(T + 45)dt = 0$ that satisfies $T(0) = 200$. (Similar to Exercise #24.)

$$dT = k(T + 45)dt \qquad \ln|T + 45| = kt + C_1 \qquad 200 = Ce^0 - 45$$

$$\int \frac{dT}{T + 45} = k\int dt \qquad T = Ce^{kt} - 45 \qquad \begin{array}{l} C = 245 \\ \text{So } T = 245e^{kt} - 45 \end{array}$$

3. Solve the homogeneous equation $4xydy - (x^2 + 2y^2)dx = 0$

   (Similar to Exercise #42.)

$$y = vx \Rightarrow dy = xdv + vdx \qquad \ln|x| = -\ln|2v^2 - 1| + C_1$$

$$4x(vx)(xdv + vdx) = (x^2 + 2v^2x^2)dx \qquad x = C(2v^2 - 1)^{-1}$$

$$\int \frac{1}{x}dx = \int \frac{-4v}{2v^2 - 1}dv \qquad \left(2\frac{y^2}{x^2} - 1\right)x = C$$

$$2y^2 - x^2 = Cx$$

4. Write a differential equation for the statement: The rate of change of y with respect to x is proportional to the square of the sum of x and 6. (Similar to Exercise #60.)

$$\frac{dy}{dx} = k(x + 6)^2$$

6.4 Homework Quiz

1. Solve the first-order linear differential equation.
   $x^2 y' + 2xy - 6x^3 = 0$.

2. Find the solution of the differential equation $y' + y\tan x = \sin x$ that satisfies $y(0) = 1$.

3. Solve the Bernoulli differentiation equation.
   $y' + \left(\dfrac{1}{3x}\right)y = xy^3$.

4. Solve the first-order differential using any method.
   $(y + e^x)\,dx - x\,dy = 0$.

6.4 Homework Quiz Solutions

1. Solve the first-order linear differential equation
$x^2 y' + 2xy - 6x^3 = 0$. (Similar to Exercise #6.)

$$P(x) = \frac{2}{x}, Q(x) = 6x \qquad\qquad y = \frac{1}{x^2}\int 6x \cdot x^2\, dx$$

$$u(x) = e^{\int \frac{2}{x} dx} = e^{2\ln|x|} = x^2 + C \qquad = \frac{1}{x^2}\left(\frac{6x^4}{4} + C\right) = \frac{3}{2}x^2 + \frac{C}{x^2}$$

2. Find the solution of the differential equation $y' + y\tan x = \sin x$
that satisfies $y(0) = 1$. (Similar to Exercise #20.)

$$P(x) = \tan x; Q(x) = \sin x \qquad\qquad \frac{y}{\cos x} = \int \frac{\sin x}{\cos x}\, dx$$

$$\int P(x) = -\ln|\cos x|$$

$$\text{Integrating factor} = (\cos x)^{-1} \qquad y = \cos x \ln|\sec x| + C\cos x$$

$$(0,1) \Rightarrow y = \cos x \ln|\sec x| + \cos x$$

3. Solve the Bernoulli differentiation equation $y' + \left(\frac{1}{3x}\right)y = xy^3$.

(Similar to Exercise #49.)

$$n = 3, Q = x, P = \frac{1}{3x} \qquad\qquad y^{-2}x^{\frac{-2}{3}} = \int -2xx^{\frac{-2}{3}}\, dx + C$$

$$e^{\int \frac{-2}{3x} dx} = e^{\frac{-2}{3}\ln x} = x^{\frac{-2}{3}} \qquad\qquad y^{-2} = 3 + Cx^{\frac{2}{3}}$$

$$\frac{1}{y^2} = 3 + Cx^{\frac{2}{3}}$$

4. Solve the first-order differential using any method
$(y + e^x)dx - x\,dy = 0$. (Similar to Exercise #63.)

$$\text{Linear: } y' + \left(\frac{1}{x}\right)y = -\frac{e^x}{x} \qquad\qquad yx = \int x \frac{-e^x}{x}\, dx$$

$$\text{Integration factor: } e^{\int \frac{1}{x} dx} = x \qquad\qquad y = \frac{-e^x}{x} + \frac{C}{x}$$

7.1 Homework Quiz

1. Set up the definite integral that gives the area of the region bounded by $y_1 = (x-1)^2 - 4; y_2 = x+1$.

2. Sketch the region bounded by the graphs of $y = x^3 - 4x^2 + 3x, y = 0, \ x = 0, x = 3$. Then find the area of the region.

3. Sketch the region bounded by the graphs. Then find the area of the region. $f(x) = \sin x, g(x) = \cos x, \dfrac{5\pi}{4} \le x \le 2\pi$

4. Find the area enclosed by the curve $y = \sqrt{x}$, the tangent to the curve at $x = 4$, and the y-axis.

7.1 Homework Quiz Solutions

1. Set up the definite integral that gives the area of the region bounded by $y_1 = (x-1)^2 - 4; y_2 = x+1$. (Similar to Exercise #2.)

$$x^2 - 2x + 1 - 4 = x + 1$$
$$x^2 - 3x - 4 = 0$$
$$(x-4)(x+1) = 0$$
$$x = -1, 4$$

$$A = \int_{-1}^{4} \left[(x+1) - \left((x-1)^2 - 4 \right) \right] dx$$

2. Sketch the region bounded by the graphs of $y = x^3 - 4x^2 + 3x, y = 0$, $x = 0, x = 3$. Then find the area of the region. (Similar to Exercise #28.)

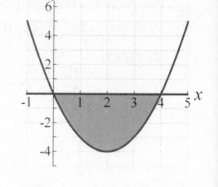

$$A = -\int_{0}^{4} (x^3 - 4x^2 + 3x) dx$$

$$= -\frac{x^4}{4} + \frac{4x^3}{3} - \frac{3x^2}{2} \Big|_{0}^{3} = \frac{9}{4}$$

3. Sketch the region bounded by the graphs. Then find the area of the region. (Similar to Exercise #48.)

$$f(x) = \sin x, g(x) = \cos x, \frac{5\pi}{4} \le x \le 2\pi$$

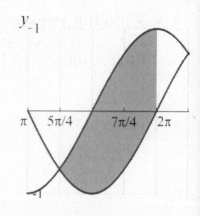

$$A = \int_{\frac{5\pi}{4}}^{2\pi} (\cos x - \sin x) dx = \sin x + \cos x \Big|_{\frac{5\pi}{4}}^{2\pi}$$

$$= 1 + \sqrt{2} \approx 2.414$$

4. Find the area enclosed by the curve $y = \sqrt{x}$, the tangent to the curve at $x = 4$, and the y-axis. (Similar to Exercise #74.)

The tangent line at $(4, 2)$ is $y = \frac{1}{4}x + 1$.

$$A = \int_{0}^{4} \left[\left(\frac{1}{4}x + 1 \right) - \sqrt{x} \right] dx = \frac{2}{3}$$

7.2 Homework Quiz

1. Find the volume of the solid that results when the region enclosed by the curves $y = \sqrt{x}$ and $y = x$ is revolved about the x-axis.

2. Find the volume of the solid that results when the region enclosed by the curves $y = 1 + x^3, x = 1$ and $y = 9$ is revolved about the y-axis.

3. Find the volume of the solid generated when the region bound by $y = \sqrt{x}, y = 0,$ and $x = 9$ is revolved about the line $x = 9$.

4. The base of a solid is the circle $x^2 + y^2 = 9$ and each cross-section perpendicular to the x-axis is an equilateral triangle with one side across the base. Find the volume of the solid.

7.2 Homework Quiz Solutions

1. Find the volume of the solid that results when the region enclosed by the curves $y = \sqrt{x}$ and $y = x$ is revolved about the x-axis. (Similar to Exercise #5.)

$$V = \pi \int_0^1 \left[\left(\sqrt{x} \right)^2 - x^2 \right] dx$$

$$= \pi \int_0^1 \left(x - x^2 \right) dx = \frac{\pi}{6}$$

2. Find the volume of the solid that results when the region enclosed by the curves $y = 1 + x^3, x = 1$ and $y = 9$ is revolved about the y-axis. (Similar to Exercise #32.)

Lower bound : $y = 1 + 1 = 2$

$$V = \pi \int_2^9 \left[(y-1)^{2/3} - 1 \right] dy = \pi \left[\left(8^{2/3} - 1 \right) - \left(1^{2/3} - 1 \right) \right] = \frac{58\pi}{5}$$

3. Find the volume of the solid generated when the region bound by $y = \sqrt{x}, y = 0,$ and $x = 9$ is revolved about the line $x = 9$. (Similar to Exercise #19.)

$$V = \pi \int_0^3 \left(9 - y^2 \right)^2 dy$$

$$= \pi \int_0^3 \left(81 - 18y^2 + y^4 \right) dy = \frac{648\pi}{5}$$

4. The base of a solid is the circle $x^2 + y^2 = 9$ and each cross-section perpendicular to the x-axis is an equilateral triangle with one side across the base. Find the volume of the solid. (Similar to Exercise #72.)

$A(x)$ is the area of an equilateral triangle whose sides are each of length $2y$, so

$$A(x) = \frac{\sqrt{3}}{4} (2y)^2 = \sqrt{3} \left(9 - x^2 \right)$$

$$V = \int_{-3}^3 \sqrt{3} \left(9 - x^2 \right) dx$$

$$= 2\sqrt{3} \int_0^3 \left(9 - x^2 \right) dx$$

$$= 36\sqrt{3}$$

7.3 Homework Quiz

1. Use the shell method to set up and evaluate the integral that gives the volume of the solid generated by revolving the plane region of $y = 2x - 1, y = -2x + 3, x = 2$ about the y-axis.

2. Use the shell method to set up and evaluate the integral that gives the volume of the solid generated by revolving the plane region of $y = x^2, x = 1, y = 0$ about the x-axis.

3. The integral $2\pi \int_0^1 (1 - y) y^2 \, dy$ represents the volume of a solid of revolution. Identify a) the plane region that is revolved and b) the axis of revolution.

4. Use the disk or the shell method to find the volume of the solid generated by revolving the region bounded by the graph of the equation $x = y^2, x = y$ about the line $y = -1$.

7.3 Homework Quiz Solutions

1. Use the shell method to set up and evaluate the integral that gives the volume of the solid generated by revolving the plane region of $y = 2x - 1, y = -2x + 3, x = 2$ about the y-axis. (Similar to Exercise #10.)

$$V = \int_1^2 2\pi x \left[(2x - 1) - (-2x + 3) \right] dx$$

$$= 8\pi \int_1^2 (x^2 - x) dx = \frac{20\pi}{3}$$

2. Use the shell method to set up and evaluate the integral that gives the volume of the solid generated by revolving the plane region of $y = x^2, x = 1, y = 0$ about the x-axis. (Similar to Exercise #22.)

$$V = \int_0^1 2\pi y \left(1 - \sqrt{y} \right) dy$$

$$= 2\pi \int_0^1 \left(y - y^{3/2} \right) dy = \frac{\pi}{5}$$

3. The integral $2\pi \int_0^1 (y - 1) y^2 dy$ represents the volume of a solid of revolution. Identify a) the plane region that is revolved and b) the axis of revolution. (Similar to Exercise # 52.)

   a) Plane region bounded by $x = y^2, x = 0, y = 1$

   b) Revolved around the line $y = 1$

4. Use the disk or the shell method to find the volume of the solid generated by revolving the region bounded by the graph of the equation $x = y^2, x = y$ about the line $y = -1$. (Similar to Exercise #30.)

   Disk Methond

$$V = \pi \int_0^1 \left[\left(\sqrt{x} + 1 \right)^2 - (x + 1)^2 \right] dx = \pi \int_0^1 \left(2\sqrt{x} - x - x^2 \right) dx = \frac{\pi}{2}$$

7.4 Homework Quiz

1. Find the distance between the points $(1,2),(3,6)$ using integration, then verify with the Distance Formula.

2. Find the arc length of the function $x = \dfrac{y^3}{24} + \dfrac{2}{y}$ from $y = 2$ to $y = 4$.

3. Set up and evaluate the definite integral for the area of the surface generated by revolving the curve $y = \sqrt{x} - \dfrac{1}{3}x^{3/2}, 1 \le x \le 3$ about the x-axis.

4. Find the area of the zone of a sphere formed by revolving the graph of $x = \sqrt{4 - y^2}, -1 \le y \le 1$, about the y-axis.

7.4 Homework Quiz Solutions

1. Find the distance between the points $(1,2),(3,6)$ using integration, then verify with the Distance Formula. (Similar to Exercise #2.)

$$m = \frac{6-2}{3-1} = 2 \Rightarrow y = 2x$$

$$L = \int_1^3 \sqrt{1+2^2}\, dx = \sqrt{5}x \Big|_1^3 = 2\sqrt{5}$$

$$d = \sqrt{(6-2)^2 + (3-1)^2}$$
$$= \sqrt{20}$$
$$= 2\sqrt{5}$$

2. Find the arc length of the function $x = \frac{y^3}{24} + \frac{2}{y}$ from $y = 2$ to $y = 4$ (Similar to Exercise #8.)

$$g'(y) = \frac{1}{8}y^2 - 2y^{-2} \Rightarrow 1 + \left[g'(y)\right]^2 = \frac{1}{64}y^4 + \frac{1}{2} + 4y^{-4}$$

$$L = \int_2^4 \sqrt{1 + \left(\frac{1}{8}y^2 - 2y^{-2}\right)^2}\, dy = \int_2^4 \left(\frac{1}{8}y^2 + 2y^{-2}\right) dy = \frac{17}{6}$$

3. Set up and evaluate the definite integral for the area of the surface generated by revolving the curve $y = \sqrt{x} - \frac{1}{3}x^{3/2}, 1 \le x \le 3$ about the x-axis. (Similar to Exercise #42.)

$$y' = \frac{1}{2}x^{-1/2} - \frac{1}{2}x^{1/2} \Rightarrow 1 + y' = \left(\frac{1}{2}x^{-1} + \frac{1}{2}x\right)^2$$

$$S = 2\pi \int_1^3 \left(x^{1/2} - \frac{1}{3}x^{3/2}\right)\left(\frac{1}{2}x^{1/2} + \frac{1}{2}x\right) dx = \frac{16\pi}{9}$$

4. Find the area of the zone of a sphere formed by revolving the graph of $x = \sqrt{4-y^2}, -1 \le y \le 1$, about the y-axis. (Similar to Exercise #57.)

$$g'(y) = \frac{-y}{\sqrt{4-y^2}} \Rightarrow 1 + \left[g'(y)\right]^2 = \frac{4}{4-y^2}$$

$$S = 2\pi \int_{-1}^1 \sqrt{4-y^2}\left(\frac{2}{\sqrt{4-y^2}}\right) dy = 4\pi \int_{-1}^1 dx = 8\pi$$

7.5 Homework Quiz

1. Determine the work done by a crane as it lifts a 550-pound beam 300 feet into the air.

2. Assume 20 ft-lb of work is required to stretch a spring 1 ft beyond its natural length. What is the spring constant?

3. A swimming pool is built in the shape of a rectangular box 10ft deep, 15ft wide, and 20 ft long. The water weighs 62.4 pounds per cubic foot. If the pool is filled 1 ft below the top, how much work is required to pump all the water into a drain at the top edge of the pool?

4. A 100-ft length of steel chain weighing 15 lb/ft is dangling from a pulley. How much work is required to wind the chain onto the pulley?

7.5 Homework Quiz Solutions

1. Determine the work done by a crane as it lifts a 550-pound beam 300 feet into the air. (Similar to Exercise # 2.)

$$W = (550)(300)$$
$$= 165,000 \text{ ft-lbs}$$

2. Assume 20 ft-lb of work is required to stretch a spring 1 ft beyond its natural length. What is the spring constant? (Similar to Exercise #12.)

$$W = \int_0^1 kx\,dx = \frac{k}{2}$$

$$\frac{k}{2} = 20 \Rightarrow k = 40 \text{ lb/ft}$$

3. A swimming pool is built in the shape of a rectangular box 10ft deep, 15ft wide, and 20 ft long. The water weighs 62.4 pounds per cubic foot. If the pool is filled 1 ft below the top, how much work is required to pump all the water into a drain at the top edge of the pool? (Similar to Exercise #21.)

$$W = \int_0^9 (10 - x)62.4(300)\,dx = 18,720\int_0^9 (10 - x)\,dx = 926,640 \text{ ft-lb}$$

4. A 100-ft length of steel chain weighing 15 lb/ft is dangling from a pulley. How much work is required to wind the chain onto the pulley? (Similar to Exercise #27.)

$$W = \int_0^{100} 15(100 - x)\,dx = 15\left[-\frac{1}{2}(100 - x)^2\right]_0^{100} = 75,000 \text{ ft-lb}$$

7.6 Homework Quiz

1. Find the center of mass of the point masses lying on the x-axis.
   $$m_1 = 2, m_2 = 8, m_3 = 5,$$
   $$x_1 = 4, x_2 = -7, x_3 = 1$$

2. Find the center of mass for the lamina of uniform density ρ bounded by $y = 3x^2, y = 2x + 1$.

3. Set up and evaluate the integrals for finding the moments about the x- and y-axes for the region bounded by the graphs of $y = 4x^2 - 1$ and $y = 0$.

4. Use the Theorem of Pappus to find the volume of the torus formed by revolving the circle $x^2 + (y + 4)^2 = 9$ about the x-axis.

7.6 Homework Quiz Solutions

1. Find the center of mass of the point masses lying on the x-axis.
$m_1 = 2, m_2 = 8, m_3 = 5, \ x_1 = 4, x_2 = -7, x_3 = 1$.
(Similar to Exercise #2.)

$$\bar{x} = \frac{2(4) + 8(-7) + 5(1)}{2 + 8 + 5}$$

$$= -\frac{43}{15}$$

2. Find the center of mass for the lamina of uniform density ρ bounded by $y = 3x^2, y = 2x + 1$. (Similar to Exercise #19.)

$$m = \rho \int_{-1/3}^{1} (2x + 1 - 3x^2) \, dx = \frac{32\rho}{27} \qquad M_y = \rho \int_{-1/3}^{1} x(2x + 1 - 3x^2) \, dx$$

$$M_x = \rho \int_{-1/3}^{1} \left[\frac{2x + 1 + 3x^2}{2} \right] [2x + 1 - 3x^2] \, dx \qquad = \frac{32\rho}{81}$$

$$= \frac{544\rho}{405}; \bar{y} = \frac{M_x}{m} = \frac{17}{15} \qquad \bar{x} = \frac{M_y}{m} = 1/3$$

3. Set up and evaluate the integrals for finding the moments about the x- and y-axes for the region bounded by the graphs of $y = 4x^2 - 1$ and $y = 0$. (Assume $\rho = 1$) (Similar to Exercise #30.)

$$M_x = -\int_{-1/2}^{1/2} \frac{(4x^2 - 1)^2}{2} \, dx = -\frac{1}{2} \int_{-1/2}^{1/2} (16x^4 - 8x^2 + 1) \, dx = -\frac{4}{15}$$

$$M_y = -\int_{-1/2}^{1/2} x(4x^2 - 1) \, dx = -\left[x^4 - \frac{x^2}{2} \right]_{-1/2}^{1/2} = 0$$

4. Use the Theorem of Pappus to find the volume of the torus formed by revolving the circle $x^2 + (y + 4)^2 = 9$ about the x-axis. (Similar to Exercise #51.)

$r = 4$ is the distance between the centroid and the x-axis.

$$A = \pi(3)^2 = 9\pi$$

$$V = 2\pi(4)(9\pi) = 72\pi^2 \approx 710.61$$

7.7 Homework Quiz

1. Find the fluid force on a horizontal piece of sheet metal measuring 5 ft by 3 ft submerged in 12 ft of water.

2. Find the fluid force on the vertical side of a semicircular tank with a diameter of 10 ft.

3. Find the fluid force on the rectangular vertical plate submerged in water, where the dimensions are in meters and the water density of water is 9800 newtons per cubic meter.

4. Find the fluid force on the vertical plate of width 4m and height 2m submerged 1m in water, and the weight-density is 9800 newtons/cubic meter.

7.7 Homework Quiz Solutions

1. Find the fluid force on a horizontal piece of sheet metal measuring 5 ft by 3 ft submerged in 12 ft of water. (Similar to Exercise #2.)

$$P = (62.4)(12) = 748.8 \text{ lb/ft}^2$$

$$F = (748.8 \text{ lb/ft}^2)(15 \text{ ft}^2) = 11232 \text{ lbs}$$

2. Find the fluid force on the vertical side of a semicircular tank with a diameter of 10 ft. (Similar to Exercise #10.)

$$h(x) = x$$

$$L(x) = 2\sqrt{25 - x^2}$$

$$F = 2(62.4)\int_0^5 x\left(\sqrt{25 - x^2}\right)dx = \frac{124.8}{-2}\left[\frac{2}{3}(25 - x^2)^{3/2}\right]_0^5 = 5200 \text{ lb}$$

3. Find the fluid force on the rectangular vertical plate submerged in water, where the dimensions are in meters and the water density is 9800 newtons per cubic meter. (Similar to Exercise #16.)

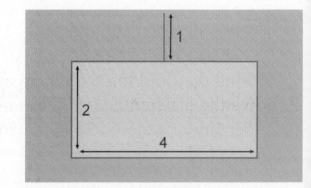

$$h(y) = 3 - y, L(y) = 4$$

$$F = 9800\int_0^3 4(4 - y)dy = 9800\left[16y - 2y^2\right]_0^3 = 294,000 \text{ newtons}$$

4. Find the fluid force on the vertical plate of width 4m and height 2m submerged 1m in water, and the weight-density is 9800 newtons/cubic meter. (Similar to Exercise #16.)

$$F = 9800\int_0^2 4(3 - y)dy$$

$$= 9800\left[12y - 2y^2\right]_0^2$$

$$= 156,800 \text{ newtons}$$

8.1 Homework Quiz

1. Select the basic integration formula you can use to find the integral. Identify u and a as appropriate.

$$\int \frac{4t-1}{2t^2 - t + 7}\, dt$$

2. Find the indefinite integral $\int \dfrac{x^2}{x+4}\, dx$.

3. Solve the differential equation $\dfrac{dy}{dx} = \left(e^x - 2\right)^2$.

4. Find the area of the region $y = \cos 2x$.
   (Similar to Exercise #78.)

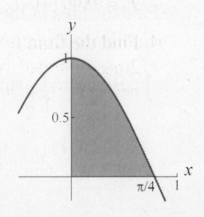

8.1 Homework Quiz Answers

1. Select the basic integration formula you can use to find the integral. Identify u and a as appropriate. (Similar to Exercise #6.)

$$\int \frac{4t-1}{2t^2-t+7}\,dt$$

$$\int \frac{du}{u} = \ln|u| + C \text{ with } u = 2t^2 - t + 7$$

2. Find the indefinite integral $\int \frac{x^2}{x+4}\,dx$. (Similar to Exercise #23.)

Let $u = x+4$. Then $x = u-4$ and $dx = du$.

$$\int \frac{x^2}{x+4}\,dx = \int \frac{(u-4)^2}{u}\,du = \int \frac{u^2-8u+16}{u}\,du = \int \left(u-8+16u^{-1}\right)du$$

$$= \frac{1}{2}u^2 - 8u + 16\ln|u| + C = \frac{1}{2}(x+4)^2 - 8(x+4) + 16\ln|x+4| + C$$

3. Solve the differential equation $\frac{dy}{dx} = \left(e^x - 2\right)^2$.

   (Similar to Exercise #59.)

   $$dy = \left(e^x - 2\right)^2 dx \qquad\qquad \int dy = \int \left(e^{2x} - 4e^x + 4\right)dx$$

   $$dy = \left(e^{2x} - 4e^x + 4\right)dx \qquad\qquad y = \frac{1}{2}e^{2x} - 4e^x + 4x + C$$

4. Find the area of the region $y = \cos 2x$.
   (Similar to Exercise #78.)

   $$\int_0^{\pi/4} \cos 2x\,dx = \left[\frac{1}{2}\sin 2x\right]_0^{\pi/4} = \frac{1}{2}$$

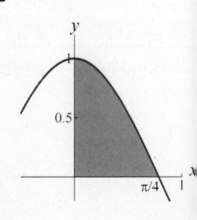

8.2 Homework Quiz

1. Evaluate the integral $\int 3xe^{3x}\,dx$ using $u = x$ and $dv = 3e^{3x}$.

2. Find the integral $\int \dfrac{2}{x(\ln x)^4}\,dx$.

3. Solve the differential equation $y' = \ln x^3$.

4. Evaluate the definite integral $\displaystyle\int_{0}^{\pi/2} x\cos 2x\,dx$.

8.2 Homework Quiz Answers

1. Evaluate the integral $\int 3xe^{3x}\,dx$ using $u = x$ and $dv = 3e^{3x}$.
   (Similar to Exercise #8.)

$$u = x \qquad dv = 3e^{3x} \qquad uv - \int v\,du = xe^{3x} - \int e^{3x}\,dx$$

$$du = dx \qquad v = e^{3x}$$

$$= xe^{3x} - \frac{1}{3}e^{3x} + C$$

2. Find the integral $\int \dfrac{2}{x(\ln x)^4}\,dx$. (Similar to Exercise #18.)

$$u = \ln x \qquad \int \frac{2}{u^4}\,du = -\frac{2}{3}u^{-3} + C$$

$$du = \frac{1}{x}\,dx$$

$$= -\frac{2}{3(\ln x)^3} + C$$

3. Solve the differential equation $y' = \ln x^3$.
   (Similar to Exercise #40.)

$$y' = 3\ln x \qquad \int 3\ln x\,dx = 3x\ln x - \int 3\,dx$$

$$u = \ln x \qquad dv = 3$$

$$= 3x\ln x - 3x + C$$

$$du = \frac{1}{x}\,dx \qquad v = 3x$$

4. Evaluate the definite integral $\displaystyle\int_0^{\pi/2} x\cos 2x\,dx$.

   (Similar to Exercise #52.)

$$u = x \qquad dv = \cos 2x$$

$$du = dx \qquad v = \frac{1}{2}\sin 2x$$

$$\int x\cos 2x\,dx = \frac{1}{2}x\sin 2x - \int \frac{1}{2}\sin 2x\,dx$$

$$= \frac{1}{2}x\sin 2x - \left(-\frac{1}{4}\cos 2x\right)$$

$$\int_0^{\pi/2} x\cos 2x\,dx = \left(0 - \frac{1}{4}\right) - \left(\frac{1}{4}\right) = -\frac{1}{2}$$

8.3 Homework Quiz

1. Find the integral $\int -\cos^4 x \sin^5 x \, dx$.

2. Use Wallis's Formulas to evaluate the integral $\displaystyle\int_0^{\pi/2} \sin^4 x \, dx$.

3. Find the integral involving secant. $\int \tan^4 x \, dx$

4. Solve the differential equation $\dfrac{dr}{d\theta} = \sin^3 \pi\theta$.

8.3 Homework Quiz Answers

1. Find the integral $\int -\cos^4 x \sin^5 x\, dx$.

   (Similar to Exercise #9.)

   $$\int -\cos^4 x \sin^5 x\, dx = \int \cos^4 x \left(1-\cos^2 x\right)^2 (-\sin x)\, dx$$

   $$= \int \cos^4 x \left(1-2\cos^2 x + \cos^4 x\right)(-\sin x)\, dx$$

   $$= \int \left(\cos^4 x - 2\cos^6 x + \cos^8 x\right)(-\sin x)\, dx$$

   $$= \frac{1}{5}\cos^5 x - \frac{2}{7}\cos^7 x + \frac{1}{9}\cos^9 x + C$$

2. Use Wallis's Formulas to evaluate the integral $\displaystyle\int_0^{\pi/2} \sin^4 x\, dx$.

   (Similar to Exercise #22.)

   $$\int_0^{\pi/2} \sin^4 x\, dx = \left(\frac{1}{2}\right)\left(\frac{3}{4}\right)\left(\frac{\pi}{2}\right)$$

   $$= \frac{3}{16}\pi$$

3. Find the integral involving secant. $\int \tan^4 x\, dx$

   (Similar to Exercise #30.)

   $$\int \tan^4 x\, dx = \int \tan^2 x \left(\tan^2 x\right) dx \qquad\qquad = \frac{\tan^3 x}{3} + \int \sec^2 x - 1\, dx$$

   $$= \int \tan^2 x \left(\sec^2 x - 1\right) dx$$

   $$= \int \tan^2 x \sec^2 x\, dx - \int \tan^2 x\, dx \qquad = \frac{\tan^3 x}{3} + \tan x - x + C$$

4. Solve the differential equation $\dfrac{dr}{d\theta} = \sin^3 \pi\theta$.

   (Similar to Exercise #43.)

   $$r = \int \sin^3 \pi\theta\, d\theta \qquad\qquad = \frac{1}{\pi}\cos \pi\theta + \frac{1}{3\pi}\cos^3 \left(\pi\theta\right) + C$$

   $$= \int \left(1-\cos^2 \pi\theta\right)\sin \pi\theta\, d\theta$$

   $$= \int \left(\sin \pi\theta - \left(\cos^2 \pi\theta\right)\sin \pi\theta\right) d\theta$$

8.4 Homework Quiz

1. State the trigonometric substitution you would use to find the integral $\int \sqrt{9+x^2}\,dx$.

2. Find the indefinite integral $\int \dfrac{1}{\sqrt{x^2-9}}\,dx$ using the substitution $x=3\sec\theta$.

3. Find the integral $\int \dfrac{x}{\sqrt{49-x^2}}\,dx$.

4. Find the particular solution to the differential equation
$x\dfrac{dy}{dx}=\sqrt{x^2-16}, x\geq 4, y(4)=1$.

255

8.4 Homework Quiz Answers

1. State the trigonometric substitution you would use to find the integral $\int \sqrt{9+x^2}\,dx$. (Similar to Exercise #2.)

   Use $u = 3\tan\theta$.

2. Find the indefinite integral $\int \dfrac{1}{\sqrt{x^2-9}}\,dx$ using the substitution $x = 3\sec\theta$. (Similar to Exercise #9.)

   $$\int \frac{1}{\sqrt{x^2-9}}\,dx = \int \frac{3\sec\theta\tan\theta}{\sqrt{9\sec^2\theta-9}}\,d\theta = \int \frac{3\sec\theta\tan\theta}{3\sqrt{\tan^2\theta}}\,d\theta = \int \frac{3\sec\theta\tan\theta}{3\tan\theta}\,d\theta$$

   $$= \int \sec\theta\,d\theta = \ln\left|\sec\theta+\tan\theta\right| + C = \ln\left|\frac{x}{3} + \frac{\sqrt{x^2-9}}{3}\right| + C$$

3. Find the integral $\int \dfrac{x}{\sqrt{49-x^2}}\,dx$. (Similar to Exercise #22.)

   Let $x = 7\sin\theta$. Then $dx = 7\cos\theta\,d\theta$.

   $$\int \frac{x}{\sqrt{49-x^2}}\,dx = \int \frac{7\sin\theta}{\sqrt{49-\left(49\sin^2\theta\right)}}\,7\cos\theta\,d\theta = \int \frac{49\sin\theta\cos\theta}{7\sqrt{1-\sin^2\theta}}$$

   $$= \int 7\sin\theta\,d\theta = -7\cos\theta + C = -\sqrt{49-x^2} + C$$

4. Find the particular solution to the differential equation
   $x\dfrac{dy}{dx} = \sqrt{x^2-16}, x \geq 4, y(4)=1$. (Similar to Exercise #53.)

   $$dy = \frac{\sqrt{x^2-16}}{x}\,dx \quad \text{Let } x = 4\sec\theta. \text{ Then } dx = 4\sec\theta\tan\theta\,d\theta.$$

   $$y = \int \frac{\sqrt{16\sec^2\theta-16}}{4\sec\theta}\,4\sec\theta\tan\theta\,d\theta = \int \frac{16\sec\theta\tan^2\theta}{4\sec\theta}\,d\theta$$

   $$y = \int 4\tan^2\theta\,d\theta = 4\int\left(\sec^2\theta-1\right)d\theta = 4\tan\theta - 4\theta + C$$

   $$y = \sqrt{x^2-16} - 4\arccos\left(\frac{4}{x}\right) + C; \, y = \sqrt{x^2-16} - 4\arccos\left(\frac{4}{x}\right) + 1$$

8.5 Homework Quiz

1. Write the form of the partial fraction decomposition of the rational expression $\dfrac{11x+17}{2x^2+7x-4}$ without solving for the constants.

2. Use partial fractions to find the integral $\displaystyle\int\dfrac{2x^2+3}{x^3-2x^2+x}dx$.

3. Use substitution to find the integral $\displaystyle\int\dfrac{\cos x}{\sin^2 x+4\sin x-5}dx$.

4. Find the area of the region bounded by the graphs of $y=\dfrac{6}{x^2+3x+2}, y=0, x=0$ and $x=1$.

8.5 Homework Quiz Solutions

1. Write the form of the partial fraction decomposition of the rational expression $\dfrac{11x+17}{2x^2+7x-4}$ without solving for the constants. (Similar to Exercise #4.)

$$\frac{11x+17}{(2x-1)(x+4)} = \frac{A}{2x-1} + \frac{B}{x+4}$$

2. Use partial fractions to find the integral $\int \dfrac{2x^2+3}{x^3-2x^2+x}dx$. (Similar to Exercise #27.)

$$\frac{2x^2+3}{x(x-1)^2} = \frac{A}{x} + \frac{B}{x-1} + \frac{C}{(x-1)^2}$$

$$2x^2+3 = A(x-1)^2 + Bx(x-1) + Cx$$

$$A=3, B=2, C=-1$$

$$3\int\frac{1}{x}dx - \int\frac{1}{x-1}dx + 5\int\frac{1}{(x-1)^2}dx$$

$$= 3\ln|x| - \ln|x-1| - \frac{5}{(x-1)} + C$$

3. Use substitution to find the integral $\int \dfrac{\cos x}{\sin^2 x + 4\sin x - 5}dx$. (Similar to Exercise #44.)

Let $u = \sin x, du = \cos x \Rightarrow \int \dfrac{1}{x^2+4x-5}dx$

$$= \frac{A}{x+5} + \frac{B}{x-1} \Rightarrow A=-\frac{1}{6}, B=\frac{1}{6}$$

$$-\frac{1}{6}\int\frac{1}{x+5}dx + \frac{1}{6}\int\frac{1}{x-1}dx$$

$$= \frac{1}{6}\ln\left|\frac{\sin x - 1}{\sin x + 5}\right| + C$$

4. Find the area of the region bounded by the graphs of $y = \dfrac{6}{x^2+3x+2}, y = 0, x = 0$ and $x = 1$. (Similar to Exercise #60.)

$$\frac{6}{(x+2)(x+1)} = \frac{A}{x+2} + \frac{B}{x+1}$$

$$\Rightarrow A=-6, B=6$$

$$6\int_0^1 \left(\frac{1}{x+1} - \frac{1}{x+2}\right)dx$$

$$= 6\left[\ln(x+1) - \ln(x+2)\right]_0^1$$

$$\approx 1.726$$

8.6 Homework Quiz

1. Use a table of integrals with forms involving the trigonometric functions to find the integral $\int \sin^4 2x\,dx$.

2. Find the indefinite integral using integration tables $\int \dfrac{x^3}{\sqrt{1+x^2}}\,dx$.

3. Use integration tables to evaluate $\displaystyle\int_0^1 \dfrac{dx}{2+2\sqrt{x}}$.

4. Find or evaluate the integral $\int \dfrac{\sin^2 x}{1+\cos x}\,dx$.

8.6 Homework Quiz Solutions

1. Use a table of integrals with forms involving the trigonometric functions to find the integral $\int \sin^4 2x\,dx$. (Similar to Exercise #7.)

$$\int \sin^4 2x\,dx = \frac{1}{2}\int \sin^4(2x)(2)\,dx$$

$$= \frac{1}{2}\left[\frac{-\sin^3(2x)\cos(2x)}{4} + \frac{3}{4}\int \sin^2(2x)(2)\,dx\right]$$

$$= \frac{1}{16}\left(6x - 3\sin 2x\cos 2x - 2\sin^3 2x\cos 2x\right) + C$$

2. Find the indefinite integral using integration tables $\int \dfrac{x^3}{\sqrt{1+x^2}}\,dx$. (Similar to Exercise #21.)

$$u = \sqrt{1+x^2} \Rightarrow x^2 = u^2 - 1 \Rightarrow x\,dx = u\,du$$

$$\int (u^2 - 1)\,du = \frac{1}{3}\left(1+x^2\right)^{3/2} - \left(1+x^2\right)^{1/2} + C$$

3. Use integration tables to evaluate $\displaystyle\int_0^1 \frac{dx}{2+2\sqrt{x}}$. (Similar to #47.)

$$u = x^{1/2} \Rightarrow x = u^2, dx = 2u\,du$$

$$\int_0^1 \frac{2u}{2+2u}\,du = \int_0^1\left(1 - \frac{1}{1+u}\right)du = \left[\sqrt{x} - \ln\left|1+\sqrt{x}\right|\right]_0^1 = 1 - \ln 2$$

4. Find or evaluate the integral $\int \dfrac{\sin^2 x}{1+\cos x}\,dx$. (Similar to Exercise #64.)

$$\int \frac{1-\cos^2 x}{1+\cos x}\,dx = \int(1-\cos x) = x - \sin x + C$$

8.7 Homework Quiz

1. Complete the table and use the result to estimate the limit $\lim\limits_{x \to +\infty} xe^{-x}$.

x	1	10	10^2	10^3	10^4	10^5
$f(x)$						

2. Evaluate the limit $\lim\limits_{x \to 0} \dfrac{1 - \cos x}{x^2}$ using L'Hôpital's Rule.

3. Evaluate the limit $\lim\limits_{x \to 0} \dfrac{e^{ax} - e^{bx}}{x}$ using L'Hôpital's Rule, if necessary.

4. Describe the type of indeterminate form that is obtained by direct substitution, and then evaluate the limit $\lim\limits_{x \to 0^+} \left(\dfrac{1}{x} - \dfrac{1}{\sin x} \right)$ using L'Hôpital's Rule, if necessary.

8.7 Homework Quiz Solutions

1. Complete the table and use the result to estimate the limit $\lim\limits_{x \to +\infty} xe^{-x}$
   (Similar to Exercise #1.)

x	1	10	10^2	10^3	10^4	10^5
$f(x)$	0.3678	4.5×10^{-4}	4×10^{-42}	0	0	0

$$\lim_{x \to +\infty} xe^{-x} = 0$$

2. Evaluate the limit $\lim\limits_{x \to 0} \dfrac{1 - \cos x}{x^2}$ using L'Hôpital's Rule.
   (Similar to Exercise #8.)

   Using L'Hôpital's Rule: $\lim\limits_{x \to 0} \dfrac{\sin x}{2x} = \lim\limits_{x \to 0} \dfrac{\cos x}{2} = \dfrac{1}{2}$

3. Evaluate the limit $\lim\limits_{x \to 0} \dfrac{e^{ax} - e^{bx}}{x}$ using L'Hôpital's Rule if necessary
   (Similar to Exercise #29.)

   Using L'Hôpital's Rule: $\lim\limits_{x \to 0} \dfrac{ae^{ax} - be^{bx}}{1} = a - b$

4. Describe the type of indeterminate form that is obtained by direct substitution, and then evaluate the limit $\lim\limits_{x \to 0^+} \left(\dfrac{1}{x} - \dfrac{1}{\sin x} \right)$ using L'Hôpital's Rule, if necessary. (Similar to Exercise #61.)

   $\lim\limits_{x \to 0^+} \dfrac{1}{x} = +\infty$, $\lim\limits_{x \to 0^+} \dfrac{1}{\sin x} = +\infty \Rightarrow$ type $\infty - \infty \Rightarrow \lim\limits_{x \to 0^+} \left(\dfrac{\sin x - x}{x \sin x} \right)$

   Using L'Hôpital's Rule: $\lim\limits_{x \to 0^+} \dfrac{\cos x - 1}{\sin x + x \cos x}$

   $= \lim\limits_{x \to 0^+} \dfrac{-\sin x}{\cos x + \cos x - x \sin x}$

   $= 0$

262

8.8 Homework Quiz

1. Decide whether the integral $\int_0^1 \dfrac{dx}{\sqrt{1-x^2}}$ is improper. Explain your reasoning.

2. Explain why the integral $\int_0^{\pi/6} \dfrac{\cos x}{\sqrt{1-2\sin x}}dx$ is improper and determine whether it diverges or converges. Evaluate the integral if it converges.

3. Determine whether the improper integral $\int_0^{+\infty} xe^{-3x}\,dx$ diverges or converges. Evaluate the integral if it converges.

4. Determine whether the improper integral $\int_0^{\pi/2} \tan x\,dx$ diverges or converges. Evaluate the integral if it converges.

8.8 Homework Quiz Solutions

1. Decide whether the integral $\int_0^1 \dfrac{dx}{\sqrt{1-x^2}}$ is improper. Explain your reasoning. (Similar to Exercise #3.)

$\int_0^1 \dfrac{dx}{\sqrt{1-x^2}}$ is improper because $\dfrac{1}{\sqrt{1-x^2}}$ is not continuous on $[0,1]$.

2. Explain why the integral $\int_0^{\pi/6} \dfrac{\cos x}{\sqrt{1-2\sin x}}\,dx$ is improper and determine whether it diverges or converges. Evaluate the integral if it converges. (Similar to Exercise #12.)

$\int_0^{\pi/6} \dfrac{\cos x}{\sqrt{1-2\sin x}}\,dx$ is not continuous at $x = \dfrac{\pi}{6} \Rightarrow$ improper integral

$$\lim_{x \to \pi/6} \int_0^{\pi/6} \dfrac{\cos x}{\sqrt{1-2\sin x}}\,dx = \lim_{a \to \pi/6}\left[-\sqrt{1-2\sin x}\right]_0^a$$

$$= \lim_{a \to \pi/6}\left(-\sqrt{1-2\sin a} + 1\right) = 1$$

3. Determine whether the improper integral $\int_0^{+\infty} xe^{-3x}\,dx$ diverges or converges. Evaluate the integral if it converges. (Similar to Exercise #23.)

By integration by parts,

$$= \lim_{b \to +\infty}\left[\left(-\dfrac{1}{3}xe^{-3x} - \dfrac{1}{9}e^{-3x}\right)\right]_0^b$$

$$= \lim_{b \to +\infty}\left(-\dfrac{1}{3}be^{-3b} - \dfrac{1}{9}e^{-3b} + \dfrac{1}{9}\right)$$

But $\lim_{b \to +\infty} be^{-3b} = \lim_{b \to +\infty} \dfrac{b}{e^{3b}} = \lim_{b \to +\infty} \dfrac{1}{3e^{3b}} = 0$

So, $\int_0^{+\infty} xe^{-3x}\,dx = \dfrac{1}{9} \Rightarrow$ converges

4. Determine whether the improper integral $\int_0^{\pi/2} \tan x\,dx$ diverges or converges. Evaluate the integral if it converges. (Similar to Exercise #43.)

$$= \lim_{b \to \pi/2}\left[-\ln(\cos x)\right]_0^b = \lim_{b \to \pi/2}\left[-\ln(\cos b)\right] = +\infty$$

$\Rightarrow$ divergent

9.1 Homework Quiz

1. Write the first five terms of the sequence. $a_n = \dfrac{(n-1)}{n!}$

2. Match the sequence with the graph.

   a. $a_n = \left(\dfrac{1}{2}\right)^n$

   b. $a_n = \left(\dfrac{-1}{2}\right)^n$

   c. $a_n = \dfrac{2}{n}$

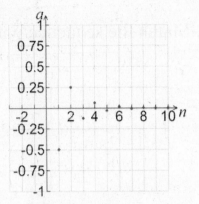

3. Determine the convergence or divergence of the sequence with the given n th term. If the sequence converges, find its limit.

$a_n = \dfrac{\sqrt{n}}{\sqrt{n}+1}$

4. Write an expression for the n th term of the sequence.

$\dfrac{-2}{4}, \dfrac{4}{5}, \dfrac{-6}{6}, \dfrac{8}{7}, \dfrac{-10}{8}, \dots$

9.1 Homework Quiz Answers

1. Write the first five terms of the sequence. $a_n = \dfrac{(n-1)}{n!}$

   (Similar to Exercise #2.)

$$0, \frac{1}{2}, \frac{1}{3}, \frac{1}{8}, \frac{1}{30}$$

2. Match the sequence with the graph. (Similar to Exercise #18.)

   a. $a_n = \left(\dfrac{1}{2}\right)^n$

   b. $a_n = \left(\dfrac{-1}{2}\right)^n$

   c. $a_n = \dfrac{2}{n}$

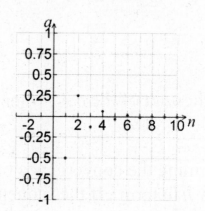

   The correct match is (b).

3. Determine the convergence or divergence of the sequence with the given n th term. If the sequence converges, find its limit.

   $a_n = \dfrac{\sqrt{n}}{\sqrt{n}+1}$ (Similar to Exercise #52.)

$$\text{Converges, } \lim_{n \to \infty} \frac{\sqrt{n}}{\sqrt{n}+1} = 1$$

4. Write an expression for the n th term of the sequence.
   $\dfrac{-2}{4}, \dfrac{4}{5}, \dfrac{-6}{6}, \dfrac{8}{7}, \dfrac{-10}{8}, \dots$ (Similar to Exercise #76.)

$$a_n = \frac{-2n}{n+3}$$

9.2 Homework Quiz

1. Match the series with the graph of its sequence of partial sums.

a. $\displaystyle\sum_{n=0}^{\infty} 2\left(\frac{1}{3}\right)^{n}$

b. $\displaystyle\sum_{n=0}^{\infty} 2\left(\frac{-2}{3}\right)^{n}$

c. $\displaystyle\sum_{n=0}^{\infty} 3\left(\frac{2}{3}\right)^{n}$

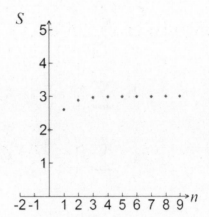

2. Find the sum of the convergent series.

$$10 + 4 + \frac{8}{5} + \frac{16}{25} + \dots$$

3. Determine the convergence or divergence of the series.

$$\sum_{n=1}^{\infty} \frac{5n+1}{3n-1}$$

4. Find all values of x for which the series converges. For these values of x, write the sum of the series as a function of x.

$$\sum_{n=0}^{\infty} \left(\frac{x-1}{2}\right)^{n}$$

9.2 Homework Quiz Answers

1. Match the series with the graph of its sequence of partial sums. (Similar to Exercise #19.)

   a. $\displaystyle\sum_{n=0}^{\infty} 2\left(\frac{1}{3}\right)^n$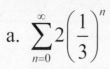

   b. $\displaystyle\sum_{n=0}^{\infty} 2\left(\frac{-2}{3}\right)^n$

   c. $\displaystyle\sum_{n=0}^{\infty} 3\left(\frac{2}{3}\right)^n$

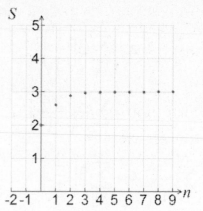

   The correct match is (a).

2. Find the sum of the convergent series.

   $$10 + 4 + \frac{8}{5} + \frac{16}{25} + \dots \qquad \text{(Similar to Exercise \#46.)}$$

   $$S = \frac{10}{1 - \dfrac{2}{5}} = \frac{50}{3}$$

3. Determine the convergence or divergence of the series.

   $$\sum_{n=1}^{\infty} \frac{5n+1}{3n-1} \qquad \text{(Similar to Exercise \#62.)}$$

   $\displaystyle\lim_{x\to\infty} \frac{5n+1}{3n+1} \neq 0.$ The series diverges by nth-Term Test for Divergence.

4. Find all values of x for which the series converges. For these values of x, write the sum of the series as a function of x.

   $$\sum_{n=0}^{\infty} \left(\frac{x-1}{2}\right)^n \qquad \text{(Similar to Exercise \#86.)}$$

   $-1 < \dfrac{x-1}{2} < 1$ simplifies to $-1 < x < 3$. This is the interval over

   which the series converges. $\text{Sum} = \dfrac{1}{1 - \dfrac{x-1}{2}} = \dfrac{2}{3-x}$

9.3 Homework Quiz

1. Use the Integral Test to determine the convergence or divergence of the series.

$$\frac{3}{2} + \frac{3}{5} + \frac{3}{10} + \frac{3}{17} + \frac{3}{26} + \ldots$$

2. Use the Integral Test to determine the convergence or divergence of the series.

$$\sum_{n=1}^{\infty} \frac{3n^2}{n^3 + 1}$$

3. Determine the convergence or divergence of the p-series.

$$\sum_{n=1}^{\infty} \frac{5}{n^{3/2}}$$

4. Match the series with the graph of its sequence of partial sums. Determine the convergence or divergence of the series.

a. $\sum_{n=1}^{\infty} \frac{3}{n}$

b. $\sum_{n=1}^{\infty} \frac{2}{\sqrt[3]{n}}$

c. $\sum_{n=1}^{\infty} \frac{1}{n^{3/2}}$

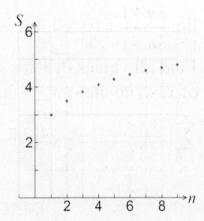

9.3 Homework Quiz Answers

1. Use the Integral Test to determine the convergence or divergence of the series.

$$\frac{3}{2}+\frac{3}{5}+\frac{3}{10}+\frac{3}{17}+\frac{3}{26}+\ldots \quad \text{(Similar to Exercise \# 7.)}$$

$$\int_{1}^{\infty}\frac{3}{x^2+1}dx=\lim_{b\to\infty}(3\tan^{-1}(b)-3\tan^{-1}1)=\frac{3\pi}{2}. \text{ The series converges.}$$

2. Use the Integral Test to determine the convergence or divergence of the series.

$$\sum_{n=1}^{\infty}\frac{3n^2}{n^3+1} \quad \text{(Similar to Exercise \#41.)}$$

$$\int_{1}^{\infty}\frac{3x^2}{x^3+1}dx=\lim_{b\to\infty}(\ln(b^3+1)-\ln(2))=\infty. \text{ The series diverges.}$$

3. Determine the convergence or divergence of the p-series.

$$\sum_{n=1}^{\infty}\frac{5}{n^{3/2}} \quad \text{(Similar to Exercise \#36.)}$$

$$p=\frac{3}{2}>1. \text{ The series converges.}$$

4. Match the series with the graph of its sequence of partial sums. Determine the convergence or divergence of the series. (Similar to Exercise \#44.)

a. $\sum_{n=1}^{\infty}\frac{3}{n}$

b. $\sum_{n=1}^{\infty}\frac{2}{\sqrt[3]{n}}$

c. $\sum_{n=1}^{\infty}\frac{1}{n^{3/2}}$

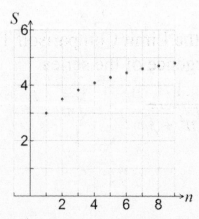

The correct match is (a).

9.4 Homework Quiz

1. Use the Direct Comparison Test to determine the convergence or divergence of the series.

$$\sum_{n=1}^{\infty} \frac{1}{n^3 + 1}$$

2. Use the Direct Comparison Test to determine the convergence or divergence of the series.

$$\sum_{n=1}^{\infty} \frac{3^n}{2^n - 1}$$

3. Use the Limit Comparison Test to determine the convergence or divergence of the series.

$$\sum_{n=1}^{\infty} \frac{1}{n(n+1)}$$

4. Use the Limit Comparison Test to determine the convergence or divergence of the series.

$$\sum_{n=0}^{\infty} \frac{1}{\sqrt{n^2 + 3}}$$

9.4 Homework Quiz Answers

1. Use the Direct Comparison Test to determine the convergence or divergence of the series.

$$\sum_{n=1}^{\infty} \frac{1}{n^3 + 1} \quad \text{(Similar to Exercise \#3.)}$$

Resembles convergent p-series $\sum_{n=1}^{\infty} \frac{1}{n^3}$. $a_n = \frac{1}{n^3 + 1} \leq \frac{1}{n^3}, n \geq 1$

which meets the requirements for convergence.

2. Use the Direct Comparison Test to determine the convergence or divergence of the series.

$$\sum_{n=1}^{\infty} \frac{3^n}{2^n - 1} \quad \text{(Similar to Exercise \#14.)}$$

Resembles divergent geometric series $\sum_{n=1}^{\infty} \left(\frac{3}{2} \right)^n$.

$a_n = \frac{3^n}{2^n} \leq \frac{3^n}{2^n - 1}, n \geq 1$ which meets the requirements for divergence.

3. Use the Limit Comparison Test to determine the convergence or divergence of the series.

$$\sum_{n=1}^{\infty} \frac{1}{n(n+1)} \quad \text{(Similar to Exercise \#22.)}$$

Like convergent p-series $\sum_{n=1}^{\infty} \frac{1}{n^2}$. $\lim_{n \to \infty} \frac{a_n}{b_n} = \lim_{n \to \infty} \left(\frac{1}{n(n+1)} \right) \left(\frac{n^2}{1} \right) = 1$

The given series converges.

4. Use the Limit Comparison Test to determine the convergence or divergence of the series.

$$\sum_{n=0}^{\infty} \frac{1}{\sqrt{n^2 + 3}} \quad \text{(Similar to Exercise \#17)}$$

Resembles divergent p-series $\sum_{n=1}^{\infty} \frac{1}{n}$. $\lim_{n \to \infty} \frac{a_n}{b_n} = \lim_{n \to \infty} \left(\frac{1}{\sqrt{n^2 + 3}} \right) \left(\frac{n}{1} \right) = 1$

The given series diverges.

9.5 Homework Quiz

1. Determine the convergence or divergence of the series.

$$\sum_{n=1}^{\infty} \frac{(-1)^n}{n+2}$$

2. Determine the convergence or divergence of the series.

$$\sum_{n=1}^{\infty} \frac{(-1)^{n+1} n}{\sqrt{n}}$$

3. Determine the number of terms required to approximate the sum of the series with an error of less than 0.001. $\displaystyle\sum_{n=1}^{\infty} \frac{(-1)^n}{10n^3}$

4. Determine whether the series converges conditionally or absolutely, or diverges. $\displaystyle\sum_{n=1}^{\infty} \frac{(-1)^{n+1}}{\sqrt[3]{n}}$

9.5 Homework Quiz Answers

1. Determine the convergence or divergence of the series.

$$\sum_{n=1}^{\infty} \frac{(-1)^n}{n+2} \quad \text{(Similar to Exercise \#11.)}$$

$\lim\limits_{n \to \infty} a_n = \lim\limits_{n \to \infty} \dfrac{1}{n+2} = 0$ and $a_{n+1} = \dfrac{1}{n+3} \leq \dfrac{1}{n+2} = a_n$ for all n. So, by the Alternating Series Test, the series converges.

2. Determine the convergence or divergence of the series.

$$\sum_{n=1}^{\infty} \frac{(-1)^{n+1} n}{\sqrt{n}} \quad \text{(Similar to Exercise \#32.)}$$

$\lim\limits_{n \to \infty} a_n = \lim\limits_{n \to \infty} \dfrac{n}{\sqrt{n}} \neq 0$. By the nth-Term Test for Divergence, the series diverges.

3. Determine the number of terms required to approximate the sum of the series with an error of less than 0.001. $\quad \sum\limits_{n=1}^{\infty} \dfrac{(-1)^n}{10n^3}$

(Similar to Exercise \#47.)

$\sum\limits_{n=1}^{\infty} \dfrac{(-1)^n}{10n^3} = \dfrac{1}{10} - \dfrac{1}{80} + \dfrac{1}{270} - \dfrac{1}{640} + \dfrac{1}{1250} - \ldots$. Since $0.001 < \dfrac{1}{1250}$, the partial sum S_4 approximates with an error of less than 0.001.

4. Determine whether the series converges conditionally or absolutely, or diverges. $\sum\limits_{n=1}^{\infty} \dfrac{(-1)^{n+1}}{\sqrt[3]{n}}$ (Similar to Exercise \#57.)

$\sum\limits_{n=1}^{\infty} \left| \dfrac{(-1)^{n+1}}{\sqrt[3]{n}} \right|$ is a divergent p-series. $\sum\limits_{n=1}^{\infty} \dfrac{(-1)^{n+1}}{\sqrt[3]{n}}$ is a converging alternating series. The series is conditionally convergent.

9.6 Homework Quiz

1. Verify the formula. $\dfrac{2^{n+1}}{(n+1)!} \cdot \dfrac{n!}{2^n} = \dfrac{2}{n+1}$

2. Use the Ratio Test to determine the convergence or divergence of the series. $\displaystyle\sum_{n=0}^{\infty} \dfrac{n!}{n2^n}$

3. Use the Ratio Test to determine the convergence or divergence of the series. $\displaystyle\sum_{n=0}^{\infty} \dfrac{5^n}{n^3}$

4. Use the Root Test to determine the convergence or divergence of the series. $\displaystyle\sum_{n=0}^{\infty} \left(\dfrac{n}{3n+1}\right)^n$

9.6 Homework Quiz Answers

1. Verify the formula. $\dfrac{2^{n+1}}{(n+1)!} \cdot \dfrac{n!}{2^n} = \dfrac{2}{n+1}$

   (Similar to Exercise #2.)

   $$\frac{2^{n+1}}{(n+1)!} \cdot \frac{n!}{2^n} = \frac{2 \cdot 2^n}{(n+1)n!} \cdot \frac{n!}{2^n} = \frac{2}{n+1}$$

2. Use the Ratio Test to determine the convergence or divergence of the series. $\displaystyle\sum_{n=0}^{\infty} \frac{n!}{n2^n}$ (Similar to Exercise #25.)

   $$\lim_{n\to\infty}\left|\frac{a_{n+1}}{a_n}\right| = \lim_{n\to\infty}\left[\frac{(n+1)!}{(n+1)2^{n+1}} \div \frac{n!}{n2^n}\right] = \lim_{n\to\infty}\left[\frac{(n+1)!}{(n+1)2^{n+1}} \cdot \frac{n2^n}{n!}\right] = \lim_{n\to\infty}\frac{n}{2} = \infty$$

   Therefore, the series diverges.

3. Use the Ratio Test to determine the convergence or divergence of the series. $\displaystyle\sum_{n=1}^{\infty} \frac{n^3}{5^n}$ (Similar to Exercise #19.)

   $$\lim_{n\to\infty}\left|\frac{a_{n+1}}{a_n}\right| = \lim_{n\to\infty}\left[\frac{(n+1)^3}{5^{n+1}} \div \frac{n^3}{5^n}\right] = \lim_{n\to\infty}\left[\frac{(n+1)^3}{5^{n+1}} \cdot \frac{5^n}{n^3}\right] = \lim_{n\to\infty}\frac{1}{5}\left(\frac{n+1}{n}\right)^3 = \frac{1}{5}$$

   Therefore, the series converges

4. Use the Root Test to determine the convergence or divergence of the series. $\displaystyle\sum_{n=0}^{\infty}\left(\frac{n}{3n+1}\right)^n$ (Similar to Exercise #37.)

   $$\lim_{n\to\infty}\sqrt[n]{|a_n|} = \lim_{n\to\infty}\sqrt[n]{\left(\frac{n}{3n+1}\right)^n} = \lim_{n\to\infty}\frac{n}{3n+1} = \frac{1}{3}$$

   Therefore, the series converges.

9.7 Homework Quiz

1. Match the Taylor polynomial approximation of the function
$f(x) = e^{-x}$.

   a. $g(x) = 1 + x + \dfrac{x^2}{2}$

   b. $g(x) = \dfrac{1}{e}[1 - (x-1) + (x-1)^2]$

   c. $g(x) = e[1 - (x+1) + (x+1)^2]$

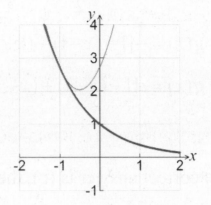

2. Find the Maclaurin polynomial of degree 6 for $f(x) = \cos x$.

3. Find the 3rd Taylor polynomial centered at $c = 1$ for $f(x) = \dfrac{1}{x^2}$.

4. Use Taylor's Theorem to obtain an upper bound for error of the
approximation $\cos(0.2) \approx 1 - \dfrac{(0.2)^2}{2!}$.

1. Match the Taylor polynomial approximation of the function
$f(x) = e^{-x}$. (Similar to Exercise #2.)

9.7 Homework Quiz Answers

a. $g(x) = 1 + x + \dfrac{x^2}{2}$

b. $g(x) = \dfrac{1}{e}[1 - (x-1) + (x-1)^2]$

c. $g(x) = e[1 - (x+1) + (x+1)^2]$

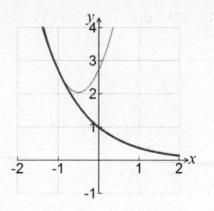

The correct answer is (c), the quadratic centered at $x = -1$.

2. Find the Maclaurin polynomial of degree 6 for $f(x) = \cos x$. (Similar to Exercise #17.)

$$f(0) = 1, f'(0) = 0, f''(0) = -1, f'''(0) = 0, f^{(4)}(0) = 1, f^{(5)}(0) = 0, f^{(6)} = -1$$

$$P_4(x) = 1 - \frac{1}{2!}x^2 + \frac{1}{4!}x^4 - \frac{1}{6!}x^6$$

3. Find the 3rd Taylor polynomial centered at $c = 1$ for $f(x) = \dfrac{1}{x^2}$. (Similar to Exercise #26.)

$$f(1) = 1, f'(1) = -2, f''(1) = 6, f'''(1) = -24$$

$$P_3(x) = 1 - 2x + \frac{6}{2!}x^2 - \frac{24}{3!}x^3 = 1 - 2x + 3x^2 - 4x^3$$

4. Use Taylor's Theorem to obtain an upper bound for error of the approximation $\cos(0.2) \approx 1 - \dfrac{(0.2)^2}{2!}$. (Similar to Exercise #45.)

$$f(x) = \cos x, \quad f^{(4)}(x) = \cos x$$

$$0 < R_4(0.2) = \frac{\cos z}{4!}(0.2)^4 < \frac{(0.2)^4}{4!} \approx 0.0000667$$

9.8 Homework Quiz

1. State where the power series is centered. $\displaystyle\sum_{n=1}^{\infty} \frac{(x+3)^n}{n^2}$

2. Find the radius of convergence of the power series. $\displaystyle\sum_{n=0}^{\infty} \frac{(3x)^n}{n}$

3. Find the interval of convergence of the power series. $\displaystyle\sum_{n=1}^{\infty} \frac{(x)^n}{(2n)!}$

4. Match the graph of the first 5 terms of the sequence of partial sums of the series $g(x) = \displaystyle\sum_{n=0}^{\infty} \left(\frac{x}{2}\right)^n$.

   a. $g(1)$
   b. $g(-1)$
   c. $g(3)$

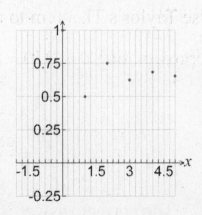

9.8 Homework Quiz Answers

1. State where the power series is centered. $\displaystyle\sum_{n=1}^{\infty}\frac{(x+3)^n}{n^2}$

   (Similar to Exercise #3.)

   $$x = -3$$

2. Find the radius of convergence of the power series. $\displaystyle\sum_{n=0}^{\infty}\frac{(3x)^n}{n}$

   (Similar to Exercise #13.)

   $$\lim_{n\to\infty}\left|\frac{u_{n+1}}{u_n}\right| = \lim_{n\to\infty}\left|\frac{(3x)^{n+1}/(n+1)}{(3x)^n/n}\right| = \lim_{n\to\infty}\left|\frac{(3x)n}{n+1}\right| = |3x|. \text{ The series}$$

   converges if $|x| < \dfrac{1}{3}$. So the radius of convergence is $R = \dfrac{1}{3}$.

3. Find the interval of convergence of the power series. $\displaystyle\sum_{n=1}^{\infty}\frac{(x)^n}{(2n)!}$

   (Similar to Exercise #16.)

   $$\lim_{n\to\infty}\left|\frac{u_{n+1}}{u_n}\right| = \lim_{n\to\infty}\left|\frac{x^{n+1}/(2n+2)!}{x^n/(2n)!}\right| = \lim_{n\to\infty}\left|\frac{x}{(2n+2)(2n+1)}\right| = 0. \text{ The series}$$

   converges for all x.

4. Match the graph of the first 5 terms of the sequence of partial sums of

   the series $g(x) = \displaystyle\sum_{n=0}^{\infty}\left(\frac{x}{2}\right)^n$. (Similar to Exercise #52.)

   a. $g(1)$
   b. $g(-1)$
   c. $g(3)$

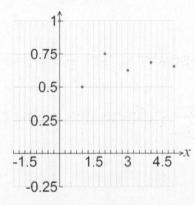

The correct answer is (b). It will yield an alternating series.

9.9 Homework Quiz

1. Find a geometric power series for the function $f(x) = \dfrac{6}{3+x}$ centered at 0.

2. Find a power series for the function $f(x) = \dfrac{2}{x+3}$ centered at $c = 1$ and determine the interval of convergence.

3. Use the power series $\dfrac{3}{2x-1} = -3\sum\limits_{n=0}^{\infty}(2x)^n$ centered at 0 for $\left(-\dfrac{1}{2}, \dfrac{1}{2}\right)$ to find $\dfrac{d}{dx}\left[\dfrac{3}{2x-1}\right]$ and determine the interval of convergence.

4. Use the power series $\dfrac{3}{2x-1} = -3\sum\limits_{n=0}^{\infty}(2x)^n$ centered at 0 for $\left(-\dfrac{1}{2}, \dfrac{1}{2}\right)$ to find $\displaystyle\int \dfrac{3}{2x-1}\,dx$ and determine the interval of convergence.

9.9 Homework Quiz Answers

1. Find a geometric power series for $f(x) = \dfrac{6}{3+x}$ centered at 0. (Similar to Exercise #11.)

$$\frac{6}{3+x} = \frac{2}{1+\dfrac{x}{3}} = \frac{2}{1-\left(-\dfrac{x}{3}\right)} = 2\sum_{n=0}^{\infty}\left(-\frac{x}{3}\right)^n$$

2. Find a power series for the function $f(x) = \dfrac{2}{x+3}$ centered at $c = 1$ and determine the interval of convergence. (Similar to Exercise #5.)

$$\frac{2}{x+3} = \frac{2}{3+1+(x-1)} = \frac{2}{4-(-(x-1))} = \frac{\dfrac{1}{2}}{1-\left(\dfrac{-1}{4}(x-1)\right)} = \sum_{n=0}^{\infty}\frac{1}{2}\left(\frac{-x+1}{4}\right)^n$$

on $\left(-\dfrac{1}{2}, \dfrac{1}{2}\right)$

3. Use the power series $\dfrac{3}{2x-1} = -3\sum_{n=0}^{\infty}(2x)^n$ centered at 0 for $\left(-\dfrac{1}{2}, \dfrac{1}{2}\right)$ to find $\dfrac{d}{dx}\left[\dfrac{3}{2x-1}\right]$ and determine the interval of convergence. (Similar to Exercise #19.)

$$\frac{d}{dx}\left[\frac{3}{2x-1}\right] = -3\sum_{n=1}^{\infty}n2^n x^{n-1} \text{ on } \left(-\frac{1}{2}, \frac{1}{2}\right).$$

4. Use the power series $\dfrac{3}{2x-1} = -3\sum_{n=0}^{\infty}(2x)^n$ centered at 0 for $\left(-\dfrac{1}{2}, \dfrac{1}{2}\right)$ to find $\displaystyle\int\frac{3}{2x-1}\,dx$ and determine the interval of convergence. (Similar to Exercise #21.)

$$\int\frac{3}{2x-1}\,dx = -3\sum_{n=0}^{\infty}\frac{2^n x^{n+1}}{n+1} \text{ on } \left[\frac{-1}{2}, \frac{1}{2}\right) \text{ since series converges at } x = -\frac{1}{2}.$$

9.10 Homework Quiz

1. Use the definition to find the Taylor series centered at $c = 1$ for the function $f(x) = \ln(2x)$.

2. Use the binomial series to find the Maclaurin series for the function $f(x) = \dfrac{1}{(1+x)^3}$.

3. Use the table of power series to find the Maclaurin series for the function $f(x) = \sin(2x)$.

4. Use the table of power series to find the Maclaurin series for the function $f(x) = e^{x^3}$.

9.10 Homework Quiz Answers

1. Use the definition to find the Taylor series centered at $c = 1$ for the function $f(x) = \ln(2x)$.   (Similar to Exercise #7.)

$$f(1) = \ln 2, \, f'(1) = 1, \, f''(1) = -1, \, f'''(1) = 2, \, f^{(4)}(1) = -6$$

$$\ln(2x) = \ln 2 + (x-1) - \frac{(x-1)^2}{2!} + \frac{2(x-1)^3}{3!} - \frac{6(x-1)^4}{4!} + \ldots$$

2. Use the binomial series to find the Maclaurin series for the function $f(x) = \dfrac{1}{(1+x)^3}$.   (Similar to Exercise # 18.)

$$\frac{1}{(1+x)^3} = 1 - 3x - \frac{3(-4)x^2}{2!} - \frac{3(-4)(-5)x^3}{3!} - \ldots$$

3. Use the table of power series to find the Maclaurin series for the function $f(x) = \sin(2x)$. (Similar to Exercise #31.)

$$\sin x = x - \frac{x^3}{3!} + \frac{x^5}{5!} - \frac{x^7}{7!} + \ldots + \frac{(-1)^n x^{2n+1}}{(2n+1)!} + \ldots$$

$$\sin 2x = 2x - \frac{(2x)^3}{3!} + \frac{(2x)^5}{5!} - \frac{(2x)^7}{7!} + \ldots + \frac{(-1)^n (2x)^{2n+1}}{(2n+1)!} + \ldots$$

4. Use the table of power series to find the Maclaurin series for the function $f(x) = e^{x^3}$. (Similar to Exercise #27.)

$$e^x = 1 + x + \frac{x^2}{2!} + \frac{x^3}{3!} + \frac{x^4}{4!} + \ldots + \frac{x^n}{n!} + \ldots$$

$$e^{x^3} = 1 + x + \frac{\left(x^3\right)^2}{2!} + \frac{\left(x^3\right)^3}{3!} + \frac{\left(x^3\right)^4}{4!} + \ldots + \frac{\left(x^3\right)^n}{n!} + \ldots$$

10.1 Homework Quiz

1. Match the equation with its graph.

    a. $\dfrac{x^2}{4} - \dfrac{y^2}{1} = 1$

    b. $\dfrac{(x-3)^2}{1} + \dfrac{(y+1)^2}{4} = 1$

    c. $\dfrac{(x+1)^2}{4} - \dfrac{(y-3)^2}{1} = 1$

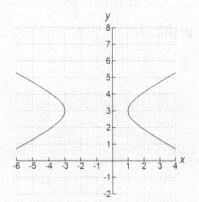

2. Find the coordinates of the center, vertices, and foci of the ellipse given by $4x^2 + 24x + 25y^2 - 150y + 161 = 0$.

3. Find the coordinates of the vertex and focus of the parabola given by $y^2 - 6y - 2x + 11 = 0$.

4. Find the arc length of the parabola $y = \dfrac{1}{2}x^2 - 1$ over the interval $0 \le x \le 4$.

10.1 Homework Quiz Answers

1. Match the equation with its graph. (Similar to Exercise #8.)

a. $\dfrac{x^2}{4} - \dfrac{y^2}{1} = 1$

b. $\dfrac{(x-3)^2}{1} + \dfrac{(y+1)^2}{4} = 1$

c. $\dfrac{(x+1)^2}{4} - \dfrac{(y-3)^2}{1} = 1$

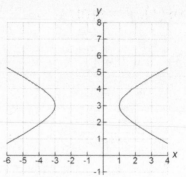

The correct answer is (c).

2. Find the coordinates of the center, vertices, and foci of the ellipse given by $4x^2 + 24x + 25y^2 - 150y + 161 = 0$.
(Similar to Exercise #33 .)

$$\dfrac{(x+3)^2}{25} + \dfrac{(y-3)^2}{4} = 1$$

Center: $(-3,3)$, Vertices:$(-8,3)$ $(2,3)$,

Foci: $(-3-\sqrt{21},3),(-3+\sqrt{21},3)$

3. Find the coordinates of the vertex and focus of the parabola given by $y^2 - 6y - 2x + 11 = 0$. (Similar to Exercise #14.)

$$2(x-1) = (y-3)^2,\ 4p = 2$$
Vertex: $(1,3)$
Focus: $(1.5,3)$

4. Find the arc length of the parabola $y = \dfrac{1}{2}x^2 - 1$ over the interval $0 \le x \le 4$. (Similar to Exercise #90.)

$$\dfrac{dy}{dx} = x$$

$$\text{Arc length} = \int_0^1 \sqrt{x^2 + 1}\ dx \approx 1.148.$$

10.2 Homework Quiz

1. Complete the table of
   values for the curve
   $x = 2\cos(t), y = \sin(t)$.

t	$-\dfrac{\pi}{2}$	$-\dfrac{\pi}{4}$	0	$\dfrac{\pi}{6}$	$\dfrac{\pi}{3}$	$\dfrac{\pi}{2}$
x						
y						

2. Match the parametric equation with the graph in rectangular form.

   a. $\begin{cases} x = 2t \\ y = 5t \end{cases}$

   b. $\begin{cases} x = 5\cos(t) - 3 \\ y = 2\sin(t) + 3 \end{cases}$

   c. $\begin{cases} x = 5(t-3) \\ y = 2\sin(t) + 3 \end{cases}$

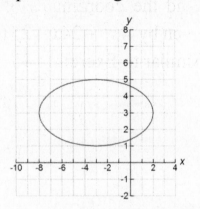

3. For $x = t^3 + 2, y = 3 - t$ eliminate the parameter t and write the corresponding rectangular equation.

4. Find a set of parametric equations for the circle with center $(3, 2)$ and radius 5.

10.2 Homework Quiz Answers

1. Complete the table of values for the curve $x = 2\cos(t), y = \sin(t)$. (Similar to Exercise #2.)

t	$-\dfrac{\pi}{2}$	$-\dfrac{\pi}{4}$	0	$\dfrac{\pi}{6}$	$\dfrac{\pi}{3}$	$\dfrac{\pi}{2}$
x	0	$\sqrt{2}$	2	$\sqrt{3}$	1	0
y	-1	$\dfrac{-\sqrt{2}}{2}$	0	$\dfrac{1}{2}$	$\dfrac{\sqrt{3}}{2}$	1

2. Match the parametric equation with the graph in rectangular form. (Similar to Exercise #19.)

a. $\begin{cases} x = 2t \\ y = 5t \end{cases}$

b. $\begin{cases} x = 5\cos(t) - 3 \\ y = 2\sin(t) + 3 \end{cases}$

c. $\begin{cases} x = 5(t - 3) \\ y = 2\sin(t) + 3 \end{cases}$

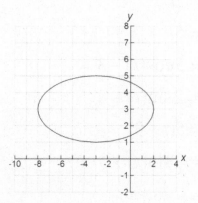

The correct answer is (b).

3. For $x = t^3 + 2, y = 3 - t$ eliminate the parameter t and write the corresponding rectangular equation. (Similar to Exercise #9.)

$$y = 3 - \sqrt[3]{x - 2}$$

4. Find a set of parametric equations for the circle with center $(3, 2)$ and radius 5. (Similar to Exercise #45.)

$$x = 5\cos(t) + 3$$
$$y = 5\sin(t) + 2$$

10.3 Homework Quiz

1. Given the curve given by $x = e^{-t}$ and $y = e^{2t}$, find dy/dx and d^2y/dx^2 at $t = 0$.

2. Find all points (if any) of vertical tangency for the curve represented by $x = t^2 + 2t - 3$ and $y = t^3 - 2t$.

3. For the curve given by $x = \dfrac{2}{3}t^{3/2}$ and $y = 2t - 1$, find the arc length of the curve on $[0,5]$.

4. Consider the curve given by $x = 2\cos t$ and $y = 2\sin t$ over the interval $0 \le t \le \dfrac{\pi}{2}$. Find the area of the surface generated if the curve is revolved about the y-axis.

10.3 Homework Quiz Answers

1. Consider the curve given by $x = e^{-t}$ and $y = e^{2t}$, find dy/dx and d^2y/dx^2 at $t=0$. (Similar to Exercise #7.)

$$\frac{dy}{dx} = \frac{2e^{2t}}{-e^{-t}} = -2e^{3t}, \left.\frac{dy}{dx}\right|_{t=0} = -2$$

$$\frac{d^2y}{dx^2} = \frac{-6e^{3t}}{-e^{-t}} = 6e^{4t}, \left.\frac{d^2y}{dx^2}\right|_{t=0} = 6$$

2. Find all points (if any) of vertical tangency for the curve represented by $x = t^2 + 2t - 3$ and $y = t^3 - 2t$. (Similar to Exercise #30.)

Vertical tangents will occur when $\frac{dx}{dt} = 0$. $\frac{dx}{dt} = 2t + 2$ which implies that at $t = -1$ there will be a vertical tangent at $(-4, 1)$.

3. For the curve given by $x = \frac{2}{3}t^{3/2}$ and $y = 2t - 1$, find the arc length of the curve on $[0, 5]$. (Similar to Exercise #55.)

$$s = \int_0^5 \sqrt{\left(t^{1/2}\right)^2 + (2)^2}\, dt = \int_0^5 \sqrt{t+4}\, dt = \left.\frac{2}{3}(t+4)^{3/2}\right|_0^5 = \frac{38}{3}$$

4. Consider the curve given by $x = 2\cos t$ and $y = 2\sin t$ over the interval $0 \le t \le \frac{\pi}{2}$. Find the area of the surface generated if the curve is revolved about the y-axis. (Similar to Exercise #69.)

$$S = 2\pi \int_0^{\pi/2} (2\sin t)\sqrt{4\sin^2 t + 4\cos^2 t}\, dt = \left.-8\pi \cos t\right|_0^{\pi/2} = 8\pi$$

10.4 Homework Quiz

1. Match the polar equation with its graph.

    a. $r = 3\sin\theta$

    b. $r = 3\sec\theta$

    c. $r = 3(1 + \sin\theta)$

    d. $r = 3\sin 3\theta$

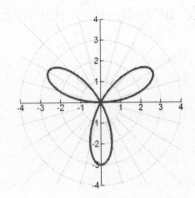

2. Find the corresponding rectangular coordinates for the point $\left(-2, \dfrac{\pi}{3}\right)$.

3. Convert the rectangular equation $x^2 + y^2 - 6x = 0$ to the polar form.

4. For the polar equation $r = 1 - \cos\theta$, find dy/dx at the point $\left(1, \dfrac{\pi}{2}\right)$.

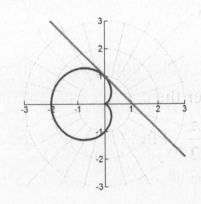

10.4 Homework Quiz Answers

1. Match the polar equation with its graph. (Similar to Exercise #24.)

   a. $r = 3\sin\theta$

   b. $r = 3\sec\theta$

   c. $r = 3(1+\sin\theta)$

   d. $r = 3\sin 3\theta$

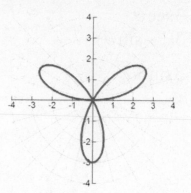

The correct solution is (d).

2. Find the corresponding rectangular coordinates for the point $\left(-2, \dfrac{\pi}{3}\right)$.

   (Similar to Exercise #3.)

$$\left(-1, -\sqrt{3}\right)$$

3. Convert the rectangular equation $x^2 + y^2 - 6x = 0$ to the polar form.
   (Similar to Exercise #28.)

$$r^2\cos^2\theta + r^2\sin^2\theta - 6r\cos\theta = 0$$

$$r^2 - 6r\cos\theta = 0 \Rightarrow r(r - 6\cos\theta) = 0$$

$$r = 6\cos\theta$$

4. For the polar equation $r = 1 - \cos\theta$,

   find dy/dx at the point $\left(1, \dfrac{\pi}{2}\right)$.

   (Similar to Exercise #60.)

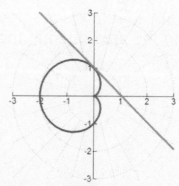

$$\frac{dy}{dx} = \frac{(1-\cos\theta)\cos\theta + \sin\theta\sin\theta}{-(1-\cos\theta)\sin\theta + \sin\theta\cos\theta} \Rightarrow \left.\frac{dy}{dx}\right|_{\frac{\pi}{2}} = -1$$

10.5 Homework Quiz

1. Find the area of the region for one petal of $r = 4\sin 2\theta$.

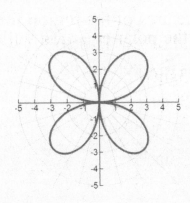

2. Find the perimeter of the cardiod $r = 1 + \cos\theta$.

3. Find the points of intersection of the graphs $r = 1 - \cos\theta$ and $r = \cos\theta$ in the interval $0 \le \theta \le 2\pi$.

4. Find the area outside the cardiod $r = 1 - \sin\theta$ and inside the circle $r = 1$.

10.5 Homework Quiz Answers

1. Find the area of the region for one petal of $r = 4\sin 2\theta$.
(Similar to Exercise #8.)

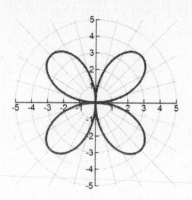

$$r = 0 \text{ when } \theta = 0, \frac{\pi}{2}, \pi, \frac{3\pi}{2}, 2\pi.$$

$$\text{Area} = \frac{1}{2}\int_0^{\pi/2} (4\sin 2\theta)^2 d\theta = 2\pi$$

2. Find the perimeter of the cardiod $r = 1 + \cos\theta$.
(Similar to Exercise #59.)

$$f(\theta) = 1 + \cos\theta, \quad f'(\theta) = -\sin\theta$$

$$2\int_0^{\pi} \sqrt{(1+\cos\theta)^2 + (-\sin\theta)^2}\, d\theta = 2\int_0^{\pi} \sqrt{2}\sqrt{1+\cos\theta}\, d\theta =$$

$$2\int_0^{\pi} \sqrt{2}\sqrt{\left(2\cos^2\frac{\theta}{2}\right)}\, d\theta = 8$$

3. Find the points of intersection of the graphs $r = 1 - \cos\theta$ and $r = \cos\theta$ in the interval $0 \le \theta \le 2\pi$. (Similar to Exercise #30.)

$$\frac{\pi}{3}, \frac{5\pi}{3}$$

4. Find the area outside the cardiod $r = 1 - \sin\theta$ and inside the circle $r = 1$. (Similar to Exercise #47.)

$$A_{region} = A_{1/2circle} - \frac{1}{2}\int_0^{\pi} (1 - \sin\theta)^2 d\theta$$

$$= \pi - \left(-2 - \frac{3\pi}{4}\right) = 2 + \frac{\pi}{4}$$

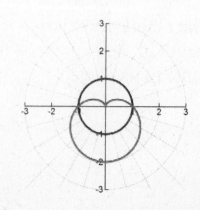

10.6 Homework Quiz

1. Match the polar equation with its graph.

    a. $r = \dfrac{1}{1 + 0.25\cos\theta}$

    b. $r = \dfrac{1}{1 + \cos\theta}$

    c. $r = \dfrac{1}{1 + 1.25\cos\theta}$

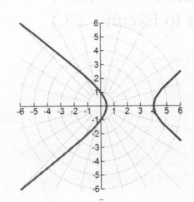

2. Find the eccentricity and distance from the pole to the directrix of the conic $r = \dfrac{4}{2 + \cos\theta}$. Identify the conic.

3. Find a polar equation for a parabola with its focus at the pole and its directrix $x = 3$.

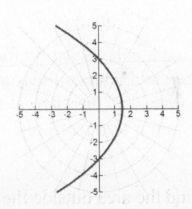

4. The elliptical orbit of a moon around its planet is $e = 0.1$. If the length of the major axis is 400,000 miles, how close does the moon come to its planet?

10.6 Homework Quiz Answers

1. Match the polar equation with its graph. (Similar to Exercise #12.)

a. $r = \dfrac{1}{1 + .25\cos\theta}$

b. $r = \dfrac{1}{1 + \cos\theta}$

c. $r = \dfrac{1}{1 + 1.25\cos\theta}$

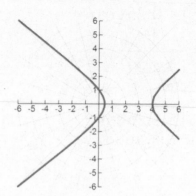

The correct solution is (c).

2. Find the eccentricity and distance from the pole to the directrix of the conic $r = \dfrac{4}{2 + \cos\theta}$. Identify the conic. (Similar to Exercise #15.)

$$r = \frac{4}{2 + \cos\theta} = \frac{(0.5)(4)}{1 + 0.5\cos\theta}$$
$$e = 0.5,\ d = 4,\ \text{ellipse}$$

3. Find a polar equation for a parabola with its focus at the pole and its directrix $x = 3$. (Similar to Exercise #33.)

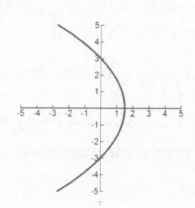

$$r = \frac{3}{1 + \cos\theta}$$

4. The elliptical orbit of a moon around its planet is $e = 0.1$. If the length of the major axis is 400,000 miles, how close does the moon come to its planet? (Similar to Exercise #59.)

$$c = ea = 0.1(200{,}000) = 20{,}000$$

Closest point is $a - c = 200{,}000 - 20{,}000 = 180{,}000$ miles.

11.1 Homework Quiz

1. Find the vectors **u** and **v** whose initial and terminal points are
   $\mathbf{u}:(4,2),(6,-3);\mathbf{v}:(0,1),(2,-4)$. Show that **u** and **v** are equivalent.

2. Find the magnitude of **v** if $\mathbf{v}=-2\mathbf{i}-\mathbf{j}$.

3. Find the component form of **v** given its magnitude is $\|\mathbf{v}\|=4\sqrt{3}$ and
   the angle it makes with the positive x-axis is $\theta=30°$.

4. If $\mathbf{v}=\langle 2,2\rangle$, find a and b such that
   $\mathbf{v}=a\mathbf{u}+b\mathbf{w}$ where $\mathbf{u}=\langle -3,1\rangle$ and $\mathbf{w}=\langle 2,0\rangle$.

11.1 Homework Quiz Solutions

1. Find the vectors **u** and **v** whose initial and terminal points are $\mathbf{u}:(4,2),(6,-3); \mathbf{v}:(0,1),(2,-4)$. Show that **u** and **v** are equivalent. (Similar to Exercise #6.)

$$\mathbf{u} = \langle 6-4, -3-2 \rangle = \langle 2, -5 \rangle$$
$$\mathbf{v} = \langle 2-0, -4-1 \rangle = \langle 2, -5 \rangle$$
$$\mathbf{u} = \mathbf{v}$$

2. Find the magnitude of **v** if $\mathbf{v} = -2\mathbf{i} - \mathbf{j}$. (Similar to Exercise #31.)

$$\|\mathbf{v}\| = \sqrt{(-2)^2 + (-1)^2}$$
$$= \sqrt{4+1}$$
$$= \sqrt{5}$$

3. Find the component form of **v** given its magnitude is $\|\mathbf{v}\| = 4\sqrt{3}$ and the angle it makes with the positive x-axis is $\theta = 30°$. (Similar to Exercise #54.)

$$\mathbf{v} = 4\sqrt{3}\left[(\cos 30°)\mathbf{i} + (\sin 30°)\mathbf{j} \right]$$
$$= 6\mathbf{i} + 2\sqrt{3}\mathbf{j}$$
$$= \langle 6, 2\sqrt{3} \rangle$$

4. If $\mathbf{v} = \langle 2,2 \rangle$, find a and b such that
$\mathbf{v} = a\mathbf{u} + b\mathbf{w}$ where $\mathbf{u} = \langle -3,1 \rangle$ and $\mathbf{w} = \langle 2,0 \rangle$.
(Similar to Exercise # 64.)

$$\mathbf{v} = 2\mathbf{i} + 2\mathbf{j} \Rightarrow -3a + 2b = 2$$
$$\text{and} \quad a = 2 \Rightarrow b = 4$$

11.2 Homework Quiz

1. Find the distance between the points $(3,-1,0)$ and $(-2,4,-2)$.

2. Find the component form and magnitude of the vector **u** with the given initial point $(2,-3,5)$ and terminal point $(-1,1,3)$. Then find a unit vector in the direction of **u**.

3. Use vectors to determine whether the points $P(-1,0,5)$, $Q(3,2,-1)$ and $R(1,1,2)$ are collinear.

4. Find the vector **v** with magnitude 5 and direction $\mathbf{u}=\langle -3,2,6 \rangle$.

11.2 Homework Quiz Solutions

1. Find the distance between the points $(3,-1,0)$ and $(-2,4,-2)$.
   (Similar to Exercise #28.)

$$d = \sqrt{(-2-3)^2 + (4-(-1))^2 + (-2-0)^2}$$
$$= \sqrt{25+25+4}$$
$$= \sqrt{54}$$
$$= 3\sqrt{6}$$

2. Find the component form and magnitude of the vector **u** with the given initial point $(2,-3,5)$ and terminal point $(-1,1,3)$. Then find a unit vector in the direction of **u**. (Similar to Exercise #54.)

$$\mathbf{u} = \langle -1-2, 1-(-3), 3-5 \rangle = \langle -3, 4, -2 \rangle$$
$$\|\langle -3,4,-2 \rangle\| = \sqrt{(-3)^2 + 4^2 + (-2)^2} = \sqrt{29}$$

$$\text{Unit vector: } \frac{\mathbf{u}}{\|\mathbf{u}\|} = \left\langle \frac{-3}{\sqrt{29}}, \frac{4}{\sqrt{29}}, \frac{-2}{\sqrt{29}} \right\rangle$$

3. Use vectors to determine whether the points $P(-1,0,5)$, $Q(3,2,-1)$ and $R(1,1,2)$ are collinear. (Similar to Exercise #74.)

$$\overline{PQ} = \langle 4,2,-6 \rangle$$
$$\overline{PR} = \langle 2,1,-3 \rangle$$
$$\langle 4,2,-6 \rangle = 2\langle 2,1,-3 \rangle \Rightarrow \overline{PQ} = \overline{PR} \Rightarrow P, Q \text{ and } R \text{ are collinear.}$$

4. Find the vector **v** with magnitude 5 and direction $\mathbf{u} = \langle -3,2,6 \rangle$.
   (Similar to Exercise #94.)

$$\|\mathbf{u}\| = \sqrt{(-3)^2 + (2)^2 + (6)^2} = \sqrt{49} = 7$$
$$\mathbf{v} = 5\frac{\mathbf{u}}{\|\mathbf{u}\|} = 5\left\langle \frac{-3}{7}, \frac{2}{7}, \frac{6}{7} \right\rangle = \left\langle \frac{-15}{7}, \frac{10}{7}, \frac{30}{7} \right\rangle$$

11.3 Homework Quiz

1. Find the angle between the vectors: $\mathbf{u} = \langle 2, 3, -2 \rangle, \mathbf{v} = \langle 4, -1, 2 \rangle$.

2. Determine whether $\mathbf{u} = \langle 2, 0, -6 \rangle$ and $\mathbf{v} = \langle 3, 2, 1 \rangle$ are orthogonal parallel, or neither.

3. Find the projection of $\mathbf{u}$ onto $\mathbf{v}$, and the vector component of $\mathbf{u}$ orthogonal to $\mathbf{v}$, where $\mathbf{u} = \mathbf{i} + 2\mathbf{j} - \mathbf{k}, \mathbf{v} = -3\mathbf{i} + \mathbf{k}$.

4. A suitcase is pulled horizontally by exerting a continual force of 30lb on the handle at an angle of 60° with the horizontal. How much work is done in moving the suitcase 25 ft?

11.3 Homework Quiz Solutions

1. Find the angle between the vectors: $\mathbf{u} = \langle 2, 3, -2 \rangle, \mathbf{v} = \langle 4, -1, 2 \rangle$.
   (Similar to Exercise #16.)

$$\cos\theta = \frac{\mathbf{u} \cdot \mathbf{v}}{\|\mathbf{u}\|\|\mathbf{v}\|} = \frac{(2)(4) + (3)(-1) + (-2)(2)}{\sqrt{17}\sqrt{21}} = \frac{1}{\sqrt{357}}$$

$$\Rightarrow \theta = \arccos\frac{1}{\sqrt{357}} \approx 86.97°$$

2. Determine whether $\mathbf{u} = \langle 2, 0, -6 \rangle$ and $\mathbf{v} = \langle 3, 2, 1 \rangle$ are orthogonal parallel, or neither. (Similar to Exercise #25.)

$$\mathbf{u} \neq c\mathbf{v} \Rightarrow \text{not parallel}$$

$$\mathbf{u} \cdot \mathbf{v} = (2)(3) + 0 + (-6)(1) = 0 \Rightarrow \text{orthogonal}$$

3. Find the projection of $\mathbf{u}$ onto $\mathbf{v}$, and the vector component of $\mathbf{u}$ orthogonal to $\mathbf{v}$, where $\mathbf{u} = \mathbf{i} + 2\mathbf{j} - \mathbf{k}, \mathbf{v} = -3\mathbf{i} + \mathbf{k}$.
   (Similar to Exercise #49.)
   Projection of $\mathbf{u}$ onto $\mathbf{v}$:

$$\mathbf{w}_1 = proj_{\mathbf{v}}\mathbf{u} = \left(\frac{\mathbf{u} \cdot \mathbf{v}}{\|\mathbf{v}\|^2}\right)\mathbf{v} = \left(\frac{-4}{10}\right)(-3\mathbf{i} + \mathbf{k}) = \frac{6}{5}\mathbf{i} - \frac{2}{5}\mathbf{k}$$

   Vector component of $\mathbf{u}$ orthog. to $\mathbf{v}$:

$$\mathbf{w}_2 = \mathbf{u} - \mathbf{w}_1 = (\mathbf{i} + 2\mathbf{j} - \mathbf{k}) - \left(\frac{6}{5}\mathbf{i} - \frac{2}{5}\mathbf{k}\right) = -\frac{1}{5}\mathbf{i} + 2\mathbf{j} - \frac{3}{5}\mathbf{k}$$

4. A suitcase is pulled horizontally by exerting a continual force of 30lb on the handle at an angle of 60° with the horizontal. How much work is done in moving the suitcase 25 ft? (Similar to Exercise #74.)

$$\mathbf{F} = 30(\cos 60°\, \mathbf{i} + \sin 60°\, \mathbf{j}) = 15\mathbf{i} + 15\sqrt{3}\mathbf{j}$$

$$\mathbf{v} = 25\mathbf{i}$$

$$W = \mathbf{F} \cdot \mathbf{v} = (15\mathbf{i} + 15\sqrt{3}\mathbf{j}) \cdot (25\mathbf{i}) = 375\, ft \cdot lb$$

11.4 Homework Quiz

1. Find the cross products $\mathbf{u} \times \mathbf{v}$ and $\mathbf{v} \times \mathbf{u}$ of $\mathbf{u} = \langle 1, 2, -3 \rangle, \mathbf{v} = \langle -4, 1, 2 \rangle$.

2. Find $\mathbf{u} \times \mathbf{v}$ and show that it is orthogonal to both $\mathbf{u}$ and $\mathbf{v}$
   $\mathbf{u} = \mathbf{i} - 5\mathbf{j} + 6\mathbf{k}, \mathbf{v} = 2\mathbf{i} + \mathbf{j} + 2\mathbf{k}$.

3. Find the area of the triangle with the vertices
   $A(1, 0, 1), B(0, 2, 3), C(2, 1, 0)$.

4. Use the triple scalar product to find the volume of the parallelepiped
   having adjacent edges $\mathbf{u} = \langle 3, 2, 1 \rangle, \mathbf{v} = \langle 1, 1, 2 \rangle, \mathbf{w} = \langle 1, 3, 3 \rangle$.

11.4 Homework Quiz Solutions

1. Find the cross products $\mathbf{u} \times \mathbf{v}$ and $\mathbf{v} \times \mathbf{u}$ of
   $\mathbf{u} = \langle 1, 2, -3 \rangle, \mathbf{v} = \langle -4, 1, 2 \rangle$. (Similar to Exercise #9.)

$$\mathbf{u} \times \mathbf{v} = \begin{vmatrix} \mathbf{i} & \mathbf{j} & \mathbf{k} \\ 1 & 2 & -3 \\ -4 & 1 & 2 \end{vmatrix}$$

$$\mathbf{v} \times \mathbf{u} = -(\mathbf{u} \times \mathbf{v})$$
$$= \langle -7, -10, -9 \rangle$$

$$= \langle 7, 10, 9 \rangle$$

2. Find $\mathbf{u} \times \mathbf{v}$ and show that it is orthogonal to both $\mathbf{u}$ and $\mathbf{v}$
   $\mathbf{u} = \mathbf{i} - 5\mathbf{j} + 6\mathbf{k}, \mathbf{v} = 2\mathbf{i} + \mathbf{j} + 2\mathbf{k}$ (Similar to Exercise #15.)

$$\mathbf{u} \times \mathbf{v} = \begin{vmatrix} \mathbf{i} & \mathbf{j} & \mathbf{k} \\ 1 & -5 & 6 \\ 2 & 1 & 2 \end{vmatrix}$$

$$\mathbf{u} \cdot (\mathbf{u} \times \mathbf{v}) = 1(-16) - 5(10) + 6(11)$$
$$= 0 \Rightarrow \mathbf{u} \perp \mathbf{u} \times \mathbf{v}$$

$$= \langle -16, 10, 11 \rangle$$

$$\mathbf{v} \cdot (\mathbf{u} \times \mathbf{v}) = 2(-16) + 1(10) + 2(11)$$
$$= 0 \Rightarrow \mathbf{v} \perp \mathbf{u} \times \mathbf{v}$$

3. Find the area of the triangle with the vertices
   $A(1,0,1), B(0,2,3), C(2,1,0)$. (Similar to Exercise #36.)

$$\overline{AB} = \langle -1, 2, 2 \rangle, \overline{AC} = \langle 1, 1, -1 \rangle \qquad \overline{AB} \times \overline{AC} = \langle -4, 1, -3 \rangle$$

$$\overline{AB} \times \overline{AC} = \begin{vmatrix} \mathbf{i} & \mathbf{j} & \mathbf{k} \\ -1 & 2 & 2 \\ 1 & 1 & -1 \end{vmatrix} \qquad A = \frac{1}{2} \| \overline{AB} \times \overline{AC} \| = \frac{\sqrt{26}}{2}$$

4. Use the triple scalar product to find the volume of the
   parallelepiped having adjacent edges
   $\mathbf{u} = \langle 3, 2, 1 \rangle, \mathbf{v} = \langle 1, 1, 2 \rangle, \mathbf{w} = \langle 1, 3, 3 \rangle$. (Similar to Exercise #46.)

$$\mathbf{u} \cdot (\mathbf{v} \times \mathbf{w}) = \begin{vmatrix} 3 & 2 & 1 \\ 1 & 1 & 2 \\ 1 & 3 & 3 \end{vmatrix} = -9$$

$$V = |\mathbf{u} \cdot (\mathbf{v} \times \mathbf{w})| = |-9| = 9$$

11.5 Homework Quiz

1. Find a set of parametric equations of the line that passes through the point $(-1,0,2)$ and is parallel to the vector $\langle 1,5,-4 \rangle$.

2. Determine whether the lines intersect, and if so, find the point of intersection.
$$x = 2+t, y = 2+3t, z = 3+t$$
$$x = 2+s, y = 3+4s, z = 4+2t$$

3. Find an equation of the plane that passes through the points $(-1,2,5)$ and $(3,0,6)$ and perpendicular to the plane $-x+2y+3z=8$.

4. Find the distance between the planes $2x-3y+4z-8=0$ and $4x-6y+8z+3=0$.

11.5 Homework Quiz Solutions

1. Find a set of parametric equations of the line that passes through the point $(-1, 0, 2)$ and is parallel to the vector $\langle 1, 5, -4 \rangle$.

   (Similar to Exercise #19.)

   Direction vector : $\langle 1, 5, -4 \rangle$

   Direction numbers : $a = 1, b = 5, c = -4$

   $\Rightarrow$ Parametric Equations : $x = -1 + t, y = 5t, z = 2 - 4t$

2. Determine whether the lines intersect, and if so, find the point of intersection.
   $$x = 2 + t, y = 2 + 3t, z = 3 + t$$
   $$x = 2 + s, y = 3 + 4s, z = 4 + 2t$$

   (Similar to Exercise #32.)

   At intersection point, $2 + t = 2 + s, 2 + 3t = 3 + 4s \Rightarrow s = t = -1$

   Since the third equation is also satisfied, the two lines intersect.

   $t = -1 \Rightarrow P(1, -1, 2)$ is point of intersection.

3. Find an equation of the plane that passes through the points $(-1, 2, 5)$ and $(3, 0, 6)$ and perpendicular to the plane $-x + 2y + 3z = 8$. (Similar to Exercise #55.)

   $\mathbf{v}$ is the vector from $(-1, 2, 5)$ to $(3, 0, 6)$: $\mathbf{v} = 4\mathbf{i} - 2\mathbf{j} + \mathbf{k}$

   $\mathbf{n}$ be a vector normal to the plane $-x + 2y + 3z = 8$:

   $\mathbf{n} = -\mathbf{i} + 2\mathbf{j} + 3\mathbf{k} \Rightarrow \mathbf{v} \times \mathbf{n} = -8\mathbf{i} - 13\mathbf{j} + 6\mathbf{k}$

   $-8(x - 3) - 13(y - 0) + 6(z - 6) = 0$

   $$-8x - 13y + 6z = 12$$

4. Find the distance between the planes $2x - 3y + 4z - 8 = 0$ and $4x - 6y + 8z + 3 = 0$. (Similar to Exercise #102.)

   $P = (4, 0, 0)$ is a point in $2x - 3y + 4z - 8 = 0$

   Then from the second plane, $a = 4, b = -6, c = 8, d = 3$.

   $$D = \frac{|4(4) + (-6)(0) + (8)(0) + 3|}{\sqrt{4^2 + (-6)^2 + 8^2}} = \frac{19}{\sqrt{116}} \approx 1.76$$

11.6 Homework Quiz

1. Describe the surface of $4x^2 + 9y^2 = 36$.

2. Identify the quadric surface $z = 4 - x^2 - y^2 - 2y$.

3. Find an equation for the surface of revolution generated by revolving the curve $yz = 3$ in the yz-plane about the y-axis.

4. Find an equation of the surface that represents the set of all points equidistant from the point $(0,0,1)$ and the plane $z = -1$.

11.6 Homework Quiz Solutions

1. Describe the surface of $4x^2 + 9y^2 = 36$.
   (Similar to Exercise #13.)

   $$\frac{x^2}{9} + \frac{y^2}{4} = 1, \ z - \text{coordinate is missing}$$

   $\Rightarrow$ an elliptical cylinder with axis in the z-plane.

2. Identify the quadric surface $z = 4 - x^2 - y^2 - 2y$.
   (Similar to Exercise #28.)

   $$x^2 + y^2 + 2y + z = 4$$

   $$z - 5 = -\left[x^2 + (y+1)^2\right]$$

   $\Rightarrow$ downward circular paraboloid, vertex $(0, -1, 5)$

3. Find an equation for the surface of revolution generated by revolving the curve $yz = 3$ in the yz-plane about the y-axis.
   (Similar to Exercise #51.)

   $$x^2 + z^2 = \left[r(y)\right]^2 \text{ and } z = r(y) = \frac{3}{y}$$

   $$\Rightarrow x^2 + z^2 = \left(\frac{3}{y}\right)^2 \Rightarrow x^2 + z^2 = \frac{9}{y^2}$$

4. Find an equation of the surface that represents the set of all points equidistant from the point $(0,0,1)$ and the plane $z = -1$.
   (Similar to Exercise #64.)

   If (x, y, z) is on the surface, then

   $$(z+1)^2 = x^2 + y^2 + (z-1)^2$$

   $$z^2 + 2z + 1 = x^2 + y^2 + z^2 - 2z + 1$$

   $$x^2 + y^2 = 4z \Rightarrow \text{Elliptic paraboloid,}$$

   Traces parallel to xy-plane are circles.

11.7 Homework Quiz

1. Convert the point $\left(4, -4\sqrt{3}, 6\right)$ from rectangular coordinates to cylindrical coordinates.

2. Find an equation in rectangular coordinates for the cylindrical equation $r = 4\sin\theta$.

3. Find an equation in spherical coordinates for the equation $x^2 = 16 - z^2$.

4. Convert the point $\left(4, \dfrac{5\pi}{6}, 4\right)$ from cylindrical coordinates to spherical coordinates.

11.7 Homework Quiz Solutions

1. Convert the point $\left(4, -4\sqrt{3}, 6\right)$ from rectangular coordinates to cylindrical coordinates. (Similar to Exercise #8.)

$$r = \sqrt{\left(4\right)^2 + \left(-4\sqrt{3}\right)^2} = 8$$

$$\theta = \arctan\frac{-4\sqrt{3}}{4} = -\frac{\pi}{3}, z = 6 \Rightarrow \left(8, -\frac{\pi}{3}, 6\right)$$

2. Find an equation in rectangular coordinates for the cylindrical equation $r = 4\sin\theta$. (Similar to Exercise #27.)

$$r^2 = 4r\sin\theta$$
$$x^2 + y^2 = 4y$$
$$x^2 + y^2 - 4y = 0$$
$$x^2 + \left(y - 2\right)^2 = 4$$

3. Find an equation in spherical coordinates for the equation $x^2 = 16 - z^2$. (Similar to Exercise #44.)

$$x^2 + y^2 + z^2 = 16 + y^2$$
$$\rho^2 = 16 + \rho^2 \sin^2\phi\sin^2\theta$$
$$\rho^2\left(1 - \sin^2\phi\sin^2\theta\right) = 16 \quad \text{(Answers may vary.)}$$

4. Convert the point $\left(4, \frac{5\pi}{6}, 4\right)$ from cylindrical coordinates to spherical coordinates. (Similar to Exercise #63.)

$$\rho = \sqrt{4^2 + 4^2} = 4\sqrt{2}$$

$$\phi = \arccos\frac{4}{4\sqrt{2}} = \frac{\pi}{4}$$

$$\theta = \frac{5\pi}{6}$$

$$\text{spherical} \Rightarrow \left(4\sqrt{2}, \frac{5\pi}{6}, \frac{\pi}{4}\right)$$

12.1 Homework Quiz

1. Find the domain of the vector-valued function.

$$\mathbf{r}(t) = t^2\mathbf{i} + \left(\frac{1}{t^2 - 1}\right)\mathbf{j} + (t - 3)\mathbf{k}$$

2. Evaluate the vector-valued function $\mathbf{r}(t) = \cos t\mathbf{i} + \sin t\mathbf{j} + \tan t\mathbf{k}$ at $t = \dfrac{\pi}{3}$.

3. Match the vector-valued function to the plane curve that it represents.

   a. $\mathbf{r}(t) = (2 + t)\mathbf{i} + (-t - 3)\mathbf{j}$
   b. $\mathbf{r}(t) = t\mathbf{i} + (-t - 3)\mathbf{j}$
   c. $\mathbf{r}(t) = (2 + t)\mathbf{i} + (-t - 1)\mathbf{j}$

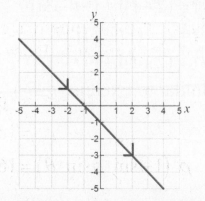

4. Represent the plane curve $x^2 + y^2 = 16$ by a vector-valued function. (There are many correct answers.)

12.1 Homework Quiz Answers

1. Find the domain of the vector-valued function.

$$\mathbf{r}(t) = t^2\mathbf{i} + \left(\frac{1}{t^2 - 1}\right)\mathbf{j} + (t - 3)\mathbf{k} \quad \text{(Similar to Exercise #1.)}$$

$$(-\infty, -1), (-1, 1), (1, \infty)$$

2. Evaluate the vector-valued function $\mathbf{r}(t) = \cos t\,\mathbf{i} + \sin t\,\mathbf{j} + \tan t\,\mathbf{k}$ at $t = \dfrac{\pi}{3}$. (Similar to Exercise #10.)

$$\mathbf{r}\left(\frac{\pi}{3}\right) = \frac{1}{2}\mathbf{i} + \frac{\sqrt{3}}{2}\mathbf{j} + \sqrt{3}\mathbf{k}$$

3. Match the vector-valued function to the plane curve that it represents.

   a. $\mathbf{r}(t) = (2 + t)\mathbf{i} + (-t - 3)\mathbf{j}$
   b. $\mathbf{r}(t) = t\mathbf{i} + (-t - 3)\mathbf{j}$
   c. $\mathbf{r}(t) = (2 + t)\mathbf{i} + (-t - 1)\mathbf{j}$
   (Similar to Exercise #27.)

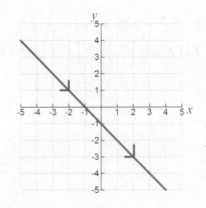

The correct solution is (a).

4. Represent the plane curve $x^2 + y^2 = 16$ by a vector-valued function. (There are many correct answers.)

$$\mathbf{r}(t) = 4\cos(t)\mathbf{i} + 4\sin(t)\mathbf{j}$$

12.2 Homework Quiz

1. Find $\dfrac{d}{dt}\left[\mathbf{r}_1 \cdot \mathbf{r}_2\right]$ if $\mathbf{r}_1(t) = \cos t\,\mathbf{i} + e^{-t}\,\mathbf{j} + t^3\,\mathbf{k}$ and $\mathbf{r}_2(t) = t^2\,\mathbf{k}$.

2. Evaluate the definite integral. $\displaystyle\int_0^1 \left(t^2\,\mathbf{i} + e^{-t}\,\mathbf{j} + 3t\,\mathbf{k}\right)dt$

3. Given $\mathbf{r}(t) = \left(3t^2\right)\mathbf{i} + \left(e^{2t}\right)\mathbf{j} + \left(\ln t\right)\mathbf{k}$, find $\mathbf{r}''\left(\dfrac{1}{3}\right)$.

4. Given $\mathbf{r}'(t) = \left(\sqrt{t}\right)\mathbf{i} + \left(2e^{2t}\right)\mathbf{j}$ and $\mathbf{r}(0) = -2\mathbf{i} + \mathbf{j}$, find $\mathbf{r}(t)$.

12.2 Homework Quiz Answers

1. Find $\dfrac{d}{dt}[\mathbf{r}_1 \cdot \mathbf{r}_2]$ if $\mathbf{r}_1(t) = \cos t\mathbf{i} + e^{-t}\mathbf{j} + t^3\mathbf{k}$ and $\mathbf{r}_2(t) = t^2\mathbf{k}$.

   (Similar to Exercise #43.)

$$\frac{d}{dt}[\mathbf{r}_1 \cdot \mathbf{r}_2] = \frac{d}{dt}\left[\left(\cos t\mathbf{i} + e^{-t}\mathbf{j} + t^3\mathbf{k}\right) \cdot \left(t^2\mathbf{k}\right)\right] = \frac{d}{dt}\left[t^5\right] = 5t^4$$

2. Evaluate the definite integral. $\displaystyle\int_0^1\left(t^2\mathbf{i} + e^{-t}\mathbf{j} + 3t\mathbf{k}\right)dt$

   (Similar to Exercise #61.)

$$\int_0^1\left(t^2\mathbf{i} + e^{-t}\mathbf{j} + 3t\mathbf{k}\right)dt = \frac{t^3}{3}\mathbf{i} - e^{-t}\mathbf{j} + \frac{3t^2}{2}\mathbf{k}\Big|_0^1 = \frac{1}{3}\mathbf{i} + \left(1 - \frac{1}{e}\right)\mathbf{j} + \frac{3}{2}\mathbf{k}$$

3. Given $\mathbf{r}(t) = \left(3t^2\right)\mathbf{i} + \left(e^{2t}\right)\mathbf{j} + \left(\ln t\right)\mathbf{k}$, find $\mathbf{r}''\left(\dfrac{1}{3}\right)$.

   (Similar to Exercise #43.)

$$\mathbf{r}'(t) = (6t)\mathbf{i} + \left(2e^{2t}\right)\mathbf{j} + \left(\frac{1}{t}\right)\mathbf{k}, \ \mathbf{r}''(t) = 6\mathbf{i} + \left(4e^{2t}\right)\mathbf{j} + \left(\frac{-1}{t^2}\right)\mathbf{k}$$

$$\mathbf{r}''\left(\frac{1}{3}\right) = 6\mathbf{i} + \left(4e^{2/3}\right)\mathbf{j} - 9\mathbf{k}$$

4. Given $\mathbf{r}'(t) = \left(\sqrt{t}\right)\mathbf{i} + \left(2e^{2t}\right)\mathbf{j}$ and $\mathbf{r}(0) = -2\mathbf{i} + \mathbf{j}$, find $\mathbf{r}(t)$.

   (Similar to Exercise #68.)

$$\int\mathbf{r}'(t)dt = \left(\int\sqrt{t}\,dt\right)\mathbf{i} + \left(\int 2e^{2t}\,dt\right)\mathbf{j} = \left(\frac{2t^{3/2}}{3} + C_1\right)\mathbf{i} + \left(e^{2t} + C_2\right)\mathbf{j}$$

$$\frac{2(0)^{3/2}}{3} + C_1 = -2, C_1 = -2 \text{ and } e^{2(0)} + C_2 = 1, C_2 = 0$$

$$\mathbf{r}(t) = \left(\frac{2t^{3/2}}{3} - 2\right)\mathbf{i} + \left(e^{2t}\right)\mathbf{j}$$

12.3 Homework Quiz

1. Sketch a graph of the path of the position vector $\mathbf{r}(t) = t\mathbf{i} + (t^2 - 4)\mathbf{j}$ in the xy-plane. Also, sketch the velocity and acceleration vectors at the point $(2,0)$.

2. Given the position function $\mathbf{r}(t) = 3t^2\mathbf{i} + (4 - t^2)\mathbf{j} + t\mathbf{k}$ that describes the path of an object moving in space, find the velocity, speed, and acceleration.

3. Use the acceleration function $\mathbf{a}(t) = 3\mathbf{i} - \mathbf{j} + \mathbf{k}$ to find the velocity and position function given $\mathbf{v}(0) = \mathbf{0}$ and $\mathbf{r}(0) = \mathbf{j} + \mathbf{k}$. Then find the position at $t = 2$.

4. Find the maximum height of a football thrown 4 feet above ground at a speed of 40 feet per second at an angle of $30°$ above the horizontal.

12.3 Homework Quiz Answers

1. Sketch a graph of the path of the position vector $\mathbf{r}(t) = t\mathbf{i} + (t^2 - 4)\mathbf{j}$ in the xy-plane. Also, sketch the velocity and acceleration vectors a the point $(2,0)$. (Similar to Exercise #4.)

$$\mathbf{r}(t) = t\mathbf{i} + (t^2 - 4)\mathbf{j},$$
$$\mathbf{v}(t) = \mathbf{i} + 2t\mathbf{j}$$
$$\mathbf{a}(t) = 2\mathbf{j}$$
$$t = 2,\ t^2 - 4 = 0$$
$$\mathbf{v}(2) = \mathbf{i} + 4\mathbf{j},\ \mathbf{a}(2) = 2\mathbf{j}$$

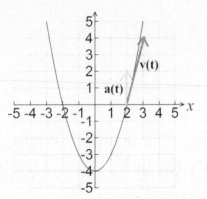

2. Given the position function $\mathbf{r}(t) = 3t^2\mathbf{i} + (4 - t^2)\mathbf{j} + t\mathbf{k}$ that describes the path of an object moving in space, find the velocity, speed, and acceleration. (Similar to Exercise #9.)

$$\mathbf{r}(t) = 3t^2\mathbf{i} + (4 - t^2)\mathbf{j} + t\mathbf{k}$$
$$\mathbf{v}(t) = 6t\mathbf{i} - 2t\mathbf{j} + \mathbf{k},\ \text{speed} = \sqrt{(6t)^2 + (-2t)^2 + (1)^2} = \sqrt{40t^2 + 1}$$
$$\mathbf{a}(t) = 6\mathbf{i} - 2\mathbf{j}$$

3. Use the acceleration function $\mathbf{a}(t) = 3\mathbf{i} - \mathbf{j} + \mathbf{k}$ to find the velocity and position function given $\mathbf{v}(0) = \mathbf{0}$ and $\mathbf{r}(0) = \mathbf{j} + \mathbf{k}$. (Similar to Exercise #12.)

$$\mathbf{v}(t) = 3t\mathbf{i} - t\mathbf{j} + t\mathbf{k} + \mathbf{C},\ \text{then}\ \mathbf{v}(t) = 3t\mathbf{i} - t\mathbf{j} + t\mathbf{k}$$
$$\mathbf{r}(t) = \frac{3t^2}{2}\mathbf{i} - \frac{t^2}{2}\mathbf{j} + \frac{t^2}{2}\mathbf{k} + \mathbf{C},\ \text{then}\ \mathbf{r}(t) = \frac{3t^2}{2}\mathbf{i} - \left(\frac{t^2}{2} - 1\right)\mathbf{j} + \left(\frac{t^2}{2} + 1\right)\mathbf{k}$$

4. Find the maximum height of a football thrown 4 feet above ground at a speed of 40 feet per second at an angle of $30°$ above the horizontal. (Similar to Exercise #24.)

$$\mathbf{r}(t) = = (20\sqrt{3})t\mathbf{i} + [4 + 20t - 16t^2]\mathbf{j}.\ \text{At maximum height}$$
$$20 - 32t = 0,\ y\left(\frac{5}{8}\right) = 4 + 20\left(\frac{5}{8}\right) - 16\left(\frac{5}{8}\right)^2 = 10.25\ \text{ft}$$

12.4 Homework Quiz

1. Sketch the unit tangent and
   normal vectors at $(0,4)$ and $(1,3)$.

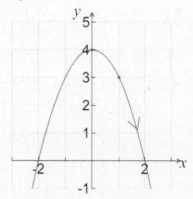

2. Find the unit tangent vector to the curve $\mathbf{r}(t) = t^2\mathbf{i} + e^t\mathbf{j}$ at $t = 1$.

3. Find the principal unit normal vector to the curve $\mathbf{r}(t) = \cos t\,\mathbf{i} + \sin t\,\mathbf{j}$
   at $t = \dfrac{\pi}{6}$.

4. Find a_T at $t = 1$ for the plane curve $\mathbf{r}(t) = t^2\mathbf{i} + 3t\mathbf{j}$.

12.4 Homework Quiz Answers

1. Sketch the unit tangent and
   normal vectors at $(0,4)$ and $(1,3)$.
   (Similar to Exercise #1.)

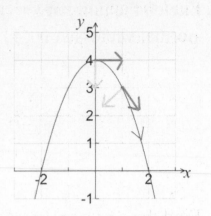

2. Find the unit tangent vector to the curve $\mathbf{r}(t) = t^2\mathbf{i} + e^t\mathbf{j}$ at $t = 1$.
   (Similar to Exercise #10.)

$$\mathbf{r}(t) = t^2\mathbf{i} + e^t\mathbf{j}$$

$$\mathbf{r}'(t) = 2t\mathbf{i} + e^t\mathbf{j} \qquad \mathbf{r}'(1) = 2\mathbf{i} + e\mathbf{j} \text{ and } \|\mathbf{r}'(1)\| = \sqrt{4 + e^2}$$

$$\mathbf{T}(1) = \left(\frac{2}{\sqrt{4 + e^2}}\right)\mathbf{i} + \left(\frac{e}{\sqrt{4 + e^2}}\right)\mathbf{j}$$

3. Find the principal unit normal vector to the curve $\mathbf{r}(t) = \cos t\mathbf{i} + \sin t\mathbf{j}$

   at $t = \dfrac{\pi}{6}$. (Similar to Exercise #26.)

$$\mathbf{r}'(t) = -\sin t\mathbf{i} + \cos t\mathbf{j} \qquad \mathbf{T}(t) = -\sin t\mathbf{i} + \cos t\mathbf{j}$$

$$\mathbf{T}'(t) = -\cos t\mathbf{i} - \sin t\mathbf{j} \qquad \|\mathbf{T}'(t)\| = 1$$

$$\mathbf{N}\left(\frac{\pi}{6}\right) = \frac{\mathbf{T}'(\pi/6)}{\|\mathbf{T}'(\pi/6)\|} = -\cos(\pi/6)\mathbf{i} - \sin(\pi/6)\mathbf{j} = -\frac{\sqrt{3}}{2}\mathbf{i} - \frac{1}{2}\mathbf{j}$$

4. Find a_T at $t = 1$ for the plane curve $\mathbf{r}(t) = t^2\mathbf{i} + 3t\mathbf{j}$.

   (Similar to Exercise #36.)

$$\mathbf{v}(t) = 2t\mathbf{i} + 3\mathbf{j} \text{ and } \mathbf{v}(1) = 2\mathbf{i} + 3\mathbf{j}$$

$$\mathbf{a}(t) = 2\mathbf{i} \text{ and } \mathbf{a}(1) = 2\mathbf{i}$$

$$\mathbf{T}(t) = \frac{2t\mathbf{i} + 3\mathbf{j}}{\sqrt{4t^2 + 9}} \text{ and } \mathbf{T}(1) = \frac{2\mathbf{i} + 3\mathbf{j}}{\sqrt{13}}$$

$$a_T = \mathbf{a} \cdot \mathbf{T} = (2\mathbf{i}) \cdot \left(\frac{2}{\sqrt{13}}\mathbf{i} + \frac{3}{\sqrt{13}}\mathbf{j}\right) = \frac{4}{\sqrt{13}}$$

12.5 Homework Quiz

1. Find the approximate length of the space curve $\mathbf{r}(t) = t\mathbf{i} + 5t\mathbf{j} + t^3\mathbf{k}$ over the interval $[0,3]$.

2. Find the curvature K of the plane curve $\mathbf{r}(t) = 2t\mathbf{i} - t\mathbf{j}$ at the parameter value $t = 1$.

3. Find the curvature K of the space curve $\mathbf{r}(t) = 8t\mathbf{i} - 6\cos t\mathbf{j} - 6\sin t\mathbf{k}$.

4. $\mathbf{r}(t) = \left(40\sqrt{2}\right)t\mathbf{i} + \left(4 + 40\sqrt{2}t - 16t^2\right)\mathbf{j}$ is the vector-valued function that describes the path of a baseball that is hit (in feet). Find the arc length of the trajectory.

12.5 Homework Quiz Answers

1. Find the approximate length of the space curve $\mathbf{r}(t) = t\mathbf{i} + 5t\mathbf{j} + t^3\mathbf{k}$ over the interval $[0,3]$. (Similar to Exercise #10.)

$$\text{Arc length} = \int_0^3 \sqrt{1^2 + 5^2 + \left(3t^2\right)^2}\, dt \approx 33.775$$

2. Find the curvature K of the plane curve $\mathbf{r}(t) = 2t\mathbf{i} - t\mathbf{j}$ at the parameter value $t = 1$. (Similar to Exercise #25.)

$$\mathbf{r}'(t) = 2\mathbf{i} - \mathbf{j} \text{ and } \mathbf{T}(t) = \frac{2\mathbf{i} - \mathbf{j}}{\sqrt{5}}$$

$$\mathbf{T}'(t) = 0 \text{ and } K = \frac{\|\mathbf{T}'(t)\|}{\|\mathbf{r}'(t)\|} = 0 \text{ (The curve is a line.)}$$

3. Find the curvature K of the space curve $\mathbf{r}(t) = 8t\mathbf{i} - 6\cos t\mathbf{j} - 6\sin t\mathbf{k}$. (Similar to Exercise #39.)

$$\mathbf{r}'(t) = 8\mathbf{i} + 6\sin t\mathbf{j} - 6\cos t\mathbf{k}$$

$$\mathbf{T}(t) = \frac{1}{5}(4\mathbf{i} + 3\sin t\mathbf{j} - 3\cos t\mathbf{k}) \text{ and } \mathbf{T}'(t) = \frac{1}{5}(3\cos t\mathbf{j} + 3\sin t\mathbf{k})$$

$$K = \frac{\|\mathbf{T}'(t)\|}{\|\mathbf{r}'(t)\|} = \frac{3/5}{10} = \frac{3}{50}$$

4. $\mathbf{r}(t) = \left(40\sqrt{2}\right)t\mathbf{i} + \left(4 + 40\sqrt{2}t - 16t^2\right)\mathbf{j}$ is the vector-valued function that describes the path of a baseball that is hit (in feet). Find the arc length of the trajectory. (Similar to Exercise #7.)

$$4 + 40\sqrt{2}t - 16t^2 = 0 \text{ when } t = 3.60488$$

$$\mathbf{r}'(t) = \left(40\sqrt{2}\right)\mathbf{i} + \left(40\sqrt{2} - 32t\right)\mathbf{j}$$

$$\text{Arc length} = \int_0^{3.60488} \|\mathbf{r}'(t)\|\, dt \approx 234.161 \text{ feet}$$

13.1 Homework Quiz

1. Given $f(x,y,z) = \dfrac{x+2xz}{yz}$, find and simplify $f(4,-2,-1)$.

   (Similar to Exercise #10.)

2. Describe the domain and range of $f(x,y) = \ln(2-3x-y)$.

3. Describe the level curves of $f(x,y) = x^2 - 6x + y^2 + 2y + 10$.

4. Sketch the graph of the level surface $f(x,y,z) = c$ at $c = 16$ for
   $f(x,y,z) = x^2 + y^2 + z^2$.

13.1 Homework Quiz Answers

1. Given $f(x,y,z) = \dfrac{x+2xz}{yz}$, find and simplify $f(4,-2,-1)$.

   (Similar to Exercise #10.)

$$f(4,-2,-1) = -2$$

2. Describe the domain and range of $f(x,y) = \ln(2-3x-y)$.

   (Similar to Exercise #21.)

   Domain: $\{(x,y): y < 2-3x\}$

   Range: all real numbers

3. Describe the level curves of $f(x,y) = x^2 - 6x + y^2 + 2y + 10$.

   (Similar to Exercise #52.)

   $f(x,y) = x^2 - 6x + 9 + y^2 + 2y + 1 = (x-3)^2 + (y+1)^2$

   Concentric circles centered at $(3,-1)$.

4. Sketch the graph of the level surface $f(x,y,z) = c$ at $c = 16$ for $f(x,y,z) = x^2 + y^2 + z^2$. (Similar to Exercise #71.)

   The graph is a sphere
   centered at (0,0,0)
   with radius 4.

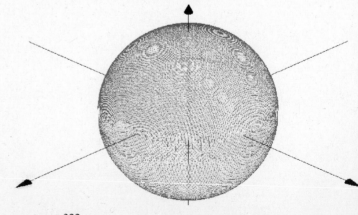

13.2 Homework Quiz

1. Use the definition of the limit of a function of two variables to verify
$$\lim_{(x,y)\to(-2,3)} x = -2 \; .$$

2. Find $\displaystyle\lim_{(x,y)\to(2,4)} \frac{x^2+2}{x+y}$ and discuss the continuity of the function.

3. Find $\displaystyle\lim_{(x,y)\to(0,0)} \frac{x-y^2}{x+y}$, if it exists. If the limit does not exist, explain

   why.

4. Discuss the continuity of $f(x,y,z) = \dfrac{3}{x^2+y^2-z^2}$.

323

13.2 Homework Quiz Answers

1. Use the definition of the limit of a function of two variables to verify $\lim\limits_{(x,y)\to(-2,3)} x = -2$. (Similar to Exercise #2.)

   Let $f(x,y) = x$ and $L = -2$. Let $\varepsilon > 0$ be given. Let $\delta = \varepsilon$. Then, whenever $\sqrt{(x+2)^2 + (y-3)^2} < \delta = \varepsilon$, it follows that

   $$|x+2| = \sqrt{(x+2)^2} \le \sqrt{(x+2)^2 + (y-3)^2} < \delta = \varepsilon, \text{ or just } |x+2| < \varepsilon.$$

2. Find $\lim\limits_{(x,y)\to(2,4)} \dfrac{x^2+2}{x+y}$ and discuss the continuity of the function. (Similar to Exercise #12.)

   We start with $\lim\limits_{(x,y)\to(2,4)} x^2 + 2 = (2)^2 + 2 = 6$ and

   $\lim\limits_{(x,y)\to(2,4)} x + y = 2 + 4 = 6$. We combine to get $\lim\limits_{(x,y)\to(2,4)} \dfrac{x^2+2}{x+y} = \dfrac{6}{6} = 1$.

   The quotient is continuous everywhere except on the line $y = -x$.

3. Find $\lim\limits_{(x,y)\to(0,0)} \dfrac{x - y^2}{x + y}$, if it exists. If the limit does not exist, explain why. (Similar to Exercise #31.)

   Along the x-axis, $y = 0$ and $x \to 0$. On this path, the limit reduces to $\lim\limits_{x\to0} \dfrac{x - 0^2}{x + 0} = \lim\limits_{x\to0} \dfrac{x}{x} = 1$. Along the y-axis, $x = 0$ and $y \to 0$. On this path, the limit reduces to $\lim\limits_{y\to0} \dfrac{0 - y^2}{0 + y} = \lim\limits_{y\to0} \dfrac{-y^2}{y} = 0$. Since the path restricted limits differ, the limit does not exist.

4. Discuss the continuity of $f(x,y,z) = \dfrac{3}{x^2 + y^2 - z^2}$.

   (Similar to Exercise #64.)

   The function $f(x,y,z) = \dfrac{3}{x^2 + y^2 - z^2}$ is continuous at each point in space except at the points on the double cone $z^2 = x^2 + y^2$.

13.3 Homework Quiz

1. Find both first partial derivatives of the function $z = xe^{(y^2+1)}$.

2. Using the function $f(x,y) = \cos(xy)$, evaluate f_x and f_y at the point $\left(3, \dfrac{3\pi}{4}\right)$.

3. Find the first partial derivatives with respect to x, y, and z of the function $f(x,y,z) = \ln\left(x^2 + 2y^2 + 3z^4\right)$.

4. Find the four second partial derivatives of $z = 3x^4 - 2x^2y^2 + 5y^4$.

13.3 Homework Quiz Answers

1. Find both first partial derivatives of the function $z = xe^{(y^2+1)}$.
(Similar to Exercise #19.)

When y is held constant, the exponential term is all constant, thus we

compute $\dfrac{\partial z}{\partial x} = \dfrac{d}{dx}(x)e^{(y^2+1)} = (1)e^{(y^2+1)} = e^{(y^2+1)}$. When x is held

constant, we need only differentiate the exponential term as follows:

$\dfrac{\partial z}{\partial y} = x\dfrac{d}{dy}\left(e^{(y^2+1)}\right) = xe^{(y^2+1)}\dfrac{d}{dy}(y^2+1) = 2xye^{(y^2+1)}$.

2. Using the function $f(x,y) = \cos(xy)$, evaluate f_x and f_y at the point
$\left(3, \dfrac{3\pi}{4}\right)$. (Similar to Exercise #48.)

The partial derivatives are $f_x(x,y) = -\sin(xy)\dfrac{d}{dx}(xy) = -y\sin(xy)$

and $f_y(x,y) = -\sin(xy)\dfrac{d}{dy}(xy) = -x\sin(xy)$. At $\left(3, \dfrac{3\pi}{4}\right)$ we get

$f_x\left(3, \dfrac{3\pi}{4}\right) = -\dfrac{3\pi}{4}\sin\left(\dfrac{9\pi}{4}\right) = \dfrac{-3\pi\sqrt{2}}{8}$ and $f_y\left(3, \dfrac{3\pi}{4}\right) = -3\sin\left(\dfrac{9\pi}{4}\right) = \dfrac{-3\sqrt{2}}{2}$.

3. Find the first partial derivatives with respect to x, y, and z of the
function $f(x,y,z) = \ln(x^2 + 2y^2 + 3z^4)$. (Similar to Exercise #63.)

The partial derivatives are: $\dfrac{\partial f}{\partial x} = \dfrac{2x}{x^2 + 2y^2 + 3z^4}$,

$\dfrac{\partial f}{\partial y} = \dfrac{4y}{x^2 + 2y^2 + 3z^4}$, and $\dfrac{\partial f}{\partial z} = \dfrac{12z^3}{x^2 + 2y^2 + 3z^4}$.

4. Find the four second partial derivatives of $z = 3x^4 - 2x^2y^2 + 5y^4$.
(Similar to Exercise #74.)

The first partials are $z_x(x,y) = 12x^3 - 4xy^2$ and $z_y(x,y) = -4x^2y + 20y^3$.

So, the second partials are $z_{xx}(x,y) = 36x^2 - 4y^2$,

$z_{xy}(x,y) = z_{yx}(x,y) = -8xy$, and $z_{yy}(x,y) = -4x^2 + 60y^2$.

13.4 Homework Quiz

1. Find the total differential of $w = z^2 e^y - \cos(x)$.

2. Let $f(x, y) = x^2 - 3y$. Evaluate $f(1,3)$ and $f(1.05, 2.9)$. Calculate Δz and use the total differential dz to approximate Δz.

3. A right circular cylinder of height 6 and radius 2 is constructed, and in the process errors $\Delta r = 0.01$ and $\Delta h = -0.02$ are made. Complete the table to compare the propagated error in volume.

Δr	Δh	dV	ΔV	$\Delta V - dV$

4. The height of a right regular pyramid is three times the quotient of the volume V and the area of the base A: $h = \dfrac{3V}{A}$. Approximate the maximum error in measuring height due to errors of 3% in V and 1% in A.

13.4 Homework Quiz Answers

1. Find the total differential of $w = z^2 e^y - \cos(x)$.
   (Similar to Exercise #8.)

   Differentiating with respect to each variable, we get
   $dw = \sin(x)dx + z^2 e^y dy + 2ze^y dz$.

2. Let $f(x,y) = x^2 - 3y$. Evaluate $f(1,3)$ and $f(1.05, 2.9)$. Calculate Δz
   and use the total differential dz to approximate Δz.
   (Similar to Exercise #12.)

   We first evaluate $f(1,3) = 1 - 9 = -8$ and $f(1.05, 2.9) = -7.5975$, so
   that $\Delta z = (-7.5975) - (-8) = 0.4025$. The differential is
   $dz = 2xdx - 3dy$ and evaluated at the point $(1,3)$ with
   $dx \approx \Delta x = 0.05$ and $dy \approx \Delta y = -0.1$ gives us the estimate for Δz,
   $\Delta z \approx dz = 2(1)(0.05) - 3(-0.1) = 0.4$.

3. A right circular cylinder of height 6 and radius 2 is constructed, and
   errors $\Delta r = 0.01$ and $\Delta h = -0.02$ are made. Complete the table to
   compare the propagated error in volume. (Similar to Exercise #27.)

Δr	Δh	dV	ΔV	$\Delta V - dV$
0.01	−0.02	0.50265	0.50202	−0.00063

   $V = \pi r^2 h$, $dV = 2\pi r h\, dr + \pi r^2\, dh$, $\Delta V = V(5.98, 2.01) - V(6,2)$

4. The height of a right regular pyramid is three times the quotient of the
   Volume V and the area of the base A: $h = \dfrac{3V}{A}$. Approximate the
   maximum percent error in measuring height due to errors of 3% in V
   and 1% in A. (Similar to Exercise #31.)

   The differential is $dh = \dfrac{3}{A}dV - \dfrac{3V}{A^2}dA$. So the maximum percent error

   is $\dfrac{\Delta h}{h} \approx \dfrac{dh}{h} = \dfrac{\dfrac{3}{A}dV - \dfrac{3V}{A^2}dA}{\dfrac{3V}{A}} = \dfrac{dV}{V} - \dfrac{dA}{A} = 0.03 - 0.01 = 0.02 = 2\%$.

13.5 Homework Quiz

1. Find $\dfrac{dw}{dt}$ by using the appropriate chain rule: $w = y\cos(x)$, $x = t + \pi/2$, $y = e^{2t}$.

2. Use the appropriate chain rule to find $\dfrac{\partial w}{\partial s}$, and $\dfrac{\partial w}{\partial t}$ at the point $s = 2$ and $t = -1$ with $w = 3x^2 - 2xy^2$, $x = s + 2t$, and $y = t - 2s$.

3. Use the appropriate chain rule to find $\dfrac{\partial w}{\partial s}$, and $\dfrac{\partial w}{\partial t}$ with $w = xye^z$ and $x = 3t$, $y = 3s$, and $z = t - s$.

4. Differentiate $2y - \cos(x + z) = 0$ implicitly to find $\dfrac{\partial z}{\partial x}$, and $\dfrac{\partial z}{\partial y}$.

13.5 Homework Quiz Answers

1. Find $\dfrac{dw}{dt}$ by using the appropriate chain rule: $w = y\cos(x)$,

   $x = t + \pi/2$, $y = e^{2t}$.   (Similar to Exercise #3.)

   The chain rule we want is $\dfrac{dw}{dt} = \dfrac{\partial w}{\partial x}\dfrac{dx}{dt} + \dfrac{\partial w}{\partial y}\dfrac{dy}{dt}$. Substituting we find

   $\dfrac{dw}{dt} = \left(-y\sin(x)\right)(1) + \left(\cos(x)\right)\left(2e^{2t}\right) = -e^{2t}\sin\left(t + \pi/2\right) + 2e^{2t}\cos\left(t + \pi/2\right)$

2. Use the appropriate chain rule to find $\dfrac{\partial w}{\partial s}$, and $\dfrac{\partial w}{\partial t}$ at the point $s = 2$

   and $t = -1$ with $w = 3x^2 - 2xy^2$, $x = s + 2t$, and $y = t - 2s$. (Similar to Exercise #16.)

   At the given point, $x = 0$ and $y = -5$. The chain rule then gives us

   $\dfrac{\partial w}{\partial s} = \dfrac{\partial w}{\partial x}\dfrac{\partial x}{\partial s} + \dfrac{\partial w}{\partial y}\dfrac{\partial y}{\partial s} = \left(6x - 2y^2\right) + \left(-4xy\right)(-2) = 6x + 8xy - 2y^2 = -50$ and

   $\dfrac{\partial w}{\partial t} = \dfrac{\partial w}{\partial x}\dfrac{\partial x}{\partial t} + \dfrac{\partial w}{\partial y}\dfrac{\partial y}{\partial t} = \left(6x - 2y^2\right)\cdot 2 + \left(-4xy\right) = 12x - 4xy - 4y^2 = -100.$

3. Use the appropriate chain rule to find $\dfrac{\partial w}{\partial s}$, and $\dfrac{\partial w}{\partial t}$ with $w = xye^z$ and

   $x = 3t$, $y = 3s$, and $z = t - s$. (Similar to Exercise #25.)

   $\dfrac{\partial w}{\partial s} = \dfrac{\partial w}{\partial y}\dfrac{\partial y}{\partial s} + \dfrac{\partial w}{\partial z}\dfrac{\partial z}{\partial s} = xe^z(3) + xye^z(-1) = 9te^{t-s} - 9ste^{t-s}$ and

   $\dfrac{\partial w}{\partial t} = \dfrac{\partial w}{\partial x}\dfrac{\partial x}{\partial t} + \dfrac{\partial w}{\partial z}\dfrac{\partial z}{\partial t} = ye^z(3) + xye^z = 9se^{t-s} + 9ste^{t-s}.$

4. Differentiate $2y - \cos(x + z) = 0$ implicitly to find $\dfrac{\partial z}{\partial x}$, and $\dfrac{\partial z}{\partial y}$.

   (Similar to Exercise #34.)

   Let $F(x, y, z) = 2y - \cos(x + z)$ and find $F_x(x, y, z) = \sin(x + z)$,

   $F_y(x, y, z) = 2$, and $F_z(x, y, z) = \sin(x + z)$. Then $\dfrac{\partial z}{\partial x} = \dfrac{F_x}{F_z} = 1$ and

   $\dfrac{\partial z}{\partial y} = \dfrac{F_y}{F_z} = \dfrac{2}{\sin(x + z)} = 2\csc(x + z).$

13.6 Homework Quiz

1. Find the directional derivative of $f(x,y) = e^y \cos(x)$ at $P\left(\frac{\pi}{3}, 1\right)$ in the direction of $\bar{v} = -\hat{j}$.

2. Find the directional derivative of $f(x,y) = 3x^2 - 2y^2$ at $P(1,2)$ in the direction of $Q(-2,-2)$.

3. Find the gradient of $f(x,y) = \ln(y^2 - 2x)$ at the point $(3,1)$.

4. Find the maximum value of the directional derivative for the function $h(x,y) = xe^y$ at the point $(3,0)$.

13.6 Homework Quiz Answers

1. Find the directional derivative of $f(x,y) = e^y \cos(x)$ at $P\left(\frac{\pi}{3}, 1\right)$ in the direction of $\vec{v} = -\hat{j}$. (Similar to Exercise #5.)

   Since $\vec{v}$ is a unit vector, $\hat{u} = \vec{v} = -\hat{j}$ so the directional derivative is $D_{\hat{u}}f(x,y) = \left(-e^y \sin(x)\right)(0) + \left(e^y \cos(x)\right)(-1)$. Evaluated at P, we get $D_{\hat{u}}f\left(\frac{\pi}{3}, 1\right) = -e^1 \cos\left(\frac{\pi}{3}\right) = -\frac{e}{2}$.

2. Find the directional derivative of $f(x,y) = 3x^2 - 2y^2$ at $P(1,2)$ in the direction of $Q(-2,-2)$. (Similar to Exercise #17.)

   The direction vector is $\vec{v} = \overrightarrow{PQ} = -3\hat{i} - 4\hat{j}$ and $\hat{u} = \frac{\vec{v}}{\|\vec{v}\|} = -\frac{3}{5}\hat{i} - \frac{4}{5}\hat{j}$. The directional derivative is $D_{\hat{u}}f(x,y) = (6x)\left(-\frac{3}{5}\right) + (-4y)\left(-\frac{4}{5}\right)$.

   Evaluated at P we get $D_{\hat{u}}f(1,2) = -\frac{18}{5} + \frac{32}{5} = \frac{14}{5}$.

3. Find the gradient of $f(x,y) = \ln\left(y^2 - 2x\right)$ at the point $(3,1)$. (Similar to Exercise #23.)

   The general gradient is $\nabla f(x,y) = \frac{-2}{y^2 - 2x}\hat{i} + \frac{2y}{y^2 - 2x}\hat{j}$ and evaluated at $(3,1)$ gives $\nabla f(3,1) = -\frac{2}{7}\hat{i} + \frac{2}{7}\hat{j}$.

4. Find the maximum value of the directional derivative for the function $h(x,y) = xe^y$ at the point $(3,0)$. (Similar to Exercise #35.)

   First we find the gradient $\nabla f(x,y) = e^y\hat{i} + xe^y\hat{j}$ at the point $(3,0)$ which is $\nabla f(3,0) = \hat{i} + 3\hat{j}$. The maximum value of the directional derivative is the magnitude $\|\nabla f(3,0)\| = \sqrt{1^2 + 3^2} = \sqrt{10}$.

13.7 Homework Quiz

1. Find a unit normal vector to the surface $x^3 - y^2 + 3z = 1$ at the point $(2,2,1)$.

2. Find the equation of the tangent plane to the surface $f(x,y) = 9x^2 + y^2$ at the point $P(1,-1,10)$.

3. Find symmetric equations of the normal line to the surface $x - \arctan(yz) = 0$ at the point $\left(\frac{\pi}{4}, -1, -1\right)$.

4. Find the angle of inclination θ of the tangent plane to the surface $y - x^2 + z^2 = 0$ at the point $P(2,5,-1)$.

13.7 Homework Quiz Answers

1. Find a unit normal vector to the surface $x^3 - y^2 + 3z = 1$ at the point $(2,2,1)$. (Similar to Exercise #11.)

   The surface is a level surface of $F(x,y,z) = x^3 - y^2 + 3z$. The gradient is $\nabla F = 3x^2\hat{i} - 2y\hat{j} + 3\hat{k}$. We evaluate and normalize:

   $$\nabla F(2,2,1) = 12\hat{i} - 4\hat{j} + 3\hat{k} \text{ and } \hat{u} = \frac{12\hat{i} - 4\hat{j} + 3\hat{k}}{\sqrt{12^2 + (-4)^2 + 3^2}} = \frac{12}{13}\hat{i} - \frac{4}{13}\hat{j} + \frac{3}{13}\hat{k}.$$

2. Find the equation of the tangent plane to the surface $f(x,y) = 9x^2 + y^2$ at the point $P(1,-1, 10)$. (Similar to Exercise #22.)

   We compute $f_x(x,y) = 18x$ and $f_y(x,y) = 2y$. Evaluated at P we get $f_x(1,-1) = 18$, $f_y(1,-1) = -2$ So an equation of the tangent plane is $18(x-1) - 2(y+1) - (z-10) = 0$ or $18x - 2y - z = 10$.

3. Find symmetric equations of the normal line to the surface $x - \arctan(yz) = 0$ at the point $\left(\frac{\pi}{4}, -1, -1\right)$. (Similar to Exercise #39.)

   If $F(x,y,z) = x - \arctan(yz)$ we get $\nabla F = \hat{i} - \frac{z}{1 + y^2 z^2}\hat{j} - \frac{y}{1 + y^2 z^2}\hat{k}$

   and $\nabla F\left(\frac{\pi}{4}, -1, -1\right) = \hat{i} + \frac{1}{2}\hat{j} + \frac{1}{2}\hat{k}$, so $\dfrac{x - \frac{\pi}{4}}{1} = \dfrac{y+1}{\frac{1}{2}} = \dfrac{z+1}{\frac{1}{2}}$ is the set of symmetric equations.

4. Find the angle of inclination θ of the tangent plane to the surface $y - x^2 + z^2 = 0$ at the point $P(2,5,-1)$. (Similar to Exercise #49.)

   The surface is a level surface of $F(x,y,z) = y - x^2 + z^2$. The gradient of F at P is given by $\nabla F(x,y,z) = -2x\hat{i} + \hat{j} - 2z\hat{k}$ and $\nabla F(2,5,-1) = -4\hat{i} + \hat{j} + 2\hat{k}$. Using the formula, we find

   $$\cos(\theta) = \frac{|\nabla F(2,5,-1) \cdot \hat{k}|}{\|\nabla F(2,5,-1)\|} = \frac{2}{\sqrt{21}} \text{ or } \theta = \arccos\left(\frac{2}{\sqrt{21}}\right) \approx 64.1°.$$

13.8 Homework Quiz

1. Examine the function $f(x,y) = x^2 + y^2 + xy - 8x - 4y + 1$ for relative extrema.

2. Examine the function $h(x,y) = y^2 - 5xy + x^2$ for relative extrema and saddle points.

3. If $f_{xx}(x_0, y_0) = 4$, $f_{yy}(x_0, y_0) = 25$, and $f_{xy}(x_0, y_0) = 10$, what can you conclude about the nature of the function $f(x,y)$ at the critical point (x_0, y_0)?

4. Find the absolute extrema of the function $f(x,y) = 10 - 4x - y$ over the triangular region with vertices at $(1,0)$, $(1,2)$, and $(2,2)$.

13.8 Homework Quiz Answers

1. Examine the function $f(x,y) = x^2 + y^2 + xy - 8x - 4y + 1$ for relative extrema. (Similar to Exercise #10.)

   First, find the critical points of f. Since $f_x(x,y) = 2x + y - 8$ and $f_y(x,y) = 2y + x - 4$, the only critical point occurs when $2x + y - 8 = 0$ and $2y + x + 4 = 0$. So the critical point is $(4,0)$. Since $f_{xx} = 2 > 0$, $f_{yy} = 2$, and $f_{xy} = 1$, we get $d = (2)(2) - 1^2 = 3 > 0$, and we conclude that $(4,0)$ is a relative minimum.

2. Examine the function $h(x,y) = y^2 - 5xy + x^2$ for relative extrema and saddle points. (Similar to Exercise #24.)

   We compute $h_x(x,y) = -5y + 2x$ and $h_y(x,y) = 2y - 5x$. Set both to zero and solve to get $(0,0)$ as the only critical point. Since $h_{xx} = 2$, $h_{yy} = 2$, and $h_{xy} = -5$, $d = (2)(2) - 5^2 = -21 < 0$ and thus $h(x,y) = y^2 - 5xy + x^2$ has a saddle point at $(0,0)$.

3. If $f_{xx}(x_0,y_0) = 4$, $f_{yy}(x_0,y_0) = 25$, and $f_{xy}(x_0,y_0) = 10$, what can you conclude about the nature of the function $f(x,y)$ at the critical point (x_0,y_0)? (Similar to Exercise #34.)

   Since $d = (4)(25) - (10)^2 = 0$, there is insufficient information to determine the nature of the critical point.

4. Find the absolute extrema of the function $f(x,y) = 10 - 4x - y$ over the triangular region with vertices at $(1,0)$, $(1,2)$, and $(2,2)$. (Similar to Exercise #48.)

   Since $f_x = -4$ and $f_y = -1$, there are no global critical points. The left boundary is $x = 1$ and the restricted function is $f(y) = 10 - 4 - y$. The top boundary is $y = 2$ and the restricted function is $f(x) = 8 - 4x$. The diagonal boundary is the line $y = 2x - 2$ and the restricted function is $f(x) = 10 - 4x - (2x - 2)$. None of these have any critical points as they are all linear. Testing only the corner points, we find $f(1,0) = 6$ (global maximum), $f(1,2) = 4$, and $f(2,2) = 0$ (global minimum).

13.9 Homework Quiz

1. Find the dimensions of the largest volume rectangular box that can be sent through the mail given the restriction that $l + 2w + 2h = 108$ in.

2. The cost for a firm to produce x and y units of two related products is $C(x, y) = 400 + 4x + 7y + 0.01(3x^2 + xy + 3y^2)$ dollars. Find the production levels x and y that maximize profit $P = 10x + 15y - C(x, y)$.

3. Find the least squares regression line.

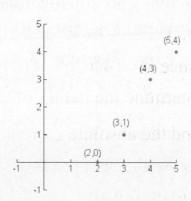

4. Use the regression capabilities of a graphing utility to find the least squares regression line for the data. Estimate demand for a price of $3.

Price, x	2.25	2.60	2.85
Demand, y	530	495	440

13.9 Homework Quiz Answers

1. Find the dimensions of the largest volume rectangular box that can be sent through the mail given the restriction that $l + 2w + 2h = 108$ in. (Similar to Exercise #10.)

   To maximize $V = lwh$, substitute for l to get $V = wh(108 - 2w - 2h)$.

   The partial derivatives are $V_w = h(108 - 2w - 2h) - 2wh = 0$ and

   $V_h = w(108 - 2w - 2h) - 2wh = 0$. Solving this system we find $w = 0$

   or $h = 0$ (min) and our max solution $w = h = 18$ in and $l = 36$ in.

2. The cost for a firm to produce x and y units of two related products is

   $C(x, y) = 400 + 4x + 7y + 0.01(3x^2 + xy + 3y^2)$ dollars. Find the

   production levels x and y that maximize profit $P = 10x + 15y - C(x, y)$.

   (Similar to Exercise #1.8)

   We compute $P_x = 10 - 4 + 0.01(6x + y) = 0$ and

   $P_y = 15 - 7 + 0.01(x + 6y) = 0$. Solving this system we get

   $6x + y = 600$ and $x + 6y = 800$ or $x = 80$ and $y = 120$. Since

   $P_{xx} P_{yy} - (P_{xy})^2 = (0.06)(0.06) - (0.01)^2 = 0.0035 > 0$ it is a maximum.

3. Find the least squares regression line. (Similar to Exercise #30.)

   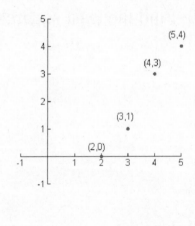

   Applying Theorem 13.18, we get

   $$a = \frac{4(35) - (14)(8)}{4(54) - (14)^2} = \frac{28}{20} = \frac{7}{5} \text{ and}$$

   $$b = \frac{1}{4}\left(8 - \frac{7}{5}(14)\right) = -\frac{58}{20} = -\frac{29}{10}. \text{ The line}$$

   is $y = \frac{7}{5}x - \frac{29}{10}$.

4. Use the regression capabilities of a graphing utility to find the least squares regression line for the data. Estimate demand for a price of $3.

Price, x	2.25	2.60	2.85
Demand, y	530	495	440

   (Similar to Exercise #48.)

   The linear regression model is $y = -146.79x + 865.09$ and when $x = 3$

   we estimate a demand of $y = 425$ units.

13.10 Homework Quiz

1. Maximize $f(x,y) = x^2 + 2y^2$ subject to the constraint $2x + 3y - 5 = 0$. Assume x and y are positive.

2. Maximize $f(x,y,z) = x^2 + y^2 + z$ subject to $x + y + z = 9$. Assume x, y, and z are positive.

3. Use Lagrange multipliers to find the minimum distance from the line $x + y = 6$ to the point $(1,0)$.

4. A rectangular box of volume 1250 cubic feet is to be made out of materials that cost $4 per square foot for the sides and $5 per square foot for the top and bottom. Use Lagrange multipliers to find the dimensions of the box of least cost.

13.10 Homework Quiz Answers

1. Maximize $f(x,y) = x^2 + 2y^2$ subject to the constraint $2x + 3y - 5 = 0$. Assume x and y are positive. (Similar to Exercise #5.)

   Let $g(x,y) = 2x + 3y - 5$ and set up the system of equations:

   $f_x(x,y) = 2x = \lambda g_x(x,y) = 2\lambda$, $f_y(x,y) = 4y = \lambda g_y(x,y) = 3\lambda$, and the original constraint $2x + 3y - 5 = 0$. Solving the linear system we get the maximum point $\left(\dfrac{20}{17}, \dfrac{15}{17} \right)$.

2. Maximize $f(x,y,z) = x^2 + y^2 + z$ subject to $x + y + z = 9$. Assume x, y, and z are positive. (Similar to Exercise #13.)

   Let $g(x,y,z) = x + y + z - 9$ and compute the partial derivatives:

   $f_x = 2x = \lambda g_x = \lambda$, $f_y = 2y = \lambda g_y = \lambda$, $f_z = 1 = \lambda g_y = \lambda$, include the constraint and solve to get the maximum $\lambda = 1$, $x = y = \dfrac{1}{2}$, and $z = 8$.

3. Use Lagrange multipliers to find the point on the line $x + y = 6$ closest to the point $(1,0)$. (Similar to Exercise #21.)

   We will minimize $f(x,y) = d^2 = (x-1)^2 + y^2$ subject to the constraint $x + y = 6$. Set $g(x,y) = x + y - 6$. Solve the system

   $f_x(x,y) = 2(x-1) = \lambda g_x(x,y) = \lambda$, $f_y(x,y) = 2y = \lambda g_y(x,y) = \lambda$,

   and the constraint $g(x,y) = 0$ to get the closest point $\left(\dfrac{7}{2}, \dfrac{5}{2} \right)$.

4. A rectangular box of volume 1250 cubic feet is to be made out of materials that cost \$4 per square foot for the sides and \$5 per square foot for the top and bottom. Use Lagrange multipliers to find the dimensions of the box of least cost. (Similar to Exercise #48.)

   Using l, w, and h for length, width, and height, we want to minimize $C(l,w,h) = 2 \cdot 5lw + 2 \cdot 4lh + 2 \cdot 4wh$ subject to $lwh = 1250$. Set $g(l,w,h) = lwh - 1250$. Solving $C_l = 10w + 8h = \lambda g_l = \lambda wh$, $C_w = 10l + 8h = \lambda g_w = lh\lambda$, $C_h = 8l + 8w = \lambda g_h = lw\lambda$ and the constraint, we get $l = w = 10$ feet and $h = 12.5$ feet.

14.1 Homework Quiz

1. Evaluate the integral $\int_{\sqrt{x}}^{x^2} \left(2y + x^2\right) dy$.

2. Evaluate the iterated integral $\int_0^2 \int_0^{\pi/3} x \sin(y)\, dy dx$.

3. Use an iterated integral to find the area of the region bounded by $x = y$, $x + y = 6$, and $y = 0$.

4. Sketch the region R and switch the order of integration $\int_0^3 \int_0^{\sqrt{9-x^2}} f(x,y)\, dy dx$.

341

14.1 Homework Quiz Answers

1. Evaluate the integral $\int_{\sqrt{x}}^{x^2}\left(2y+x^2\right)dy$. (Similar to Exercise #6.)

Integrating with respect to y we get $\int_{\sqrt{x}}^{x^2}\left(2y+x^2\right)dy = y^2 + yx^2\Big|_{\sqrt{x}}^{x^2}$ or

$\left(x^4 + x^4\right)-\left(x + \sqrt{x}x^2\right)= 2x^4 - x - x^{5/2}$.

2. Evaluate the iterated integral $\int_0^2\int_0^{\pi/3} x\sin(y)\,dy\,dx$.
(Similar to Exercise #15.)

We start on the inside with $\int_0^2\int_0^{\pi/3} x\sin(y)\,dy\,dx = \int_0^2 -x\cos(y)\Big|_0^{\pi/3}\,dx$ or

$\int_0^2\left(-\dfrac{x}{2}+x\right)dx = \int_0^2 \dfrac{x}{2}\,dx$. We then compute the single integral as

$\int_0^2 \dfrac{x}{2}\,dx = \dfrac{x^2}{4}\Big|_0^2 = 1 - 0 = 1$.

3. Use an iterated integral to find the area of the region bounded by
$x = y$, $x + y = 6$, and $y = 0$. (Similar to Exercise #41.)

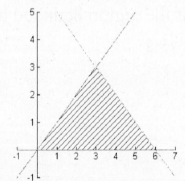

Using horizontal slicing, we get

$A = \int_0^3\int_y^{-y+6} 1\,dx\,dy$

$= \int_0^3 x\Big|_y^{-y+6}\,dy = \int_0^3\left(-y+6-y\right)dy$

$= \int_0^3\left(-2y+6\right)dy = -y^2 + 6y\Big|_0^3 = 9$.

4. Sketch the region R and switch the order of integration

$\int_0^3\int_0^{\sqrt{9-x^2}} f(x,y)\,dy\,dx$. (Similar to Exercise #49.)

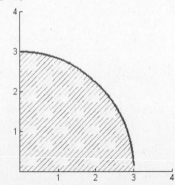

If $y = \sqrt{9-x^2}$, then the same curve in terms of y is $x = \sqrt{9-y^2}$ and the

integral is $\int_0^3\int_0^{\sqrt{9-y^2}} f(x,y)\,dx\,dy$.

14.2 Homework Quiz

1. Sketch the region R and evaluate the iterated integral $\displaystyle\int_0^2 \int_{y/3}^{\sqrt{y}} xy\,dx\,dy$.

2. Set up integrals for both orders of integration and use one to evaluate the integral $\displaystyle\iint_R ye^x\,dA$ with R: triangle bounded by $y = 3 - x$, $y = 0$, and $x = 0$.

3. Use a double integral to find the volume of the solid in the first octant below the plane $6x + 2y + 3z = 12$.

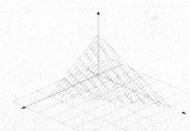

4. Find the average value of $f(x,y) = y$ over R: rectangle with vertices $(0,0)$, $(3,0)$, $(3,4)$, $(0,4)$.

14.2 Homework Quiz Answers

1. Sketch the region R and evaluate the iterated integral $\int_0^2 \int_{y/3}^{\sqrt{y}} xy\,dx\,dy$. (Similar to Exercise #10.)

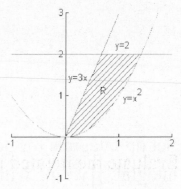

$$\int_0^2 \int_{y/3}^{\sqrt{y}} xy\,dx\,dy = \int_0^2 \frac{x^2 y}{2}\Big|_{y/3}^{\sqrt{y}}\,dy = \int_0^2 \frac{y^2}{2} - \frac{y^3}{18}\,dy$$

$$= \left(\frac{y^3}{6} - \frac{y^4}{72}\right)\Big|_0^2 = \frac{8}{6} - \frac{16}{72} = \frac{10}{9}.$$

2. Set up integrals for both orders of integration and use one to evaluate the integral $\iint\limits_R ye^x\,dA$ with R: triangle bounded by $y = 3 - x$, $y = 0$, and $x = 0$. (Similar to Exercise #16.)

The two choices are $\int_0^3 \int_0^{3-x} ye^x\,dy\,dx$ and $\int_0^3 \int_0^{3-y} ye^x\,dx\,dy$. We evaluate

$\int_0^3 \int_0^{3-y} ye^x\,dx\,dy = \int_0^3 ye^x\Big|_0^{3-y}\,dy = \int_0^2 \left(ye^{(3-y)} - y\right)dy$. Integrate by parts to

get $e^3\left(-ye^{-y} - e^{-y}\right) - \frac{y^2}{2}\Big|_0^2 = -3e - 2 + e^3.$

3. Use a double integral to find the volume of the solid in the first octant below the plane $6x + 2y + 3z = 12$. (Similar to Exercise #25.)

$$V = \int_0^2 \int_0^{-3x+6} \left(4 - 2x - \tfrac{2}{3}y\right)dy\,dx$$

$$= \int_0^2 4(-3x+6) - 2x(-3x+6) - \frac{1}{3}(-3x+6)^2\,dx$$

$$= 8$$

4. Find the average value of $f(x,y) = y$ over R: rectangle with vertices $(0,0)$, $(3,0)$, $(3,4)$, $(0,4)$. (Similar to Exercise #59.)

The average value is $\frac{1}{A}\int_0^3 \int_0^4 y\,dy\,dx = \frac{1}{12}\int_0^3 \frac{y^2}{2}\Big|_0^4\,dx = \frac{1}{12}\int_0^3 8\,dx = \frac{24}{12} = 2.$

344

14.3 Homework Quiz

1. Evaluate the integral $\int_0^{\pi/2} \int_0^{2\cos(\theta)} r\,dr\,d\theta$ and sketch the region.

2. Evaluate the iterated integral $\int_0^2 \int_0^{\sqrt{2y-y^2}} xy\,dx\,dy$ by converting to polar coordinates.

3. Use a double integral in polar coordinates to compute the volume of the solid bounded by $z = 2xy$, $x^2 + y^2 = 4$ and the first octant.

4. Use a double integral to find the area inside the rose $r = 2\cos(3\theta)$.

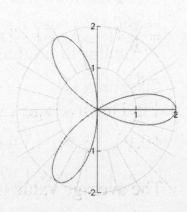

14.3 Homework Quiz Answers

1. Evaluate the integral $\int_0^{\pi/2} \int_0^{2\cos(\theta)} r\,dr\,d\theta$ and sketch the region. (Similar to Exercise #9.)

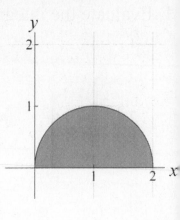

$$\int_0^{\pi/2} \int_0^{2\cos(\theta)} r\,dr\,d\theta = \int_0^{\pi/2} \frac{r^2}{2}\bigg|_0^{2\cos(\theta)} d\theta$$

$$= 2\int_0^{\pi/2} \cos^2(\theta)\,d\theta = \frac{1}{2}\sin(2\theta) + \theta\bigg|_0^{\pi/2} = \frac{\pi}{2}.$$

2. Evaluate the iterated integral $\int_0^2 \int_0^{\sqrt{2y-y^2}} xy\,dx\,dy$ by converting to polar coordinates. (Similar to Exercise #23.)

   The curve $x = \sqrt{2y - y^2}$ is the right side of the circle $x^2 + y^2 - 2y = 0$ or $x^2 + (y-1)^2 = 1$. This is the curve $r = 2\sin(\theta)$. In polar we get

   $$\int_0^{\pi/2} \int_0^{2\sin(\theta)} r\cos(\theta) r\sin(\theta) r\,dr\,d\theta = \int_0^{\pi/2} 4\sin^5(\theta)\cos(\theta)\,d\theta = \frac{2}{3}.$$

3. Use a double integral in polar coordinates to compute the volume of the solid bounded by $z = 2xy$, $x^2 + y^2 = 4$ and the first octant. (Similar to Exercise #33.)

   $$V = \int_0^{\pi/2} \int_0^2 2r\cos(\theta) r\sin\theta\, r\,dr\,d\theta = \int_0^{\pi/2} \frac{r^4}{4}\sin(\theta)\cos(\theta)\bigg|_0^2 d\theta$$

   $$= \int_0^{\pi/2} 8\sin(\theta)\cos(\theta)\,d\theta = 4.$$

4. Use a double integral to find the area inside the rose $r = 2\cos(3\theta)$. (Similar to Exercise #49.)

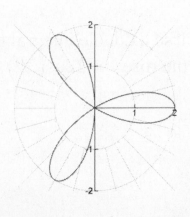

   The area is

   $$A = 6\int_0^{\pi/3} \int_0^{2\cos(3\theta)} r\,dr\,d\theta$$

   $$= \int_0^{\pi/3} 12\cos^2(3\theta)\,d\theta.$$

   $$= 3\pi$$

14.4 Homework Quiz

1. Find the mass of the lamina bounded by $0 \le x \le 2$, $0 \le y \le 4 - x^2$ with density $\rho(x, y) = xy$.

2. Find the center of mass of the lamina bounded by $x = \sqrt{y}$, $x = 0$, and $y = 1$ with density $\rho = xy$.

3. Find I_x, I_y, I_0, $\bar{x}$, and $\bar{y}$ for the rectangular lamina bounded by $0 \le x \le 2$ and $0 \le y \le 3$ with density $\rho = 2y$.

4. Set up, but do not evaluate, the double integral required to find the moment of inertia for the circular lamina $x^2 + y^2 = 4$ about the line c with density $\rho = k$.

14.4 Homework Quiz Answers

1. Find the mass of the lamina bounded by $0 \le x \le 2$, $0 \le y \le 4 - x^2$ with density $\rho(x, y) = xy$. (Similar to Exercise #2.)

The total mass is

$$\int_0^2 \int_0^{4-x^2} xy\, dy\, dx = \frac{1}{2} \int_0^2 16x - 8x^3 + x^5\, dx = 4x^2 - x^4 + \frac{x^6}{12}\Big|_0^2 = \frac{16}{3}.$$

2. Find the center of mass of the lamina bounded by $x = \sqrt{y}$, $x = 0$, and $y = 1$ with density $\rho = xy$. (Similar to Exercise #11.)

The mass is $m = \int_0^1 \int_{x^2}^1 xy\, dy\, dx = \frac{1}{6}$. The

moments are $M_x = \int_0^1 \int_{x^2}^1 xy^2\, dy\, dx = \frac{1}{8}$ and

$M_y = \int_0^1 \int_{x^2}^1 x^2 y\, dy\, dx = \frac{2}{21}$. The center of mass

then is $\left(\dfrac{M_y}{m}, \dfrac{M_x}{m} \right) = \left(\dfrac{4}{7}, \dfrac{3}{4} \right)$.

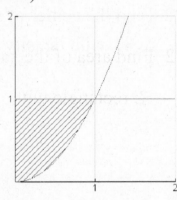

3. Find I_x, I_y, I_0, $\bar{x}$, and $\bar{y}$ for the rectangular lamina bounded by $0 \le x \le 2$ and $0 \le y \le 3$ with density $\rho = 2y$. (Similar to Exercise #33.)

First, we find $m = \int_0^2 \int_0^3 2y\, dy\, dx = 18$, $M_x = \int_0^2 \int_0^3 2y^2\, dy\, dx = 36$, and

$M_y = \int_0^2 \int_0^3 2xy\, dy\, dx = 18$, so that $\bar{x} = 1$ and $\bar{y} = 2$. Then we find

$I_x = \int_0^2 \int_0^3 2y^3\, dy\, dx = 81$, $I_y = \int_0^2 \int_0^3 2x^2 y\, dy\, dx = 24$, so that

$I_0 = I_x + I_y = 105$.

4. Set up, but do not evaluate, the double integral required to find the moment of inertia for the circular lamina $x^2 + y^2 = 4$ about the line $y = 3$ with density $\rho = k$. (Similar to Exercise #41.)

The distance from any point in the lamina to the line is $d = 3 - y$, so the inertia is $I = \iint_R (3 - y)^2 k\, dA$. Using polar, we set up

$$I = \int_0^{2\pi} \int_0^2 k(3 - r\sin(\theta))^2 r\, dr\, d\theta.$$

14.5 Homework Quiz

1. Find the area of the surface $z = 3x + y$ over the region R: triangle with vertices $(0,0)$, $(2,0)$, $(0,2)$.

2. Find area of the surface $f(x,y) = 3 + \dfrac{2}{3} y^{3/2}$ over the region

   R: rectangle with vertices $(0,0), (2,0), (2,3), (0,3)$.

3. Find the area of the portion of the sphere $x^2 + y^2 + z^2 = 16$ that is inside the cylinder $x^2 + y^2 = 12$.

4. Set up a double integral that gives the area of the surface on the graph of $f(x,y) = e^y \sin(x)$ over the region $R: \ 0 \le x \le y, \ 0 \le y \le 5$.

14.5 Homework Quiz Answers

1. Find the area of the surface $z = 3x + y$ over the region R: triangle with vertices $(0,0)$, $(2,0)$, $(0,2)$. (Similar to Exercise #1.)

The surface area is $\int_0^2 \int_0^{2-x} \sqrt{1+3^2+1^2}\, dy\, dx = \int_0^2 (2-x)\sqrt{11}\, dx = 2\sqrt{11}$.

2. Find area of the surface $f(x,y) = 3 + \dfrac{2}{3} y^{3/2}$ over the region

   R: rectangle with vertices $(0,0),(2,0),(2,3),(0,3)$.
   (Similar to Exercise #8.)

   The surface area is $\int_0^2 \int_0^3 \sqrt{1 + (0)^2 + \left(y^{1/2}\right)^2}\, dy\, dx = \int_0^2 \int_0^3 \sqrt{1+y}\, dy\, dx$.

   Use a substitution $u = 1 + y$ to get $\int_0^2 \dfrac{2}{3}(1+y)^{3/2}\Big|_0^3 \, dx = \int_0^2 \dfrac{14}{3}\, dx = \dfrac{28}{3}$.

3. Find the area of the portion of the sphere $x^2 + y^2 + z^2 = 16$ that is inside the cylinder $x^2 + y^2 = 12$. (Similar to Exercise #17.)

   The top half is the portion of the hemisphere $z = \sqrt{16 - x^2 - y^2}$ above the circle R: $x^2 + y^2 = 12$. Double to get the total surface area of

   $$2 \iint_R \sqrt{1 + \left(\frac{-x}{\sqrt{16-x^2-y^2}}\right)^2 + \left(\frac{-y}{\sqrt{16-x^2-y^2}}\right)^2}\, dA.\ \text{Using polar, we}$$

   find $2 \int_0^{2\pi} \int_0^{\sqrt{12}} \dfrac{4}{\sqrt{16-r^2}} r\, dr\, d\theta = 8 \int_0^{2\pi} -\sqrt{4} + \sqrt{16}\, d\theta = 32\pi$.

4. Set up a double integral that gives the area of the surface on the graph of $f(x,y) = e^y \sin(x)$ over the region R: $0 \le x \le y$, $0 \le y \le 5$. (Similar to Exercise #34.)

   We first compute the partial derivatives
   $f_x(x,y) = e^y \cos(x)$ and $f_y(x,y) = e^y \sin(x)$. Then, plug them into the

   surface area formula to get $\int_0^5 \int_0^y \sqrt{1 + e^{2y}\cos^2(x) + e^{2y}\sin^2(x)}\, dx\, dy$

   which simplifies to $S.A. = \int_0^5 \int_0^y \sqrt{1 + e^{2y}}\, dx\, dy$.

14.6 Homework Quiz

1. Evaluate the iterated integral $\int_0^2 \int_0^{\pi/2} \int_0^{1-z} z\cos(x)\,dy\,dx\,dz$.

2. Set up a triple integral for the volume of the solid bounded by $z = 4 - y^2$, $z = 0$, $x = 0$, and $x = 2y$.

3. Rewrite the integral $\int_0^3 \int_0^x \int_0^{4-2x-y} dz\,dy\,dx$ using the order $dz\,dx\,dy$.

4. Find $\bar{y}$ for the solid bounded by $Q: 2x + 2x + 7z = 14$, $x = 0$, $y = 0$, and $z = 0$ with density $\rho(x,y,z) = 7y$.

14.6 Homework Quiz Answers

1. Evaluate the iterated integral $\int_0^2 \int_0^{\pi/2} \int_0^{1-z} z\cos(x)\,dy\,dx\,dz$.
   (Similar to Exercise #7.)

   Starting on the inside, we compute $\int_0^2 \int_0^{\pi/2} z(1-z)\cos(x)\,dx\,dz$ then

   $\int_0^2 z(1-z)\sin(x)\Big|_0^{\pi/2}\,dz = \int_0^2 z - z^2\,dz$ and finally $\dfrac{z^2}{2} - \dfrac{z^3}{3}\bigg|_0^2 = 2 - \dfrac{8}{3} = -\dfrac{2}{3}$.

2. Set up a triple integral for the volume of the solid bounded by
   $z = 4 - y^2$, $z = 0$, $x = 0$, and $x = 2y$. (Similar to Exercise #14.)
   The surface is the portion of a parabolic cylinder $z = 4 - y^2$ above the
   triangle in the xy-plane with vertices $(0,0)$, $(0,2)$, and $(4,2)$. So, the

   volume is $\iiint_V 1\,dV = \int_0^2 \int_0^{2y} \int_0^{4-y^2} 1\,dz\,dx\,dy$ or $\iiint_V 1\,dV = \int_0^4 \int_{x/2}^2 \int_0^{4-y^2} 1\,dz\,dy\,dx$.

3. Rewrite the integral $\int_0^3 \int_0^x \int_0^{4-2x-y} dz\,dy\,dx$ using the order $dz\,dx\,dy$.
   (Similar to Exercise #30.)

   The bounding surface on the top and bottom remain the same, so we
   need only rewrite the projection in the xy-plane in reverse order.
   Horizontal slices through the triangle range from $x = 3$ on the right to
   $x = y$ on the left, so the integral becomes $\int_0^3 \int_y^3 \int_0^{4-2x-y} dz\,dy\,dx$.

4. Find $\bar{y}$ for the solid bounded by Q: $2x + 2x + 7z = 14$,
   $x = 0$, $y = 0$, and $z = 0$ with density $\rho(x,y,z) = 7y$.
   (Similar to Exercise #40.)

   We first compute the mass $m = \int_0^7 \int_0^{7-x} \int_0^{\frac{14-2x-2y}{7}} 7y\,dz\,dy\,dx$

   $= \int_0^7 \int_0^{7-x} 14y - 2xy - 2y^2\,dy\,dx = \dfrac{1}{3}\int_0^7 (7-x)^3\,dx = \dfrac{7^4}{12}$. Then we find

   $M_{xz} = \int_0^7 \int_0^{7-x} \int_0^{\frac{14-2x-2y}{7}} 7y^2\,dz\,dy\,dx = \dfrac{7^5}{30}$, so that $\bar{y} = \dfrac{M_{xz}}{m} = \dfrac{\frac{7^5}{30}}{\frac{7^4}{12}} = \dfrac{14}{5}$.

14.7 Homework Quiz

1. Evaluate the iterated integral $\int_0^\pi \int_0^{\pi/4} \int_0^{2\cos\phi} \left(\rho^2 \sin\phi\right) d\rho \, d\phi \, d\theta$.

2. Sketch the solid region whose volume is given by the iterated integral $\int_0^{2\pi} \int_0^3 \int_0^{9-r^2} r \, dz \, dr \, d\theta$ and evaluate.

3. Use cylindrical coordinates to find the volume of the solid bounded above by $z = 3y$ and below by $z = 3x^2 + 3y^2$.

4. Use spherical coordinates to find the volume of the solid inside the sphere $x^2 + y^2 + z^2 = 25$, outside the cone $z = \sqrt{3x^2 + 3y^2}$ and above the xy-plane.

14.7 Homework Quiz Answers

1. Evaluate the iterated integral $\displaystyle\int_0^\pi \int_0^{\pi/4} \int_0^{2\cos\phi} \left(\rho^2 \sin\phi\right) d\rho\, d\phi\, d\theta$.

   (Similar to Exercise #5.)

   Starting on the inside, we compute $\displaystyle\int_0^\pi \int_0^{\pi/4} \frac{8}{3}\cos^3\phi \sin\phi\, d\phi\, d\theta$

   $\displaystyle = \int_0^\pi -\frac{2}{3}\cos^4\phi \Big|_0^{\pi/4} d\theta = \int_0^\pi -\frac{2}{3}\left(\frac{1}{4}-1\right) d\theta = \frac{\pi}{2}.$

2. Sketch the solid region whose volume is given by the iterated integral

   $\displaystyle\int_0^{2\pi} \int_0^3 \int_0^{9-r^2} r\, dz\, dr\, d\theta$ and evaluate. (Similar to Exercise #10.)

   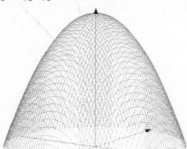

   The solid is bounded by a paraboloid above the xy-plane. The volume is

   $$V = \int_0^{2\pi} \int_0^3 \int_0^{9-r^2} r\, dz\, dr\, d\theta$$

   $$= \int_0^{2\pi} \int_0^3 9r - r^3\, dr\, d\theta = \int_0^{2\pi} \frac{81}{2} - \frac{81}{4} d\theta = \frac{81\pi}{2}.$$

3. Use cylindrical coordinates to find the volume of the solid bounded above by $z = 3y$ and below by $z = 3x^2 + 3y^2$ (Similar to Exercise #19.)

   The paraboloid and plane intersect on the circle $3y = 3x^2 + 3y^2$ which in polar is $r\sin(\theta) = r^2$ or just $r = \sin(\theta)$. The volume is obtained with the triple integral $V = \displaystyle\iiint_Q 1dV = \int_0^\pi \int_0^{\sin(\theta)} \int_{3r^2}^{3r\sin(\theta)} r\, dz\, dr\, d\theta$. We then

   compute $V = \displaystyle\int_0^\pi \int_0^{\sin(\theta)} 3r^2\sin\theta - 3r^3\, dr\, d\theta = \frac{1}{4}\int_0^\pi \sin^4\theta\, d\theta = \frac{3\pi}{32}.$

4. Use spherical coordinates to find the volume of the solid inside the sphere $x^2 + y^2 + z^2 = 25$, outside the cone $z = \sqrt{3x^2 + 3y^2}$ and above the xy-plane. (Similar to Exercise #33.)

   The cone has angle $\phi = \tan^{-1}\left(\dfrac{r}{z}\right) = \tan^{-1}\left(\dfrac{1}{\sqrt{3}}\right) = \dfrac{\pi}{6}$. So, in spherical

   coordinates, we find $\displaystyle\iiint_V 1dV = \int_0^{2\pi} \int_{\pi/6}^{\pi/2} \int_0^5 \rho^2 \sin\phi\, d\rho\, d\phi\, d\theta = \frac{125\pi\sqrt{3}}{3}.$

354

14.8 Homework Quiz

1. Find the Jacobian $\dfrac{\partial(x,y)}{\partial(u,v)}$ for the change of variables

   $x = 2v - uv$, $y = uv - 2u$.

2. Sketch the image S in the uv-plane of the region R in the xy-plane after the transformation $x = 2u$, $y = u + v$.

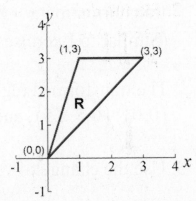

3. Use the change of variables $x = \dfrac{1}{2}(u + v)$, $y = \dfrac{1}{2}(u - v)$ to evaluate the integral $\iint\limits_{R} (x^2 + y^2)\, dA$ over the square region R with vertices at

   $(1,1)$, $(2,0)$, $(1,-1)$, $(0,0)$.

4. Use a change of variables to find the volume of the solid region below $f(x,y) = \sqrt{(x-y)(x+2y)}$ and above the plane region R: bounded by the parallelogram $(0,0), (1,1), (3,0), (2,-1)$.

14.8 Homework Quiz Answers

1. Find the Jacobian $\dfrac{\partial(x,y)}{\partial(u,v)}$ for the change of variables

$x = 2v - uv$, $y = uv - 2u$. (Similar to Exercise #4.)
The Jacobian is

$$\dfrac{\partial(x,y)}{\partial(u,v)} = \begin{vmatrix} -v & 2-u \\ v-2 & u \end{vmatrix} = -uv - (v-2)(2-u) = 4 - 2u - 2v.$$

2. Sketch the image S in the uv-plane of the region R in the xy-plane after the transformation $x = 2u$, $y = u+v$.
(Similar to Exercise #9.)

The transformed region S has vertices at $(0,0)$, $(0.5, 2.5)$, and $(1.5, 1.5)$.

3. Use the change of variables $x = \dfrac{1}{2}(u+v)$, $y = \dfrac{1}{2}(u-v)$ to evaluate the

integral $\displaystyle\iint_R (x^2 + y^2)\,dA$ over the square region R with vertices at

$(1,1)$, $(2,0)$, $(1,-1)$, $(0,0)$. (Similar to Exercise #15.)
The transformed region S has vertices at

$(2,0)$, $(2,2)$, $(0,2)$, and $(0,0)$. The Jacobian is $\begin{vmatrix} 0.5 & 0.5 \\ 0.5 & -0.5 \end{vmatrix} = -0.5$,

so $\displaystyle\iint_R (x^2 + y^2)\,dA = \int_0^2 \int_0^2 \frac{1}{2}(u^2 + v^2)\frac{1}{2}\,du\,dv = \frac{8}{3}.$

4. Use a change of variables to find the volume of the solid region below
$f(x,y) = \sqrt{(x-y)(x+2y)}$ and above the plane region R: bounded by
the parallelogram $(0,0),(1,1),(3,0),(2,-1)$. (Similar to Exercise #25.)

Let $u = x - y$ and $v = x + 2y$ so that $x = \dfrac{1}{3}(2u+v)$ and $y = \dfrac{1}{3}(v-u)$.

The region becomes $S: 0 \le u \le 3$, $0 \le v \le 3$, the Jacobian is

$\begin{vmatrix} \frac{2}{3} & \frac{1}{3} \\ -\frac{1}{3} & \frac{1}{3} \end{vmatrix} = \dfrac{1}{3}$ and thus $V = \int_0^3 \int_0^3 \frac{1}{3}\sqrt{uv}\,du\,dv = \int_0^3 \frac{2}{9}\sqrt{v}(3)^{3/2}\,dv = 4.$

15.1 Homework Quiz

1. Let $\bar{F}(x,y) = x\hat{i} + 3y\hat{j}$. Compute $\|\bar{F}\|$ and sketch several representative vectors in the vector field.

2. Let $\bar{F}(x,y,z) = xy^2z\hat{i} - yz^2\hat{j} + x^2y\hat{k}$. Find curl $\bar{F}$ at $(-1,1,2)$.

3. Determine whether the vector field $\bar{F}(x,y,z) = 2xyz\hat{i} + x^2z\hat{j} + x^2y\hat{k}$ is conservative. If so, find a potential function.

4. Find the divergence of the vector field
$\bar{F}(x,y,z) = e^y\cos(x)\hat{i} - e^y\sin(x)\hat{j} + z^3\hat{k}$ at the point $\left(\frac{\pi}{2},0,1\right)$.

15.1 Homework Quiz Answers

1. Let $\vec{F}(x, y) = x\hat{i} + 3y\hat{j}$. Compute $\|\vec{F}\|$ and sketch several representative vectors in the vector field. (Similar to Exercise #13.)

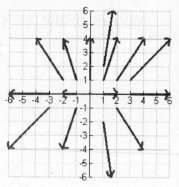

The magnitude is $\|\vec{F}\| = \sqrt{x^2 + 9y^2}$.

2. Let $\vec{F}(x, y, z) = xy^2 z\hat{i} - yz^2 \hat{j} + x^2 y\hat{k}$. Find curl $\vec{F}$ at $(-1, 1, 2)$. (Similar to Exercise #50.)

$$\text{curl } \vec{F} = \begin{vmatrix} \hat{i} & \hat{j} & \hat{k} \\ \dfrac{\partial}{\partial x} & \dfrac{\partial}{\partial y} & \dfrac{\partial}{\partial z} \\ xy^2 z & -yz^2 & x^2 y \end{vmatrix} = \hat{i}(x^2 + 2yz) - \hat{j}(2xy - xy^2) + \hat{k}(0 - 2xyz)$$

At the point, we get curl $\vec{F}(-1, 1, 2) = 5\hat{i} + 3\hat{j} + 4\hat{k}$.

3. Determine whether the vector field $\vec{F}(x, y, z) = 2xyz\hat{i} + x^2 z\hat{j} + x^2 y\hat{k}$ is conservative. If so, find a potential function. (Similar to Exercise #58.)

Using $M = 2xyz$, $N = x^2 z$, and $P = x^2 y$, we calculate

$$\frac{\partial P}{\partial y} = x^2 = \frac{\partial N}{\partial z}, \quad \frac{\partial P}{\partial x} = 2xy = \frac{\partial M}{\partial z}, \quad \text{and} \quad \frac{\partial N}{\partial x} = 2xz = \frac{\partial M}{\partial y}. \text{ So, the vector}$$

field is conservative. To find the potential we integrate and compare:
$f = \int 2xyz\, dx$, $f = \int x^2 z\, dy$, and $f = \int x^2 y\, dz$ to find $f(x, y, z) = x^2 yz + C$.

4. Find the divergence of the vector field

$\vec{F}(x, y, z) = e^y \cos(x)\hat{i} - e^y \sin(x)\hat{j} + z^3 \hat{k}$ at the point $\left(\frac{\pi}{2}, 0, 1\right)$. (Similar to Exercise #69.)

The divergence is $div\ \vec{F} = \nabla \cdot \vec{F} = -e^y \sin(x) - e^y \sin(x) + 3z^2$. At the point, we get $div\ \vec{F}\left(\frac{\pi}{2}, 0, 1\right) = -2 + 3 = 1$.

15.2 Homework Quiz

1. Find the total mass of the wire $\vec{r}(t) = (2t)\hat{i} + (3t)\hat{j} + (t)\hat{k}$, $0 \le t \le 2$ with density $\rho(x, y, z) = x + y + z$.

2. Let $\vec{F}(x, y) = 2x\hat{i} + y\hat{j}$ and C be the curve parameterized by $\vec{r}(t) = \sin(t)\hat{i} + \cos(t)\hat{j}$, $0 \le t \le \pi/2$. Evaluate $\int_C \vec{F} \cdot d\vec{r}$.

3. Find the work done by the force field $\vec{F}(x, y) = x^2\hat{i} + y\hat{j}$ in moving a particle along the cubic curve $y = x^3$ from the point $(1,1)$ to the point $(2,8)$.

4. Evaluate the integral $\int_C (x - 2y)\,dx + (2x + y)\,dy$ where C is the arc on $y = x^2$ from $(0,0)$ to $(1,1)$.

15.2 Homework Quiz Answers

1. Find the total mass of the wire $\bar{r}(t) = (2t)\hat{i} + (3t)\hat{j} + (t)\hat{k}$, $0 \le t \le 2$ with density $\rho(x,y,z) = x + y + z$. (Similar to Exercise #25.)

    Since $ds = \|\bar{r}'(t)\| dt = \sqrt{2^2 + 3^2 + 1^2}\, dt = \sqrt{14}\, dt$, we can use a line integral to compute Mass $= \int_C \rho\, ds = \int_0^2 (2t + 3t + t)\sqrt{14}\, dt = 12\sqrt{14}$.

2. Let $\bar{F}(x,y) = 2x\hat{i} + y\hat{j}$ and C be the curve parameterized by $\bar{r}(t) = \sin(t)\hat{i} + \cos(t)\hat{j}$, $0 \le t \le \pi/2$. Evaluate $\int_C \bar{F} \cdot d\bar{r}$.

    (Similar to Exercise #29.)

    We first find $\bar{r}'(t) = \cos(t)\hat{i} - \sin(t)\hat{j}$ and $\bar{F}(t) = 2\sin(t)\hat{i} + \cos(t)\hat{j}$ so that $\int_C \bar{F} \cdot d\bar{r} = \int_0^{\pi/2} 2\sin(t)\cos(t) - \sin(t)\cos(t)\, dt = \dfrac{1}{2}$.

3. Find the work done by the force field $\bar{F}(x,y) = x^2\hat{i} + y\hat{j}$ in moving a particle along the cubic curve $y = x^3$ from the point $(1,1)$ to the point $(2,8)$. (Similar to Exercise #35.)

    Let $x = t$. We can parameterize the path as $\bar{r}(t) = t\hat{i} + t^3\hat{j}$, $1 \le t \le 2$. The work is $W = \int_C \bar{F} \cdot d\bar{r}$, so we compute $\bar{r}'(t) = \hat{i} + 3t^2\hat{j}$ and

    $\bar{F}(t) = t^2\hat{i} + t^3\hat{j}$ to evaluate $W = \int_1^2 t^2 + 3t^5\, dt = \left(\dfrac{t^3}{3} + \dfrac{t^6}{6}\right)\Big|_1^2 = \dfrac{203}{6}$.

4. Evaluate the integral $\int_C (x - 2y)dx + (2x + y)dy$ where C is the arc on $y = x^2$ from $(0,0)$ to $(1,1)$. (Similar to Exercise #59.)

    We parameterize C with $\bar{r}(t) = t\hat{i} + t^2\hat{j}$, $0 \le t \le 1$ and evaluate

    $\int_0^1 (t - 2t^2)(1) + (2t + t^2)(2t)\, dt = \int_0^1 t + 2t^2 + 2t^3\, dt = \dfrac{5}{3}$.

15.3 Homework Quiz

1. Find the value of the line integral $\int_C \vec{F} \cdot d\vec{r}$ with $\vec{F}(x,y) = y^2\hat{i} + 2xy\hat{j}$

   and $C: \vec{r}(t) = t^2\hat{i} + t^3\hat{j},\ 0 \le t \le 1.$

2. Find the value of the line integral $\int_C \left(x^2 + y^2\right)dx + 2xy\,dy$ with

   $C:$ ellipse $\dfrac{x^2}{9} + \dfrac{y^2}{4} = 1$ from $(3,0)$ to $(0,2).$

3. Evaluate $\int_C \left(2x\hat{i} + 2y\hat{j}\right) \cdot d\vec{r}$ where C is any smooth curve from

   $(1,0)$ to $(2,3).$

4. Find the work done by the force field $\vec{F}(x,y) = \left(1 + 2y^3\right)\hat{i} + \left(6xy^2\right)\hat{j}$
   in moving a particle from $(0,0)$ to $(3,4).$

15.3 Homework Quiz Answers

1. Find the value of the line integral $\int_C \vec{F} \cdot d\vec{r}$ with $\vec{F}(x,y) = y^2\hat{i} + 2xy\hat{j}$

   and $C: \vec{r}(t) = t^2\hat{i} + t^3\hat{j}$, $0 \le t \le 1$. (Similar to Exercise #11.)

   Since $\dfrac{\partial M}{\partial y} = 2y = \dfrac{\partial N}{\partial x}$, the vector field is conservative with potential

   function $f(x,y) = xy^2$. The path begins at $(0,0)$ and ends at $(1,1)$. The

   fundamental theorem of line integrals gives $\int_C \vec{F} \cdot d\vec{r} = \left(xy^2\right)\Big|_{(0,0)}^{(1,1)} = 1$.

2. Find the value of the line integral $\int_C \left(x^2 + y^2\right)dx + 2xy\,dy$ with

   $C:$ ellipse $\dfrac{x^2}{9} + \dfrac{y^2}{4} = 1$ from $(3,0)$ to $(0,2)$.

   (Similar to Exercise #17.)

   Let $\vec{F}(x,y) = \left(x^2 + y^2\right)\hat{i} + (2xy)\hat{j}$ then the integral is $\int_C \vec{F} \cdot d\vec{r}$. But,

   $\dfrac{\partial M}{\partial y} = 2y = \dfrac{\partial N}{\partial x}$, so the vector field is conservative with potential

   function $f(x,y) = \dfrac{x^3}{3} + xy^2$. Thus, $\int_C \vec{F} \cdot d\vec{r} = f(0,2) - f(3,0) = -9$.

3. Evaluate $\int_C \left(2x\hat{i} + 2y\hat{j}\right) \cdot d\vec{r}$ where C is any smooth curve from

   $(1,0)$ to $(2,3)$. (Similar to Exercise #25.)

   Let $\vec{F}(x,y) = 2x\hat{i} + 2y\hat{j}$ and find $\dfrac{\partial M}{\partial y} = 0 = \dfrac{\partial N}{\partial x}$. So $\vec{F}$ is conservative

   with potential $f(x,y) = x^2 + y^2$ and $\int_C \vec{F} \cdot d\vec{r} = f(2,3) - f(1,0) = 12$.

4. Find the work done by the force field $\vec{F}(x,y) = \left(1 + 2y^3\right)\hat{i} + \left(6xy^2\right)\hat{j}$

   in moving a particle from $(0,0)$ to $(3,4)$. (Similar to Exercise #35.)

   Note that $\dfrac{\partial M}{\partial y} = 6y^2 = \dfrac{\partial N}{\partial x}$ so $\vec{F}$ is conservative with potential

   $f(x,y) = x + 2xy^3$ and $\int_C \vec{F} \cdot d\vec{r} = f(3,4) - f(0,0) = 387$.

15.4 Homework Quiz

1. Use Green's Theorem to evaluate the integral

$$\int_C (3x + y)\,dx + (2x - 2y)\,dy \quad \text{for } C: x = \cos(\theta),\ y = 2\sin(\theta).$$

2. Use Green's Theorem to evaluate $\int_C \left(2e^y \cos(2x)\right) dx + \left(e^y \sin(2x)\right) dy$

   with $C: x^2 + y^2 = 9$ counterclockwise.

3. Use Green's Theorem to calculate the work done by the force

   $\vec{F}(x, y) = \left(e^{x^2} - 2y\right)\hat{i} + \left(\cos(e^y) + 3x\right)\hat{j}$ on a particle that moves

   counterclockwise around $C: r = 4\cos(\theta)$.

4. Use a line integral to find the area of the region

   $R:$ region bounded by $\dfrac{x^2}{4} + \dfrac{y^2}{9} = 1$.

15.4 Homework Quiz Answers

1. Use Green's Theorem to evaluate $\int_C (3x + y)dx + (2x - 2y)dy$ for

   $C: x = \cos(\theta), y = 2\sin(\theta)$. (Similar to Exercise #8.)

   We first find $\dfrac{\partial N}{\partial x} = 2$ and $\dfrac{\partial M}{\partial y} = 1$. The curve C is a counter-

   clockwise parameterization of the ellipse $x^2 + \dfrac{y^2}{4} = 1$. Applying

   Green's theorem, $\int_C (3x + y)dx + (2x - y)dy = \iint_R (2 - 1)dA = \text{Area}$

   bounded by $C = 2\pi$.

2. Use Green's Theorem to evaluate $\int_C (2e^y \cos(2x))dx + (e^y \sin(2x))dy$

   with $C: x^2 + y^2 = 9$ counterclockwise. (Similar to Exercise #15.)

   We first find $\dfrac{\partial N}{\partial x} = 2e^y \cos(2x) = \dfrac{\partial M}{\partial y}$, so by Green's Theorem

   $\int_C (2e^y \cos(2x))dx - (e^y \sin(2x))dy = \iint_R (0)dA = 0$.

3. Use Green's Theorem to calculate the work done by the force

   $\vec{F}(x, y) = \left(e^{x^2} - 2y\right)\hat{i} + \left(\cos(e^y) + 3x\right)\hat{j}$ on a particle that moves

   counterclockwise around $C: r = 4\cos(\theta)$. (Similar to Exercise #22.)

   If $\vec{F} = M\hat{i} + N\hat{j}$, we find $\dfrac{\partial N}{\partial x} = 3$ and $\dfrac{\partial M}{\partial y} = -2$. Applying Green's

   Theorem, we get $\int_C \vec{F} \cdot d\vec{r} = \iint_R (3 + 2)dA = 5(\text{Area of R}) = 20\pi$.

4. Use a line integral to find the area of the region

   R: region bounded by $\dfrac{x^2}{4} + \dfrac{y^2}{9} = 1$. (Similar to Exercise #25.)

   A counterclockwise parameterization of the ellipse C is $x = 2\cos(\theta)$,

   $y = 3\sin(\theta)$ $0 \le \theta \le 2\pi$. The area is $A = \dfrac{1}{2}\int_C x\,dy - y\,dx$

   $= \dfrac{1}{2}\int_0^{2\pi} 2\cos(\theta)3\cos(\theta) - 3\sin(\theta)(-2\sin(\theta))d\theta = \int_0^{2\pi} 3\,d\theta = 6\pi$.

364

15.5 Homework Quiz

1. Find the rectangular equation for the surface
$\vec{r}(u,v) = u\hat{i} + 3\cos(v)\hat{j} + 3\sin(v)\hat{k}$. Identify the surface and sketch.

2. Find a vector-valued function whose graph is the ellipsoid
$\dfrac{x^2}{4} + y^2 + \dfrac{z^2}{9} = 1$.

3. Use Green's Theorem to calculate the work done by the force
$\vec{F}(x,y) = \left(e^{x^2} - 2y\right)\hat{i} + \left(\cos(e^y) + 3x\right)\hat{j}$ on a particle that moves counterclockwise around $C: r = 4\cos(\theta)$.

4. Find the area of the portion of the paraboloid
$\vec{r}(u,v) = 4v\cos(u)\hat{i} + 4v\sin(u)\hat{j} + v^2\hat{k}$, for $0 \le u \le \pi$, and $0 \le v \le 4$.

15.5 Homework Quiz Answers

1. Find the rectangular equation for the surface $\vec{r}(u,v) = u\hat{i} + 3\cos(v)\hat{j} + 3\sin(v)\hat{k}$. Identify the surface and sketch.
(Similar to Exercise #9.)

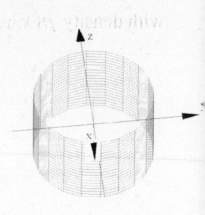

We notice that $x = u$ has no restrictions and $y^2 + z^2 = 9\cos^2(v) + 9\sin^2(v) = 9$. So the equation is $y^2 + z^2 = 9$ and is a cylinder of radius 3 extending in the x-direction.

2. Find a vector-valued function whose graph is the ellipsoid $\dfrac{x^2}{4} + y^2 + \dfrac{z^2}{9} = 1$. (Similar to Exercise #28.)

We let $x = 2\sin(u)\sin(v)$, $y = \cos(u)\sin(v)$, and $z = 3\cos(v)$, then the parameterization is $0 \le u \le 2\pi, 0 \le v \le 2\pi$ and
$\vec{r}(u,v) = 2\sin(u)\sin(v)\hat{i} + \cos(u)\sin(v)\hat{j} + 3\cos(v)\hat{k}$.

3. Find an equation for the tangent plane to the surface $\vec{r}(u,v) = uv\hat{i} + u\hat{j} + v\hat{k}$ at the point $(6,2,3)$. (Similar to Exercise #36.)

A normal vector is given by $\vec{r}_u \times \vec{r}_v = \begin{vmatrix} \hat{i} & \hat{j} & \hat{k} \\ v & 1 & 0 \\ u & 0 & 1 \end{vmatrix} = \hat{i} - v\hat{j} - u\hat{k}$. So

$\vec{N}(6,2,3) = i - 3\hat{j} - 2\hat{k}$. The plane is $(x-6) - 3(y-2) - 2(z-3) = 0$.

4. Find the area of the portion of the paraboloid $\vec{r}(u,v) = 4v\cos(u)\hat{i} + 4v\sin(u)\hat{j} + v^2\hat{k}$, with $0 \le u \le \pi$, and $0 \le v \le 4$.
(Similar to Exercise #40.)
We first find

$\vec{r}_u \times \vec{r}_v = \begin{vmatrix} \hat{i} & \hat{j} & \hat{k} \\ -4v\sin(u) & 4v\cos(u) & 0 \\ 4\cos(u) & 4\sin(u) & 2v \end{vmatrix} = 8v^2\cos(u)\hat{i} - 8v^2\sin(u)\hat{j} - 16v^2\hat{k}$

and $ds = \|\vec{r}_u \times \vec{r}_v\| dA = \sqrt{320}v^2\,dvdu$. $A = \int_0^\pi \int_0^4 \sqrt{320}v^2\,dvdu = \dfrac{512\sqrt{5}\pi}{3}$.

15.6 Homework Quiz

1. Find the mass of the surface lamina $S: x + y + z = 1$ in the first octant
   with density $\rho(x, y, z) = x^2 + 2y$.

2. Let $S: \bar{r}(u, v) = v\hat{i} + \cos(u)\hat{j} + \sin(u)\hat{k}, \ 0 \le u \le \pi, \ 0 \le v \le 1$.
   Evaluate $\iint_S (2x + y)\, dS$.

3. Let $S: z = x^2 + y^2, \ 1 \le x^2 + y^2 \le 4$. Evaluate $\iint_S (1 + 4x^2 + 4y^2)\, dS$.

4. Find the flux $\iint_S \bar{F} \cdot \bar{N}\, dS$ of $\bar{F}(x, y, z) = x\hat{i} + y\hat{j} + \hat{k}$ through

   $S: z = 4 - x^2 - y^2, \ z \ge 0$ oriented upward.

15.6 Homework Quiz Answers

1. Find the mass of the surface lamina $S: x + y + z = 1$ in the first octant with density $\rho(x, y, z) = x^2 + 2y$. (Similar to Exercise #11.)

   The mass is $m = \iint_S \rho \, dS$. Projecting S onto the xy-plane gives the region $R: 0 \le x \le 1, \ 0 \le y \le 1 - x$ and the plane can be written as $z = 1 - x - y = g(x, y)$. So, $dS = \sqrt{1 + 1 + 1} \, dA = \sqrt{3} \, dA$ and the mass is

   $$\int_0^1 \int_0^{1-x} (x^2 + 2y) \sqrt{3} \, dy \, dx = \sqrt{3} \int_0^1 -x^3 + 2x^2 - 2x + 1 \, dx = \frac{5\sqrt{3}}{12}.$$

2. Let $S: \vec{r}(u, v) = v\hat{i} + \cos(u)\hat{j} + \sin(u)\hat{k}, \ 0 \le u \le \pi, \ 0 \le v \le 1$.

   Evaluate $\iint_S (2x + y) \, dS$. (Similar to Exercise #15.)

   We first find $\vec{r}_u \times \vec{r}_v = \cos(u)\hat{j} + \sin(u)\hat{k}$, so that

   $dS = \sqrt{\cos^2 u + \sin^2 u} \, dA = dA$. The surface integral becomes

   $\int_0^\pi \int_0^1 2v + \cos(u) \, dv \, du = \pi.$

3. Let $S: z = x^2 + y^2, \ 1 \le x^2 + y^2 \le 4$. Evaluate $\iint_S (1 + 4x^2 + 4y^2) \, dS$.

   (Similar to Exercise #18.)

   We convert to an area integral $\iint_R (1 + 4x^2 + 4y^2) \sqrt{1 + (2x)^2 + (2y)^2} \, dA$

   and use polar to compute

   $$\int_0^{2\pi} \int_1^2 (1 + 4r^2)^{3/2} r \, dr \, d\theta = \frac{2}{40} \int_0^{2\pi} (1 + 4r^2)^{5/2} \Big|_1^2 \, d\theta = \frac{\pi}{10}(17^{5/2} - 2^{5/2}).$$

4. Find the flux $\iint_S \vec{F} \cdot \vec{N} \, dS$ of $\vec{F}(x, y, z) = x\hat{i} + y\hat{j} + \hat{k}$ through

   $S: z = 4 - x^2 - y^2, \ z \ge 0$ oriented upward. (Similar to Exercise #25.)

   The flux is $\iint_S \vec{F} \cdot \vec{N} \, dS = \iint_R \vec{F} \cdot (2x\hat{i} + 2y\hat{j} + \hat{k}) \, dA = \iint_R 2x^2 + 2y^2 + 1 \, dA.$

   Using polar, we compute $\int_0^{2\pi} \int_0^2 (2r^2 + 1) r \, dr \, d\theta = 20\pi.$

15.7 Homework Quiz

1. Evaluate $\iint_S \vec{F} \cdot \vec{N} dS$ as a surface integral with

    $\vec{F}(x, y, z) = x^2 \hat{i} + y\hat{j} + 2\hat{k}$ and S :surface bounded by the plane
    $6x + 2y + 3z = 12$ and the coordinate planes.

2. Verify the Divergence Theorem by evaluating $\iint_S \vec{F} \cdot \vec{N} dS$ as a triple

    integral with $\vec{F}$ and S as in Question 1.

3. Use the Divergence Theorem to evaluate $\iint_S \vec{F} \cdot \vec{N} dS$ to find the

    outward flux of $\vec{F}(x, y, z) = y\hat{i} + x\hat{j} + z\hat{k}$ through the surface
    $S: z = \sqrt{9 - x^2 - y^2}$, $z = 0$.

4. Find the outward flux of $\vec{F} = x^2 \hat{i} - y^2 \hat{j} + z\hat{k}$ through
    $S: x^2 + y^2 = 4$, $z = 0$, $z = 5$.

15.7 Homework Quiz Answers

1. Evaluate $\iint\limits_{S} \vec{F} \cdot \vec{N} dS$ as a surface integral with

   $\vec{F}(x,y,z) = x^2 \hat{i} + y\hat{j} + 2\hat{k}$ and S :surface bounded by the plane
   $6x + 2y + 3z = 12$ and the coordinate planes. (Similar to Exercise #3.)
   On the top surface, we get

   $$S_1 = \int_0^2 \int_0^{6-3x} \left(2x^2 + \frac{2}{3}y + 2\right) dy dx = 28 \text{, in}$$

   the xy-plane we have

   $$S_2 = \int_0^2 \int_0^{6-3x} -2 dy dx = -12 \text{, in the } yz\text{-plane}$$

   we have $S_3 = \int_0^4 \int_0^{4-\frac{2}{3}y} -x^2 dz dy = 0$, and in the xz-plane we get

   $$S_4 = \int_0^4 \int_0^{4-2x} -y dz dx = 0. \text{ In total, we have } S_1 + S_2 + S_3 + S_4 = 16.$$

2. Verify the Divergence Theorem by evaluating $\iint\limits_{S} \vec{F} \cdot \vec{N} dS$ as a triple

   integral with $\vec{F}$ and S as in question 1. (Similar to Exercise #3.)
   We compute $Div\ \vec{F} = (2x+1)$ and the triple integral

   $$\int_0^2 \int_0^{6-3x} \int_0^{4-2x-\frac{2}{3}y} (2x+1) dz dy dx = \int_0^2 \int_0^{6-3x} (2x+1)\left(4 - 2x - \frac{2}{3}y\right) dy dx$$

   $$= \int_0^2 6x^3 - 21x^2 + 12x + 12 dx = 16.$$

3. Use the Divergence Theorem to evaluate $\iint\limits_{S} \vec{F} \cdot \vec{N} dS$ to find the

   outward flux of $\vec{F}(x,y,z) = y\hat{i} + x\hat{j} + z\hat{k}$ through the surface
   $S: z = \sqrt{9 - x^2 - y^2}$, $z = 0$. (Similar to Exercise #9.)

   Since $\nabla \cdot \vec{F} = 1$, $\iint\limits_{S} \vec{F} \cdot \vec{N} dS = \iiint\limits_{V} 1 dV = $ Volume $= \frac{1}{2}\left(\frac{4}{3}\pi(3)^3\right) = 18\pi.$

4. Find the outward flux of $\vec{F} = x^2 \hat{i} - y^2 \hat{j} + z\hat{k}$ through

   $S: x^2 + y^2 = 4$, $z = 0$, $z = 5$. (Similar to Exercise #13.)
   Since $\nabla \cdot \vec{F} = 2x - 2y + 1$, we use the Divergence Theorem to get

   $$\iiint\limits_{V} (2x - 2y + 1) dV = \int_0^{2\pi} \int_0^2 \int_0^5 (2r\cos(\theta) - 2r\sin(\theta) + 1) r dz dr d\theta = 20\pi.$$

15.8 Homework Quiz

1. Find the curl of $\bar{F}(x,y,z) = z^2 + xe^y\hat{j} + \arcsin(y)\hat{k}$.

2. Use a line integral to compute $\displaystyle\int_C \bar{F}\cdot\bar{T}\,ds = \int_C \bar{F}\cdot d\bar{r}$ with

   $\bar{F}(x,y,z) = (x+2y)\hat{i} + (-2x+y)\hat{j} + z\hat{k}$ and C the counterclockwise boundary of S : $z = 16 - x^2 - y^2$, $z \geq 0$.

3. Use Stokes's Theorem with a double (surface) integral to compute the line integral from Question 2.

4. Use Stokes's Theorem to evaluate $\displaystyle\int_C \bar{F}\cdot d\bar{r}$ for

   $\bar{F}(x,y,z) = xz\hat{i} + \arctan(y)\hat{j} + xy\hat{k}$ with S : $z = 3 - x - y$ over $r = 2\sin(\theta)$ in the first octant.

15.8 Homework Quiz Answers

1. Find the curl of $\vec{F}(x,y,z) = z^2 + xe^y\hat{j} + \arcsin(y)\hat{k}$.

   (Similar to Exercise #6.)

   We compute

$$curl\ \vec{F} = \nabla \times \vec{F} = \begin{vmatrix} \hat{i} & \hat{j} & \hat{k} \\ \dfrac{\partial}{\partial x} & \dfrac{\partial}{\partial y} & \dfrac{\partial}{\partial z} \\ z^2 & xe^y & \arcsin(y) \end{vmatrix} = \left(\dfrac{1}{\sqrt{1-y^2}}\right)\hat{i} + 2z\hat{j} + e^y\hat{k}.$$

2. Use a line integral to compute $\displaystyle\int_C \vec{F}\cdot\vec{T}ds = \int_C \vec{F}\cdot d\vec{r}$ with

   $\vec{F}(x,y,z) = (x+2y)\hat{i} + (-2x+y)\hat{j} + z\hat{k}$ and C the counterclockwise boundary of S: $z = 16 - x^2 - y^2$, $z \geq 0$. (Similar to Exercise #7.)
   We parameterize C with $\vec{r}(t) = 4\cos(t)\hat{i} + 4\sin(t)\hat{j}$, $0 \leq t \leq 2\pi$ and
   compute $\displaystyle\int_C \vec{F}\cdot d\vec{r} = \int_C (x+2y)dx + (-2x+y)dy + zdz$

$$= \int_0^{2\pi} -32\sin^2(t) - 32\cos^2(t)\,dt = -64\pi.$$

3. Use Stokes's Theorem with a double (surface) integral to compute the line integral from Question 2. (Similar to Exercise #7.)

   Since $curl\ \vec{F} = -4\hat{k}$ and $z = 16 - x^2 - y^2 = g(x,y)$, we compute

$$\int_C \vec{F}\cdot d\vec{r} = \iint_S (curl\ \vec{F})\cdot\vec{N}dS = \iint_R -4dA \text{ or } -4\pi(4)^2 = -64\pi.$$

4. Use Stokes's Theorem to evaluate $\displaystyle\int_C \vec{F}\cdot d\vec{r}$ for

   $\vec{F}(x,y,z) = xz\hat{i} + \arctan(y)\hat{j} + xy\hat{k}$ with S: $z = 3 - x - y$ over $r = 2\sin(\theta)$ in the first octant. (Similar to Exercise #17.)
   Since $curl\ \vec{F} = x\hat{i} + (x-y)\hat{j}$, we compute $\displaystyle\int_C \vec{F}\cdot d\vec{r} = \iint_S (curl\ \vec{F})\cdot\vec{N}dS$

$$= \iint_R 2x - ydA = \int_0^{\pi/2}\int_0^{2\sin(\theta)} 2r^2\cos(\theta) - r^2\sin(\theta)\,drd\theta$$

$$= \int_0^{2\pi} \frac{16}{3}\sin^3(\theta)\cos(\theta) - \frac{8}{3}\sin^4(\theta)\,d\theta = \frac{13}{6} - \frac{\pi}{2}.$$

372

Section I

This section contains 45 multiple-choice questions and contains two parts: Part A and Part B. Part A has 28 questions that must be solved without a calculator. Part B has 17 questions, including some questions that require the use of a graphing calculator.

Part A Multiple-Choice

You may not use a calculator on this portion of the exam.

Directions: Solve each problem in the provided space. Then choose the best option from among the choices given. Be efficient with the use of your time.

Throughout this exam:
(1) The domain of each function f is the set of all real numbers for which $f(x)$ is defined. If the domain of a particular function differs from this, it will be specified in the problem.
(2) For trigonometric functions, the inverse may be represented with "$^{-1}$" or "arc". For example, the inverse cosine function may be represented as $\cos^{-1} x$ or $\arccos x$.

1. $\int \sin\left(\dfrac{1}{4}x\right) dx =$

   (A) $-\cos\left(\dfrac{1}{4}x\right) + C$

   (B) $-4\cos\left(\dfrac{1}{4}x\right) + C$

   (C) $4\cos\left(\dfrac{1}{4}x\right) + C$

   (D) $-\dfrac{1}{4}\cos\left(\dfrac{1}{4}x\right) + C$

   (E) $\dfrac{1}{4}\cos\left(\dfrac{1}{4}x\right) + C$

2. Find $\lim\limits_{x\to 1}\dfrac{x^2-3x+2}{x-1}$.

   (A) 2

   (B) 1

   (C) 0

   (D) -1

   (E) Does not exist

3. For what value(s) of k, if any, is $f(x)=\begin{cases} k^2-x^2 & \text{if } x<2 \\ 2(x+k) & \text{if } x\ge 2 \end{cases}$ continuous on $(-\infty,\infty)$?

   (A) $-4,-2$

   (B) 2

   (C) 4

   (D) $-2,4$

   (E) Does not exist

4. If $f(x)=2x\sqrt{8x-1}$, then $f'(x)$ is

   (A) $x\sqrt{8x-1}$

   (B) $\dfrac{8x}{\sqrt{8x-1}}$

   (C) $2\sqrt{8x-1}+8x$

   (D) $2\sqrt{8x-1}+\dfrac{8x}{\sqrt{8x-1}}$

   (E) $2+\dfrac{8x}{\sqrt{8x-1}}$

5. $\int \dfrac{8}{1+8x}\,dx =$

   (A) $8x + \ln 8x + C$

   (B) $\ln|1+8x| + C$

   (C) $\ln|8x| + C$

   (D) $\dfrac{1}{8}\ln|1+8x| + C$

   (E) $-\dfrac{1}{8}\ln|1+8x| + C$

6. A particle moves along the x-axis so that at any time $t \geq 0$, its velocity is given by $v(t) = \cos(4t)$. If the position of the particle at time $t = \dfrac{\pi}{8}$ is $x = \dfrac{7}{4}$, what is the particle's position at time $t = 0$?

   (A) $\dfrac{2}{3}$

   (B) $\dfrac{5}{4}$

   (C) $-\dfrac{1}{2}$

   (D) 0

   (E) $\dfrac{3}{2}$

7. The function f is continuous on the closed interval $[0,9]$ and has the values given in the table below.

x	0	3	6	9
$f(x)$	8	15	k	12

The trapezoidal approximation for $\int_0^9 f(x)dx$ found with three subintervals of equal length is 90. What is the value of k?

(A) 2

(B) 5

(C) 7

(D) 11

(E) 17

8. $\dfrac{d}{dx}\left(\sin^3\left(x^2\right)\right) =$

(A) $6x\cos^2(2x)$

(B) $6x\sin^2\left(x^2\right)\cos\left(x^2\right)$

(C) $2x\sin^3(x^2)+3x^2\sin^2(2x)$

(D) $6x\sin^2\left(x^2\right)$

(E) $3\cos^2(2x)$

9. A colony of bacteria starts with 500 and grows at a rate proportional to its size. After 3 hours there are 8000 bacteria. When will the population reach 25,000?

(A) 3.87267 hours

(B) 4.01239 hours

(C) 4.23289 hours

(D) 4.98778 hours

(E) 5.43927 hours

10. Given $f(x) = \dfrac{x^4 - 27}{x^2}$, for what values of x is the graph of f concave downwards?

(A) $-3 < x < 0$

(B) $0 < x < 3$

(C) $3 < x < \infty$

(D) $-3 < x < 0$ and $0 < x < 3$

(E) $-\infty < x < -3$ and $3 < x < \infty$

11. Let f be defined by $f(x) = |x - 6|$ for all real numbers x. For what values of x is the function increasing?

(A) $(-\infty, -6)$

(B) $(-\infty, 6)$

(C) $[-6, 0)$

(D) $(0, 6)$

(E) $(6, \infty)$

12. Find an equation for the line tangent to the graph of $f(x) = \sqrt{x - 7}$ at the point where $x = 16$

(A) $y = 6x - 2$

(B) $y = \dfrac{1}{6}x - \dfrac{1}{3}$

(C) $y = \dfrac{1}{6}x + \dfrac{1}{3}$

(D) $y = -6x - 2$

(E) $y = -\dfrac{1}{6}x + \dfrac{1}{3}$

13. $\dfrac{d}{dx}\left(\sin x \cos(2x)\right) =$

   (A) $\cos(x)\cos(2x) - 2\sin(x)\sin(2x)$

   (B) $2\cos(x)\cos(2x) - \sin(x)\sin(2x)$

   (C) $\cos(x)\cos(2x) + 2\sin(x)\sin(2x)$

   (D) $2\cos(x)\cos(2x) - 2\sin(x)\sin(2x)$

   (E) $2\cos(x)\cos(2x) + 2\sin(x)\sin(2x)$

14. Find the function $y = f(x)$ if $\dfrac{dy}{dx} = 2x - 1$ and $f(1) = 3$.

   (A) $x^2 - x + 3$

   (B) $x^2 - x + 5$

   (C) $2x^2 + x - 3$

   (D) $\dfrac{1}{2}x^2 - x + \dfrac{5}{2}$

   (E) $x^2 - 4x + 6$

15. $\displaystyle\int_{1}^{2} xe^{6x^2}\,dx =$

   (A) $\dfrac{e^{12} - e^4}{8}$

   (B) $\dfrac{e^{24} - e^6}{12}$

   (C) $\dfrac{e^{24} - e^{12}}{12}$

   (D) $\dfrac{e^{24} + e^6}{12}$

   (E) $\dfrac{e^2 - e^{12}}{12}$

16. How many points of inflection does $f(x) = 3x(x+2)^3$.

    (A) 0

    (B) 1

    (C) 2

    (D) 3

    (E) 4

17. Find the area of the region bound by $f(x) = x^2$ and $g(x) = x^3$.

    (A) $\dfrac{1}{6}$

    (B) $\dfrac{1}{2}$

    (C) $\dfrac{1}{8}$

    (D) $\dfrac{1}{12}$

    (E) $\dfrac{1}{16}$

18. If $F(x) = \displaystyle\int_{1}^{x^3-10} f(u)\,du$ and $f(-2) = 5$, then $F'(2) =$

    (A) 60

    (B) 30

    (C) 10

    (D) −5

    (E) −10

19. What is the equation of the line tangent to the curve $y = x^3 - 2x^2$ at the point $(2,0)$?

    (A) $y = -4x - 8$

    (B) $y = 4x + 8$

    (C) $y = 4x - 8$

    (D) $y = \frac{1}{4}x - 8$

    (E) $y = -\frac{1}{4}x + 8$

20. A particle moves along the x-axis so that its velocity at any time $t \geq 0$ is given by $v(t) = 4t^3 - 4t$. Which of the following expressions could represent the position $x(t)$ of the particle at any time $t \geq 0$?

    (A) $t^3 - 2t^2 + 4$

    (B) $t^3 - 2t^3$

    (C) $t^4 - 2t^2 + 4$

    (D) $t^4 - 2t - 3$

    (E) $t^4 - 4t^2 + 4$

21. What is the slope of the tangent line to $x^2 + xy + y^2 = 3$ that lies in the first quadrant at the point where $y = 1$?

    (A) -2

    (B) -3

    (C) 3

    (D) -1

    (E) 1

22. If $f(x) = \ln|2x|$ then what is the derivative of the inverse of $f(x)$ at $x = 4$?

(A) $\dfrac{1}{2}e^2$

(B) $\dfrac{1}{4}e^4$

(C) $\dfrac{1}{4}e^2$

(D) $\dfrac{1}{2}e^4$

(E) Undefined

23. The function $f(x) = \dfrac{3x^4 - 5x^3 + 79}{7x^4 + 9x^2 + 11}$ has horizontal asymptote(s) at

(A) $y = \pm 3$

(B) $y = \pm\dfrac{7}{3}$

(C) $y = \dfrac{3}{7}$

(D) $y = 0$

(E) $y = 1$

24. Find the derivative of $f(x) = \dfrac{x-4}{\left(x^2+1\right)^2}$.

(A) $\dfrac{-3x^2+16x+1}{\left(x^2+1\right)^{-2}}$

(B) $\dfrac{-3x^2+16x+1}{\left(x^2+1\right)^2}$

(C) $\dfrac{3x^2-16x-1}{\left(x^2+1\right)^3}$

(D) $\dfrac{-3x^2+16x+1}{\left(x^2+1\right)^4}$

(E) $\dfrac{-3x^2+16x+1}{\left(x^2+1\right)^3}$

25. Evaluate $\dfrac{d}{dx}\displaystyle\int_0^x \left(t^5-7t+9\right)dt$ for $x \geq 0$.

(A) x^4-7

(B) t^5-7t

(C) $5x^4-7x$

(D) t^5-7t+9

(E) x^5-7x+9

26. Find $\displaystyle\lim_{x\to 2}\dfrac{x^3-8}{x-2}$

(A) 8

(B) 12

(C) 16

(D) 4

(E) ∞

27. Which of the following statements is true about $f(x) = -x^3 - 6x^2 - 9x - 2$?

    (A) f is decreasing on $(-3, -1)$

    (B) f is increasing on $(-3, -1)$

    (C) f is increasing on $(-\infty, -3)$

    (D) f is increasing on $(-2, \infty)$

    (E) f is decreasing for all real values

28. For which points on the graph of f is $f'(x)$ positive?

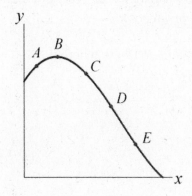

    (A) A and E

    (B) A only

    (C) C only

    (D) C, D, and E

    (E) B only

Part B Multiple-Choice

This portion of the exam requires a graphing calculator for some questions.

This part of the exam contains 17 questions.

Directions: Solve each problem in the provided space. Then choose the best option from among the choices given. Be efficient with the use of your time.

Throughout this exam:
(1) Sometimes the exact numerical value of the solution is not given as a choice. In this event, pick the best numerical approximation from the given choices.
(2) The domain of each function f is the set of all real numbers for which $f(x)$ is defined. If the domain of a particular function differs from this, it will be specified in the problem.
(3) For trigonometric functions, the inverse may be represented with "$^{-1}$" or "arc". For example, the inverse cosine function may be represented as $\cos^{-1} x$ or $\arccos x$.

29. Find the position function, $P(t)$, given $a(t) = 8$, $v(2) = 9$, and $P(1) = 0$ where the acceleration is given by $a(t)$ and the velocity is given by $v(t)$.

    (A) $P(t) = 4t^2 - 7t - 3$

    (B) $P(t) = 4t^2 - 7t + 3$

    (C) $P(t) = t^2 - 7t + 3$

    (D) $P(t) = 4t^2 + 7t + 3$

    (E) $P(t) = t^2 + 7t + 3$

30. Give a value of c that satisfies the conclusion of the Mean Value Theorem for Derivatives for the function $f(x) = -2x^2 - x + 2$ on the interval $[1,3]$.

    (A) $\dfrac{9}{4}$

    (B) $\dfrac{3}{2}$

    (C) $\dfrac{1}{2}$

    (D) 2

    (E) $\dfrac{5}{4}$

31. The volume of a sphere with radius r is $V = \frac{4}{3}\pi r^3$. At the time when the volume and radius are changing at the same numerical amount, what is the volume?

    (A) 4.18879

    (B) 0.282095

    (C) 0.094032

    (D) 0.023508

    (E) 0.376126

32. Given $f(x) = (1+5x)^{\frac{1}{3x}}$ find $\lim\limits_{x \to 0} f(x)$.

    (A) 1.66667

    (B) 1.82212

    (C) 5.29449

    (D) 1.06894

    (E) 0.000000305902

33. Find the value of c on the interval $[0, \pi]$ that satisfies the Mean Value Theorem for Derivatives given $f(x) = x - \cos x$.

    (A) 1.6366

    (B) 0.6901

    (C) 0.6366

    (D) 1.9471

    (E) 3.1415

34. If $f'(x) = 2x\sin(2x)$ for $0 < x < 4$ then f has a local max at $x \approx$

(A) 3.990

(B) 3.142

(C) 1.782

(D) 6.345

(E) 1.571

35. A rock is thrown upwards (vertically) from the ground with an initial velocity of 40 feet per second. If the acceleration due to gravity is $-10\dfrac{ft}{\sec^2}$, how high will the rock go?

(A) 20 feet

(B) 40 feet

(C) 80 feet

(D) 100 feet

(E) 120 feet

36. What is the average value of the function $f(x) = x^3 + 4x^2 - 5x + 7$ on the interval $[2,6]$?

(A) 545.333

(B) 272.667

(C) 181.778

(D) 155.809

(E) 136.333

37. An object moves along the x-axis so that its velocity at any time $t \geq 0$ is given by $v(t) = 4t^3 - 4t$. Find the total displacement of the particle from $t = 0$ to $t = 2$.

(A) 0

(B) 8

(C) 9

(D) 10

(E) 12

38. Estimate the area under the curve of $f(x) = \cos(x) + 1$ from $x = 1$ to $x = 4$. Use three sub-intervals and right endpoints.

(A) 1.402

(B) 2.942

(C) 1.030

(D) 0.940

(E) 2.596

39. The base of a solid is the region in the xy-plane enclosed by the curves $f(x) = \sin(x), g(x) = \cos(x)$ over the interval $\left[0, \dfrac{\pi}{4}\right]$. Cross sections of the solid perpendicular to the x-axis are squares. Determine the volume of the solid.

(A) 0.2854

(B) 0.3123

(C) 0.2758

(D) 0.3085

(E) 0.3171

40. The first derivative of the function f is given by $f'(x) = 4x^3 - 18x^2$. How many points of inflection does the graph of f have?

(A) one

(B) two

(C) three

(D) four

(E) zero

41. Find the average value of $f(x) = \sin x$ on the interval $\left[\dfrac{\pi}{4}, \dfrac{\pi}{2}\right]$.

(A) 0.900316

(B) 0.707107

(C) 0.31831

(D) 0.450158

(E) −0.777594

42. If $f(x) = x^2 e^{-4x}$, then the y-value of one of the horizontal tangents is

(A) 0.5

(B) 7.38906

(C) 0.541341

(D) 0.033834

(E) 0.045112

43. Find the interval(s) on which the curve $f(x) = -x^4 + 2x^2 + 3$ is concave up.

(A) $\left(-\dfrac{\sqrt{3}}{3}, 0\right)$

(B) $\left(0, \dfrac{\sqrt{3}}{3}\right)$

(C) $\left(-\dfrac{3}{4}, \dfrac{3}{4}\right)$

(D) $\left(-\dfrac{\sqrt{3}}{3}, \dfrac{\sqrt{3}}{3}\right)$

(E) $\left(-\dfrac{\sqrt{3}}{4}, \dfrac{\sqrt{3}}{4}\right)$

44. The velocity of a particle moving along a line is $2t$ meters per second. Find the distance traveled in meters during the time interval $1 \le t \le 3$.

   (A) 9

   (B) 5

   (C) 6

   (D) 4

   (E) 8

45. If $F(x) = \int_{x^2-1}^{0} f(t)dt$ and $f(8) = -4$ then $F'(3) =$

   (A) 24

   (B) −24

   (C) 12

   (D) −12

   (E) 32

Section II

This section contains six free response problems and has two parts: Part A and Part B. Part A has three questions that may require a calculator. A calculator may not be used on the three questions in Part B.

Directions: Solve each problem in the provided space. Be efficient with the use of your time. A calculator may be used on Part A to solve equations, find derivatives at specific points, and evaluate definite integrals. A calculator may not be used on Part B.

Write neatly so that your work can be read. Cross out any mistakes. Work that is erased or crossed out will not be scored.

Before beginning work on Section II, you may want to look over all of the questions. Not everyone is expected to be able to complete every question.

As you work this exam, be sure to do the following:

- Show your work. Label tables, functions, and graphs that you create. Your solutions will be scored based on the correctness of the problem solving process used in addition to the final answer. To receive full credit, you must provide supporting work. When justifying your answers, use mathematical reasons.

- Use standard mathematical notation instead of calculator syntax. For example, $\text{fnInt}\left(x^2 - 2x, x, 3, 7\right)$ may not be used to represent $\int_{3}^{7}\left(x^2 - 2x\right)dx$.

- Numeric and algebraic answers do not need to be simplified (unless otherwise specified). Decimal approximations in final answers should be accurate to three decimal places.

- The domain of each function f is the set of all real numbers for which $f(x)$ is defined. If the domain of a particular function differs from this, it will be specified in the problem.

Part A   A calculator may be required to solve some problems.

Question 1

Let S be the region bounded by the graphs of $f(x) = e^{-x^2}$ and $g(x) = 2x^2$.

(a) Find the area of the region S.

(b) Find the volume of the solid generated when the region S is rotated about the x-axis.

(c) The region S is the base of a solid for which each cross section perpendicular to the x-axis is a square with diameter in the xy plane. Find the volume of the solid.

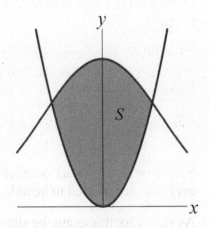

Question 2

Let $F(x) = \int_0^x \sin^2(t)\,dt$ on the interval $[0, \pi]$.

(a) Approximate $F(\pi)$ using the trapezoid rule with $n = 4$.

(b) Find $F'(x)$.

(c) Find the average value of $F'(x)$ on the interval $[0, \pi]$.

Question 3

A particle moves along the x-axis so that its acceleration at any time $t \geq 0$ is given by $a(t) = 2t - 4$. At time $t = 1$, the velocity of the particle is $v(1) = -1$ and its position is $x(1) = \dfrac{4}{3}$.

(a) Write an expression for the velocity of the particle $v(t)$.

(b) At what value(s) of t does the particle change direction?

(c) Write an expression for the position $x(t)$ of the particle.

(d) Find the total distance traveled by the particle from $t = 1$ to $t = 4$.

Part B   A calculator may not be used.

Question 4

Consider the differential equation $\dfrac{dy}{dx} = \dfrac{y}{x^2}$.

(a) On the given axes, draw a slope field for the differential equation at the nine points shown.

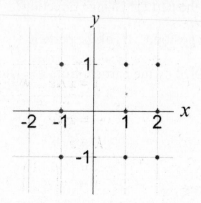

(b) Find the particular solution $y = g(x)$ to the differential equation with initial condition $g(1) = -1$. Then state the domain of $g(x)$.

(a)

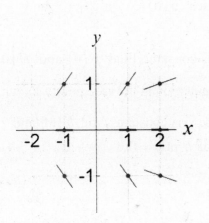

(b)

$$\frac{dy}{dx} = \frac{y}{x^2}$$

$$\frac{1}{y}\,dy = \frac{1}{x^2}\,dx$$

$$\ln|y| = -\frac{1}{x} + C$$

$$e^{\ln|y|} = e^{-\frac{1}{x}+C}$$

$$y = \pm Ke^{-\frac{1}{x}} \text{ with } K > 0$$

$$-1 = \pm Ke^{-\frac{1}{1}}$$

$$K = e$$

$$y = -e\left(e^{-\frac{1}{x}}\right) \text{ since } y < 0 \text{ when } x = 1$$

$$y = -e^{1-\frac{1}{x}}$$

The domain is all real numbers x with $x \neq 0$.

Question 5

A twice-differentiable function g has the following properties: $g(0)=3$, $g'(0)=5$, and $g''(0)=-1$.

(a) A function f is defined as $f(x)=3^{kx}+g(x)$ where k is constant. Find $f'(0)$ and $f''(0)$ in terms of k. Show how you obtained your answer.

(b) The function h is defined as $h(x)=\sin(ax)g(x)$ where a is constant. Find $h'(x)$ and determine the equation of the tangent line of the graph of h at $x=0$.

Question 6

t (minutes)	0	10	20	30	40	50	60	70	80
$v(t)$ (meters per minute)	0	180	172	160	158	164	166	152	170

The velocity of Runner A at selected times during a race are shown in the table above. At all times during the race, the runner's velocity was nonnegative. The runner had initial position 0 meters. (She was at the starting line.)

(a) Find the average acceleration of the Runner A from $t = 0$ minutes to $t = 80$ minutes. Label your answer with appropriate units.

(b) Explain the meaning of $\int_0^{80} v(t)\, dt$ as related to the runner, making sure to use appropriate units as a part of your explanation. Then use a midpoint Riemann sum with 4 subintervals of the same length to approximate $\int_0^{80} v(t)\, dt$.

(c) At time $t = 8$, Runner B leaves the starting line with a velocity of 160 meters per minute. Runner B accelerates by $a(t) = \dfrac{1}{\sqrt{t+1}}$ meters per minute per minute. Is Runner A or Runner B running faster at $t = 80$ minutes?

Section I

This section contains 45 multiple-choice questions and contains two parts: Part A and Part B. Part A has 28 questions that must be solved without a calculator. Part B has 17 questions, including some questions that require the use of a graphing calculator.

Part A Multiple-Choice

You may not use a calculator on this portion of the exam.

Directions: Solve each problem in the provided space. Then choose the best option from among the choices given. Be efficient with the use of your time.

Throughout this exam:
(1) The domain of each function f is the set of all real numbers for which $f(x)$ is defined. If the domain of a particular function differs from this, it will be specified in the problem.
(2) For trigonometric functions, the inverse may be represented with " $^{-1}$ " or "arc". For example, the inverse cosine function may be represented as $\cos^{-1} x$ or $\arccos x$.

1. $\displaystyle \int \cos\left(\frac{3}{4}x\right) dx =$

(A) $\dfrac{4}{3}\sin\left(\dfrac{3}{4}x\right) + C$

(B) $\sin\left(\dfrac{3}{4}x\right) + C$

(C) $\dfrac{3}{4}\sin\left(\dfrac{3}{4}x\right) + C$

(D) $-\dfrac{3}{4}\sin\left(\dfrac{3}{4}x\right) + C$

(E) $\dfrac{4}{3}\cos\left(\dfrac{3}{4}x\right) + C$

2. Find $\lim\limits_{x \to 2} \dfrac{x^2 - 4}{x - 2}$.

   (A) 2

   (B) 1

   (C) 0

   (D) 4

   (E) Does not exist

3. For what value(s) of k, if any, is $f(x) = \begin{cases} k^2 - x & \text{if } x < 3 \\ 2k & \text{if } x \geq 3 \end{cases}$ continuous on $(-\infty, \infty)$?

   (A) $1, -3$

   (B) 1

   (C) $-1, 3$

   (D) 3

   (E) Does not exist

4. If $f(x) = 3x\sqrt{7x - 1}$, then $f'(x)$ is

   (A) $x\sqrt{7x - 1}$

   (B) $\dfrac{21}{2\sqrt{7x - 1}}$

   (C) $3\sqrt{7x - 1} + 3x$

   (D) $3\sqrt{7x - 1} + \dfrac{21x}{2\sqrt{7x - 1}}$

   (E) $3 + \dfrac{7x}{\sqrt{7x - 1}}$

5. $\int \dfrac{12}{1+12x} dx =$

(A) $\ln|1+12x| + C$

(B) $12x + \ln 12x + C$

(C) $\ln|12x| + C$

(D) $\dfrac{1}{12} \ln|1+12x| + C$

(E) $-\dfrac{1}{12} \ln|1+12x| + C$

6. A particle moves along the x-axis so that at any time $t \geq 0$, its velocity is given by $v(t) = \cos(4t)$. If the position of the particle at time $t = \dfrac{\pi}{3}$ is $x = 2$, what is the particle's position at time $t = 0$?

(A) $\dfrac{5}{3}$

(B) $\dfrac{5}{4}$

(C) $\dfrac{4}{3}$

(D) 0

(E) $\dfrac{3}{2}$

7. The function f is continuous on the closed interval $[0,8]$ and has the values given in the table below.

x	0	2	4	6	8
$f(x)$	8	4	k	5	6

The trapezoidal approximation for $\int_0^8 f(x)dx$ found with four subintervals of equal length is 52. What is the value of k?

(A) 2

(B) 5

(C) 7

(D) 10

(E) 17

8. $\dfrac{d}{dx}\left(\sin^2(3x+7)\right) =$

(A) $\cos^2(3x+7)$

(B) $2\sin(3x+7)$

(C) $-6\cos(3x+7)\sin(3x+7)$

(D) $3\sin^2(3x+7)$

(E) $3\cos x \sin x$

9. A colony of bacteria starts with 400 and grows at a rate proportional to its size. After 2 hours there are 5000 bacteria. When will the population reach 20,000?

(A) 4.1235 hours

(B) 12.5000 hours

(C) 3.5355 hours

(D) 8 hours

(E) 3.0977 hours

10. Given $f(x) = \dfrac{2x}{x+4}$, for what values of x is the graph of f concave downwards?

(A) $0 < x < 4$

(B) $\infty < x < -4$

(C) $-4 < x < \infty$

(D) $\infty < x < -4$ and $4 < x < \infty$

(E) $x = -4$

11. Let f be defined by $f(x) = |x + 9|$ for all real numbers x. For what values of x is the function increasing?

(A) $(-\infty, -9)$

(B) $(-\infty, 9)$

(C) $[-9, 0)$

(D) $(0, 9)$

(E) $(-9, \infty)$

12. Find an equation for the line tangent to the graph of $f(x) = \sqrt{2x+1}$ at the point where $x = 4$

(A) $y = 2x + 1$

(B) $y = \dfrac{1}{6}x + \dfrac{7}{3}$

(C) $y = 4$

(D) $y = \dfrac{1}{3}x + \dfrac{5}{3}$

(E) $y = -\dfrac{1}{2}x + 5$

13. $\dfrac{d}{dx}\big(\sin(3x)\cos(x)\big) =$

(A) $3\cos(3x)\cos(x) - \sin(x)\sin(3x)$

(B) $3\cos(x)\cos(3x) + \sin(x)\sin(3x)$

(C) $\cos(x)\cos(3x) + \sin(x)\sin(3x)$

(D) $-3\cos(3x)\sin(x)$

(E) $3\cos(x)\cos(3x) + 3\sin(x)\sin(3x)$

14. Find the function $y = f(x)$ if $\dfrac{dy}{dx} = 3x^2 - 7$ and $f(3) = 5$.

(A) $\dfrac{x^3}{3} - 7x + 5$

(B) $x^2 - 3x + 5$

(C) $x^3 + 5$

(D) $x^3 - 7x - 1$

(E) $6x$

15. $\displaystyle\int_{-1}^{1} 4xe^{x^2}\,dx =$

(A) $4e$

(B) 0

(C) $16e$

(D) $4 - e$

(E) 7

16. How many points of inflection does $f(x) = 6x(x+2)^4$.

    (A) 0

    (B) 1

    (C) 2

    (D) 3

    (E) 4

17. Find the area of the region bound by $f(x) = x^3 - x^2$ and $g(x) = x^3 + x$.

    (A) $\dfrac{1}{6}$

    (B) $\dfrac{1}{2}$

    (C) $\dfrac{1}{8}$

    (D) $\dfrac{1}{12}$

    (E) $\dfrac{1}{16}$

18. If $F(x) = \displaystyle\int_{1}^{x^2+1} f(u)\,du$ and $f(5) = 7$, then $F'(2) =$

    (A) 4

    (B) 28

    (C) 7

    (D) −18

    (E) 16

19. What is the equation of the line tangent to the curve $y = x^3 - \sin x$ at the point $(0,0)$?

   (A) $y = -2x + 1$

   (B) $y = 3x + 4$

   (C) $y = x$

   (D) $y = 0$

   (E) $y = -x$

20. A particle moves along the x-axis so that its velocity at any time $t \geq 0$ is given by $v(t) = 3t^2 - 6t$. Which of the following expressions could represent the position $x(t)$ of the particle at any time $t \geq 0$?

   (A) $t^3 - 3t^2 + 7$

   (B) $t^3 - 6$

   (C) $t^2 - 2t$

   (D) $3t^3 - 6t^2 - 3$

   (E) $3t(t-2)$

21. What is the slope of the tangent line to $x^3 - 2xy - y^2 = 12$ that lies in the fourth quadrant at the point where $x = 2$?

   (A) 0

   (B) 16

   (C) -2

   (D) 12

   (E) undefined

22. If $f(x) = \ln|x - 3|$ then what is a derivative of the inverse of $f(x)$ at $x = 5$?

(A) $-e^5$

(B) $3 - e^5$

(C) $3e^4$

(D) $\ln 2$

(E) undefined

23. The function $f(x) = \dfrac{4x^3 - 7x^2 + 21}{6x^3 + 5x^2 + 17}$ has horizontal asymptote(s) at

(A) $y = \dfrac{2}{3}, y = -\dfrac{7}{5}$

(B) $y = -\dfrac{7}{5}$

(C) $y = \dfrac{2}{3}$

(D) $y = 0$

(E) no horizontal asymptotes

24. Find the derivative of $f(x) = \dfrac{3x-5}{\left(x^2-9\right)^2}$.

(A) $-9x^2 + 20x - 7$

(B) $\dfrac{3}{4x\left(x^2-9\right)}$

(C) $\dfrac{-9x^2 + 20x - 7}{\left(x^2-9\right)^3}$

(D) $\dfrac{15x^2 - 20x - 7}{\left(x^2-9\right)^3}$

(E) $\dfrac{3}{2\left(x^2-9\right)}$

25. Evaluate $\dfrac{d}{dx}\displaystyle\int_0^x \left(5t^4 - 9t + 6\right)dt$ for $x \geq 0$.

(A) $20t^3 - 9$

(B) $5x^4 - 9x + 6$

(C) $5t^4 - 9t$

(D) $20x^3 - 9$

(E) $x^5 - 4.5x + 6x$

26. Find $\displaystyle\lim_{x \to 3}\dfrac{x^3 - 27}{x-3}$

(A) does not exist

(B) 9

(C) 3

(D) 27

(E) ∞

27. Which of the following statements is true about $f(x) = 4x^3 - 12x^2 + 7$?

(A) f is decreasing on $(-\infty, 1)$

(B) f is increasing on $(2, \infty)$

(C) f is increasing on $(0, 2)$

(D) f is decreasing on $(2, \infty)$

(E) f is increasing for all real values

28. For which points on the graph of f is $f'(x)$ negative?

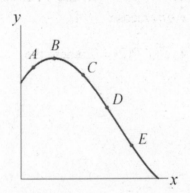

(A) A and E

(B) A only

(C) C only

(D) C, D, and E

(E) B only

Part B Multiple-Choice

This portion of the exam requires a graphing calculator for some questions.

This part of the exam contains 17 questions.

Directions: Solve each problem in the provided space. Then choose the best option from among the choices given. Be efficient with the use of your time.

Throughout this exam:
(1) Sometimes the exact numerical value of the solution is not given as a choice. In this event, pick the best numerical approximation from the given choices.
(2) The domain of each function f is the set of all real numbers for which $f(x)$ is defined. If the domain of a particular function differs from this, it will be specified in the problem.
(3) For trigonometric functions, the inverse may be represented with "$^{-1}$" or "arc". For example, the inverse cosine function may be represented as $\cos^{-1}x$ or $\arccos x$.

29. Find the position function, $P(t)$, given $a(t) = 5$, $v(3) = 4$, and $P(2) = 0$ where the acceleration is given by $a(t)$ and the velocity is given by $v(t)$.

(A) $P(t) = 2.5t^2 - 11t - 12$

(B) $P(t) = 4t^2 - 7t + 3$

(C) $P(t) = 5t^2 + 4t$

(D) $P(t) = 2.5t^2 - 11t + 12$

(E) $P(t) = t^2 + 7t + 3$

30. Give a value of c that satisfies the conclusion of the Mean Value Theorem for Derivatives for the function $f(x) = -3x^2 + 4x - 5$ on the interval $[1,2]$.

(A) $\dfrac{2}{3}$

(B) $\dfrac{3}{2}$

(C) $\dfrac{4}{5}$

(D) -5

(E) $\dfrac{5}{4}$

31. The area of a circle with radius r is $V = \pi r^2$. At the time when the area and radius are changing at the same numerical amount, what is the area?

    (A) 3.14159

    (B) 0.31831

    (C) 1.61803

    (D) 0.78539

    (E) 0.76126

32. Given $f(x) = (3x+1)^{\frac{1}{x}}$ find $\lim\limits_{x \to 0} f(x)$.

    (A) 20.0855

    (B) 1.0000

    (C) 0.0498

    (D) 20.0765

    (E) 19.9955

33. Find the value of c on the interval $[0, \pi]$ that satisfies the Mean Value Theorem for Derivatives given $f(x) = 2x - \sin x$.

    (A) 0.7854

    (B) 1.4297

    (C) 2.0000

    (D) 1.5708

    (E) 3.1415

34. If $f'(x) = 2x\sin(2x)$ for $0 < x < 4$ then f has a local max at $x \approx$

    (A) 3.990

    (B) 1.9293

    (C) 1.782

    (D) 6.345

    (E) 1.571

35. A rock is thrown upwards (vertically) from the ground with an initial velocity of 48 feet per second. If the acceleration due to gravity is $-32\dfrac{ft}{\sec^2}$, how high will the rock go?

(A) 48 feet

(B) 40 feet

(C) 36 feet

(D) 80 feet

(E) 32 feet

36. What is the average value of the function $f(x) = \sin 3x + \ln x$ on the interval $[1,5]$?

(A) 3.9704

(B) 0.9926

(C) 2.1186

(D) 0.5297

(E) 1.5971

37. An object moves along the x-axis so that its velocity at any time $t \geq 0$ is given by $v(t) = t^3 - 16t$. Find the total displacement of the particle from $t = 0$ to $t = 6$.

(A) 164

(B) 81

(C) 120

(D) 36

(E) 40

38. Estimate the area under the curve of $f(x) = \cos^2(x) + 1$ from $x = 2$ to $x = 4$. Use four sub-intervals and right endpoints.

(A) 8.0993

(B) 6.9261

(C) 1.030

(D) 3.4631

(E) 3.3361

39. The base of a solid is the region in the xy-plane enclosed by the curves $f(x) = -\sin(x), g(x) = \cos(x)$ over the interval $\left[0, \dfrac{3\pi}{4}\right]$. Cross sections of the solid perpendicular to the x-axis are squares. Determine the volume of the solid.

    (A) 2.3562

    (B) 2.8562

    (C) 1.4142

    (D) 0.7071

    (E) 1.8657

40. The first derivative of the function f is given by $f'(x) = 5x^4 - 40x^2$. How many points of inflection does the graph of f have?

    (A) one

    (B) two

    (C) three

    (D) four

    (E) zero

41. Find the average value of $f(x) = \cos 2x + \sin x$ on the interval $\left[0, \dfrac{\pi}{2}\right]$.

    (A) 0.8660

    (B) 0.7071

    (C) 0.0000

    (D) 0.6366

    (E) 1.0000

42. If $f(x) = 7xe^{-2x}$, then the y-value of the horizontal tangent line is

    (A) 0.5531

    (B) 1.2807

    (C) 9.5140

    (D) 0.5000

    (E) 1.2876

43. Find the interval(s) on which the curve $f(x) = x^3 - \sin x$ is concave up.

    (A) $(-0.1247, \infty)$

    (B) $(0, \infty)$

    (C) $(-\infty, 0)$

    (D) $(0.0314, \infty)$

    (E) $(-31.3742, -29.3371)$ and $(0.0314, \infty)$

44. The velocity of a particle moving along a line is $v(t) = \pi \cos(\pi t)$ meters per second. Find the distance traveled in meters during the time interval $1 \leq t \leq 3$.

    (A) 0

    (B) 2

    (C) π

    (D) 4

    (E) 5

45. If $F(x) = \displaystyle\int_{0}^{x^2+4} f(t)\,dt$ and $f(13) = -5$ then $F'(3) =$

(A) 30

(B) 6

(C) –5

(D) –30

(E) –20

Section II

This section contains six free response problems and has two parts: Part A and Part B. Part A has three questions that may require a calculator. A calculator may not be used on the three questions in Part B.

Directions: Solve each problem in the provided space. Be efficient with the use of your time. A calculator may be used on Part A to solve equations, find derivatives at specific points, and evaluate definite integrals. A calculator may not be used on Part B.

Write neatly so that your work can be read. Cross out any mistakes. Work that is erased or crossed out will not be scored.

Before beginning work on Section II, you may want to look over all of the questions. Not everyone is expected to be able to complete every question.

As you work this exam, be sure to do the following:

- Show your work. Label tables, functions, and graphs that you create. Your solutions will be scored based on the correctness of the problem solving process used in addition to the final answer. To receive full credit, you must provide supporting work. When justifying your answers, use mathematical reasons.

- Use standard mathematical notation instead of calculator syntax. For example, $\text{fnInt}\left(x^2 - 2x, x, 3, 7\right)$ may not be used to represent $\int_{3}^{7}\left(x^2 - 2x\right)dx$.

- Numeric and algebraic answers do not need to be simplified (unless otherwise specified). Decimal approximations in final answers should be accurate to three decimal places.

- The domain of each function f is the set of all real numbers for which $f\left(x\right)$ is defined. If the domain of a particular function differs from this, it will be specified in the problem.

Part A   A calculator may be required to solve some problems.

Question 1

Let S be the region bounded by the graphs of $f(x) = \dfrac{1}{x^2 + 1}$

and $g(x) = x^2$.

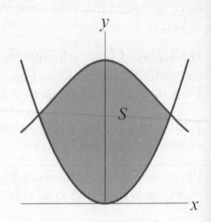

(a) Find the area of the region S.

(b) Find the volume of the solid generated when the region S is rotated about the x-axis.

(c) The region S is the base of a solid for which each cross section perpendicular to the x-axis is a square with diameter in the xy plane. Find the volume of the solid.

Question 2

Let $F(x) = \int_0^x \ln(t^2 + 1)\, dt$ on the interval $[0, 2]$.

(a) Approximate $F(2)$ using the trapezoid rule with $n = 4$.

(b) Find $F'(x)$.

(c) Find the average value of $F'(x)$ on the interval $[0, 2]$.

Question 3

A particle moves along the x-axis so that its acceleration at any time $t \geq 0$ is given by $a(t) = 3t - 5$. At time $t = 1$, the velocity of the particle is $v(1) = -2$ and its position is $x(1) = 4$.

(a) Write an expression for the velocity of the particle $v(t)$.

(b) At what value(s) of t does the particle change direction?

(c) Write an expression for the position $x(t)$ of the particle.

(d) Find the total distance traveled by the particle from $t = 0$ to $t = 3$.

Part B   A calculator may not be used.

Question 4

Consider the differential equation $\dfrac{dy}{dx} = 2x(y+1)$.

(a) On the given axes, draw a slope field for the differential equation at the nine points shown.

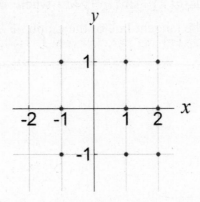

(b) Find the particular solution $y = g(x)$ to the differential equation with initial condition
$g(1) = 2$. Then state the domain of $g(x)$.

Question 5

A twice-differentiable function g has the following properties: $g(0)=4$, $g'(0)=-6$, and $g''(0)=2$.

(a) A function f is defined as $f(x)=4^{kx}+g(x)$ where k is constant. Find $f'(0)$ and $f''(0)$ in terms of k. Show how you obtained your answer.

(b) The function h is defined as $h(x)=\sin(ax)g(x)$ where a is constant. Find $h'(x)$ and determine the equation of the tangent line of the graph of h at $x=0$.

Question 6

t (minutes)	0	10	20	30	40	50	60	70	80
$v(t)$ (meters per minute)	0	150	164	170	162	174	166	158	174

The velocity of Runner A at selected times during a race are shown in the table above. At all times during the race, the runner's velocity was nonnegative. The runner had initial position 0 meters. (She was at the starting line.)

(a) Find the average acceleration of the Runner A from $t = 0$ minutes to $t = 80$ minutes. Label your answer with appropriate units.

(b) Explain the meaning of $\int_0^{80} v(t)\,dt$ as related to the runner, making sure to use appropriate units as a part of your explanation. Then use a midpoint Riemann sum with 4 subintervals of the same length to approximate $\int_0^{80} v(t)\,dt$.

(c) At time $t = 7$, Runner B leaves the starting line with a velocity of 158 meters per minute. Runner B accelerates by $a(t) = \dfrac{1}{\sqrt{t+9}}$ meters per minute per minute. Is Runner A or Runner B running faster at $t = 40$ minutes?

___

Section I

This section contains 45 multiple-choice questions and contains two parts: Part A and Part B. Part A has 28 questions that must be solved without a calculator. Part B has 17 questions, including some questions that require the use of a graphing calculator.

Part A Multiple-Choice

You may not use a calculator on this portion of the exam.

Directions: Solve each problem in the provided space. Then choose the best option from among the choices given. Be efficient with the use of your time.

Throughout this exam:

(1) The domain of each function f is the set of all real numbers for which $f(x)$ is defined. If the domain of a particular function differs from this, it will be specified in the problem.

(2) For trigonometric functions, the inverse may be represented with " $^{-1}$ " or "arc". For example the inverse cosine function may be represented as $\cos^{-1} x$ or $\arccos x$.

1. If $f(x) = \dfrac{4x+3}{2x-7}$, then $f'(x) =$

(A) $\dfrac{12}{(2x-7)^2}$

(B) $\dfrac{7}{(2x-7)^2}$

(C) $\dfrac{16x+9}{(2x-7)^2}$

(D) $\dfrac{34}{(2x-7)^2}$

(E) $\dfrac{-34}{(2x-7)^2}$

2. Find $\lim\limits_{x \to \infty} \dfrac{e^{2x}}{\ln x}$

(A) 0

(B) 1

(C) $-\infty$

(D) ∞

(E) Cannot be determined

3. What is the value of $\sum\limits_{n=0}^{\infty} \left(-\dfrac{3}{5}\right)^{n}$?

(A) $\dfrac{3}{5}$

(B) 1

(C) $\dfrac{5}{8}$

(D) 0

(E) Does not exist

4. The length of the curve $y = \dfrac{2}{3}x^3$ from $x = 2$ to $x = 6$ is given by

(A) $\displaystyle\int_2^6 \sqrt{1 + 4x^4}\, dx$

(B) $\displaystyle\int_2^6 \sqrt{1 + \dfrac{2}{3}x^6}\, dx$

(C) $\displaystyle\int_2^6 \sqrt{1 + \dfrac{4}{9}x^6}\, dx$

(D) $\displaystyle\int_2^6 \sqrt{1 + 2x^3}\, dx$

(E) $\displaystyle\int_2^6 \sqrt{1 + 6x^3}\, dx$

5. $\displaystyle\int \dfrac{8}{1 + 8x}\, dx =$

(A) $8x + \ln 8x + C$

(B) $\ln|1 + 8x| + C$

(C) $\ln|8x| + C$

(D) $\dfrac{1}{8}\ln|1 + 8x| + C$

(E) $-\dfrac{1}{8}\ln|1 + 8x| + C$

6. A particle moves along the x-axis so that at any time $t \geq 0$, its velocity is given by $v(t) = \cos(4t)$. If the position of the particle at time $t = \dfrac{\pi}{8}$ is $x = \dfrac{7}{4}$, what is the particle's position at time $t = 0$?

(A) $\dfrac{2}{3}$

(B) $\dfrac{5}{4}$

(C) $-\dfrac{1}{2}$

(D) 0

(E) $\dfrac{3}{2}$

7. The function f is continuous on the closed interval $[0,9]$ and has the values given in the table below.

x	0	3	6	9
$f(x)$	8	15	k	12

The trapezoidal approximation for $\displaystyle\int_0^9 f(x)dx = 90$ found with three subintervals of equal length is 90. What is the value of k?

(A) 2

(B) 5

(C) 7

(D) 11

(E) 17

8. Let $y = f(x)$ be the solution to the differential equation $\dfrac{dy}{dx} = x + y + 2$ with the initial condition $f(3) = 4$. What is the *approximation* for $f(3.4)$ if Euler's method is used, starting at $x = 3$ with two steps of equal size?

(A) 10.68

(B) 8.00

(C) 31.20

(D) 5.40

(E) 6.40

9. Solve $\dfrac{dy}{dx} = y(2x + 1)$

(A) $y = Ce^{x^2 + x}$

(B) $y = Ce^{x^2}$

(C) $y = \ln\left|x^2 + x\right| + C$

(D) $y = Ce^{x^2 + 1}$

(E) $y = Ce^{x^2 + \ln x}$

10. What is the equation of the line tangent to the curve $y = x^3 - 2x^2$ at the point $(2, 0)$?

(A) $y = -4x - 8$

(B) $y = 4x + 8$

(C) $y = 4x - 8$

(D) $y = \dfrac{1}{4}x - 8$

(E) $y = -\dfrac{1}{4}x + 8$

11. If $f(x) = 3(2x+1)^3$ find $f'(-2) =$

(A) -81

(B) 64

(C) 225

(D) 441

(E) 81

12. What are the first three terms in the Maclaurin Series for e^{2x} ?

(A) $1 + \frac{1}{4}x + \frac{1}{32}x^2$

(B) $1 + \frac{1}{2}x + \frac{1}{8}x^2$

(C) $1 + x + \frac{1}{2}x^2$

(D) $1 + x + x^2$

(E) $1 + 2x + 2x^2$

13. Which of the following series diverge?

$I. = \sum_{n=1}^{x} \frac{2}{n^4}, \quad II. = \sum_{n=1}^{x} \frac{1}{n}, \quad III. = 8\sum_{n=1}^{x} \frac{1}{n^{1/2}}$

(A) I only

(B) II only

(C) III only

(D) I & III

(E) II & III

14. Find $\int 2x \cos x\, dx$

  (A) $2x \sin x + \cos x + C$

  (B) $2x \sin x + 2 \cos x + C$

  (C) $x^2 \sin x + C$

  (D) $-2 \sin x + C$

  (E) $2x \sin x - 2 \cos x + C$

15. Give a value of c that satisfies the conclusion of the Mean Value Theorem for Derivatives for the function $f(x) = -2x^2 - x + 2$ on the interval $[1,3]$.

  (A) $\dfrac{9}{4}$

  (B) $\dfrac{3}{2}$

  (C) $\dfrac{1}{2}$

  (D) 2

  (E) $\dfrac{5}{4}$

16. $\displaystyle\int_{1}^{5} \dfrac{\ln x}{x}\, dx =$

  (A) $\dfrac{1}{2}(\ln 5)^2$

  (B) $\dfrac{1}{2}(\ln 5)^2 + \dfrac{1}{2}$

  (C) 12

  (D) $\dfrac{-24 - \ln 5}{25}$

  (E) Cannot be determined from given information

17. Which of the following differential equations represents the slope field shown?

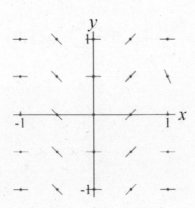

(A) $\dfrac{dy}{dx} = \sin x$

(B) $\dfrac{dy}{dx} = \cos x$

(C) $\dfrac{dy}{dx} = y^2$

(D) $\dfrac{dy}{dx} = \sin(\pi x)$

(E) $\dfrac{dy}{dx} = \cos(\pi x)$

18. Give the radius of convergence for the series $\displaystyle\sum_{n=1}^{\infty} \dfrac{3^{(n+2)} x^n}{n+1}$

(A) The series diverges for all x

(B) 1

(C) 0

(D) $\dfrac{1}{3}$

(E) 3

19. Which of the following series converge?

$$I = \sum_{n=1}^{\infty} \frac{1}{n^{\frac{3}{4}}}, \quad II = \sum_{n=1}^{\infty} \frac{1}{\sqrt{n^5}}, \quad III = \sum_{n=1}^{\infty} \frac{(-1)^n}{\sqrt{n}}$$

(A) II only

(B) I, II, and III

(C) II and III

(D) I and II

(E) I and III

20. Find the y-coordinate of the point of inflection of the function $y = x^3 - x^2$

(A) $-\dfrac{2}{27}$

(B) $\dfrac{1}{3}$

(C) $\dfrac{2}{27}$

(D) $-\dfrac{1}{3}$

(E) $-\dfrac{2}{9}$

21. $\int \dfrac{x}{x^2+2x-8}\,dx$

(A) $\dfrac{1}{2}\ln\big((x-2)(x+4)\big)+C$

(B) $\dfrac{1}{3}\ln\big(|x-2|\big)+\dfrac{2}{3}\ln\big(|x+4|\big)+C$

(C) $-\dfrac{2}{3}\ln\big(|x-2|\big)-\dfrac{1}{3}\ln\big(|x+4|\big)+C$

(D) $-\dfrac{2}{3}\ln\big(x+4\big)-\dfrac{1}{3}\ln\big(|x-2|\big)+C$

(E) $\dfrac{1}{2}\ln\big(\big|(x-2)(x+4)\big|\big)+C$

22. Evaluate $\displaystyle\int_{1}^{\infty}\dfrac{8}{x^3}\,dx$

(A) 8

(B) −24

(C) 4

(D) 0

(E) Divergent

23. Solve the differential equation $y'=5y(1000-y)$ subject to the condition $y(0)=500$. Then evaluate $\lim\limits_{t\to\infty} y(t)$.

(A) 5000

(B) 4500

(C) 3000

(D) 2000

(E) 1000

24. Give the first 3 nonzero terms in the Taylor series expansion about $x = 0$ for the function $f(x) = \cos(2x)$.

   (A) $1 - 2x^2 + 4x^4$

   (B) $1 - 2x^2 + \dfrac{2}{3}x^4$

   (C) $x - \dfrac{4}{3}x^3 + \dfrac{4}{15}x^5$

   (D) $1 + 2x + 2x^2$

   (E) $1 - 2x^2$

25. If $f(x) = x \ln(3x)$ find $f'(x)$.

   (A) 1

   (B) $\dfrac{\ln(3x) - 1}{\left(\ln(3x)\right)^2}$

   (C) $\dfrac{1}{3x}$

   (D) $\ln(3x) + 1$

   (E) $\ln(3x)$

26. Give the exact value of $\displaystyle\sum_{n=0}^{\infty} \dfrac{\cos(n\pi)5^n}{n!}$

   (A) e^{-5}

   (B) $\sin(5)$

   (C) $\cos(5)$

   (D) e^5

   (E) $-\sin(5)$

27. Find the area of the region bounded by the curve $r = \sin\theta$.

(A) $\dfrac{3}{2}\pi$

(B) $\dfrac{\pi}{2}$

(C) $\dfrac{\pi}{4}$

(D) $\dfrac{\pi}{6}$

(E) $\dfrac{\pi}{3}$

28. A rectangle has both a changing height and a changing width, but the height and width change so that the area of the rectangle is always 200 square feet. Give the rate of change of the width (in ft/sec) when the height is 5 feet, if the height is decreasing at that moment at the rate of 1/2 ft/sec.

(A) 4

(B) −4

(C) $\dfrac{1}{4}$

(D) 8

(E) 40

Part B Multiple-Choice

This portion of the exam requires a graphing calculator for some questions.

This part of the exam contains 17 questions.

Directions: Solve each problem in the provided space. Then choose the best option from among the choices given. Be efficient with the use of your time.

Throughout this exam:
(1) Sometimes the exact numerical value of the solution is not given as a choice. In this event, pick the best numerical approximation from the given choices.
(2) The domain of each function f is the set of all real numbers for which $f(x)$ is defined. If the domain of a particular function differs from this, it will be specified in the problem.
(3) For trigonometric functions, the inverse may be represented with "$^{-1}$" or "arc". For example, the inverse cosine function may be represented as $\cos^{-1} x$ or $\arccos x$.

29. Give the minimum value of the function $f(x) = 2x^3 - 9x + 5$ for $x \geq 0$.

    (A) -2.175

    (B) -2.258

    (C) -2.213

    (D) -2.349

    (E) -2.368

30. Approximate the area under the curve given by $y = e^x$ using right endpoints between $x = 0$ and $x = 6$ using three equal subintervals.

    (A) 342.434

    (B) 930.832

    (C) 125.974

    (D) 305.559

    (E) 210.731

31. Find the value of the limit $\lim\limits_{n \to \infty} \sqrt{\dfrac{x + 8x^2}{2x^2 - 1}}$.

    (A) −2

    (B) 2

    (C) 4

    (D) 1

    (E) 0

32. Find the area of the region inside the curve $r = 4\sin\theta$ but not inside the curve $r = 2\sin\theta$.

    (A) 12π

    (B) 2π

    (C) π

    (D) 6π

    (E) 3π

33. Give the minimum value of the function $f(x) = 2x^3 - 9x + 5$ for $x \geq 0$.

    (A) −2.175

    (B) −2.258

    (C) −2.213

    (D) −2.349

    (E) −2.368

34. The function f satisfies the equation $\displaystyle\int_0^{2x} f(t)\,dt = 2\sin(x) + x$. Evaluate $f\left(\dfrac{\pi}{3}\right)$.

(A) 1

(B) 1.366

(C) 2.732

(D) 2

(E) 1.411

35. The base of a solid is the region in the xy plane enclosed by the curves $f(x) = \sin(x), g(x) = \cos(x)$ over the interval $\left[0, \dfrac{\pi}{4}\right]$. Cross sections of the solid perpendicular to the x-axis are squares. Determine the volume of the solid.

(A) 0.2855

(B) 0.3123

(C) 0.2758

(D) 0.3085

(E) 0.3171

36. The graph of the derivative of f is given below.

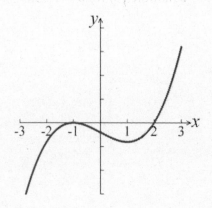

Which of the following is FALSE about the function f?

(A) The function f is decreasing on the interval $(-3, -1)$.

(B) f is concave down on the interval $(-1, 1)$.

(C) f has a critical value at $x = -1$.

(D) f is concave down on the interval $(-3, 0)$.

(E) f is increasing on the interval $(2, 3)$.

37. Find the 4th-degree Taylor polynomial for $f(x) = \sqrt{x}$, centered about the point $x = 4$. Use this polynomial to approximate $\sqrt{4.2}$.

(A) 2.049

(B) 2.797

(C) 3.153

(D) 3.660

(E) 4.118

38. Give the length of the curve determined by $x = 2t, y = t^3 + 3t$ for t from 0 to 2.

   (A) 16.165

   (B) 16.195

   (C) 16.230

   (D) 16.224

   (E) 16.165

39. If $\int_0^3 f(x)dx = 12$ and $\int_0^6 f(x)dx = 42$, find the value of $\int_3^6 [2f(x) - 3]dx$.

   (A) 50

   (B) 51

   (C) 52

   (D) 53

   (E) 54

40. The function of g is the derivative of $\int_0^x (t^3 - 5)dt$. What is the derivative of the inverse of g at $x = 3$?

   (A) 4

   (B) $\dfrac{1}{4}$

   (C) 12

   (D) $\dfrac{1}{3}$

   (E) $\dfrac{1}{12}$

41. Select the TRUE statement associated with the function $f(x) = \dfrac{\sin(x)}{x^2}$.

    (A) The function does not have a horizontal asymptote.

    (B) The function has a vertical asymptote at $x = 0$.

    (C) The graph of the function passes through the origin.

    (D) The graph of the function is symmetric about the x-axis.

    (E) The graph is always concave up.

42. Particles A and B leave the origin at the same time and move along the y-axis. Their positions are determined by the functions $y_A = 2\sin(2t)$, $y_B = 4\cos(t)$ for t between 0 and 8. What is the velocity of particle B when particle A stops for the first time?

    (A) -2

    (B) 0

    (C) $-2\sqrt{2}$

    (D) 4

    (E) $2\sqrt{2}$

43. Give the error that occurs when the area between the curve $y = x^3 + 1$ and the x-axis over the interval $[0,1]$ is approximated by the trapezoid rule with $n = 4$.

    (A) 0.008

    (B) 0.025

    (C) 0.128

    (D) 0.016

    (E) 0.046

44. A rectangular box has a square base and top. The distance around the box (across the top, down the side, across the bottom, and up the side) is 130 inches. What box dimensions maximize the volume?

(A) $16 \times 16 \times 49$ cubic inches

(B) $21.67 \times 21.67 \times 43.33$ cubic inches

(C) $22.15 \times 22.15 \times 44.30$ cubic inches

(D) $43.33 \times 22.15 \times 22.15$ cubic inches

(E) $21.67 \times 43.33 \times 43.33$ cubic inches

45. If a ball is thrown into the air with a velocity of 80 feet per second, its height in feet after t seconds is given by $y = 80t - 16t^2$. It will be at maximum height when its instantaneous velocity is zero. Find its average velocity (in feet per second) from the time it is thrown $(t = 0)$ to the time it reaches its maximum height.

(A) 32

(B) 40

(C) 48

(D) 50

(E) 60

Section II

This section contains six free response problems and has two parts: Part A and Part B. Part A has three questions that may require a calculator. A calculator may not be used on the three questions in Part B.

Directions: Solve each problem in the provided space. Be efficient with the use of your time. A calculator may be used on Part A to solve equations, find derivatives at specific points, and evaluate definite integrals. A calculator may not be used on Part B.

Write neatly so that your work can be read. Cross out any mistakes. Work that is erased or crossed out will not be scored.

Before beginning work on Section II, you may want to look over all of the questions. Not everyone is expected to be able to complete every question.

As you work this exam, be sure to do the following:

- Show your work. Label tables, functions, and graphs that you create. Your solutions will be scored based on the correctness of the problem solving process used in addition to the final answer. To receive full credit, you must provide supporting work. When justifying your answers, use mathematical reasons.

- Use standard mathematical notation instead of calculator syntax. For example,

  $\text{fnInt}\left(x^2 - 2x, x, 3, 7\right)$ may not be used to represent $\displaystyle\int_3^7 \left(x^2 - 2x\right)dx$.

- Numeric and algebraic answers do not need to be simplified (unless otherwise specified). Decimal approximations in final answers should be accurate to three decimal places.

- The domain of each function f is the set of all real numbers for which $f\left(x\right)$ is defined. If the domain of a particular function differs from this, it will be specified in the problem.

Part A   A calculator may be required to solve some problems.

Question 1

Let S be the region bounded by the graphs of $f(x) = e^{-x^2}$ and $g(x) = 2x^2$.

(a) Find the area of the region S.

(b) Find the volume of the solid generated when the region S is rotated about the x-axis.

(c) The region S is the base of a solid for which each cross section perpendicular to the x-axis is a square with diameter in the xy plane. Find the volume of the solid.

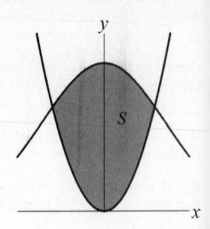

Question 2

Let $F(x) = \int_0^x \sin^2(t)\,dt$ on the interval $[0, \pi]$.

(a) Approximate $F(\pi)$ using the trapezoid rule with $n = 4$.

(b) Find $F'(x)$.

(c) Find the average value of $F'(x)$ on the interval $[0, \pi]$.

Question 3

The function f has derivative $f'(x) = (x-8)e^x$ for $x > 0$. Additionally, $f(1) = 7$.

(a) Given that $f'(8) = 0$, determine whether f has a relative maximum, relative minimum, or neither at $x = 8$. Show the work that justifies your answer.

(b) Is the graph of f simultaneously decreasing and concave up on any interval? Explain your reasoning.

(c) Determine the value of $f(10)$.

Part B   A calculator may not be used.

Question 4

Consider the differential equation $\dfrac{dy}{dx} = 8x^2 - \dfrac{6}{10-y}$ for $y \neq 10$. Define $y = f(x)$ to be the

particular solution to this differential equation. Let the initial condition be $f(0) = 7$.

(a) Evaluate $\dfrac{dy}{dx}$ and $\dfrac{d^2y}{dx^2}$ at $(0,7)$.

(b) Can the x-axis be a tangent line of the graph of f at some point? Explain.

(c) Determine the second-degree Taylor polynomial for f about $x = 0$.

(d) Starting at $x = 0$ and using two equally-sized steps, use Euler's method to approximate $f(1)$.
   Show all work leading to your solution.

Question 5

Let f be the function defined by the power series $f(x) = \dfrac{x}{1} - \dfrac{x^2}{4} + \dfrac{x^3}{9} - \ldots + (-1)^{n+1} \dfrac{x^n}{n^2} + \ldots$ for all real numbers x for which the series converges. Let g be the function defined by the power series $g(x) = 1 + \dfrac{x}{3!} + \dfrac{x^2}{5!} + \dfrac{x^3}{7!} - \ldots + \dfrac{x^n}{(2n+1)!} + \ldots$ for all real numbers x for which the series converges.

(a) Find the interval of convergence of the power series for f. Justify your conclusion.

(b) The graph of $y = g(x) - f(x)$ passes through the point $(0,1)$. Find $y'(0)$ and $y''(0)$. Then figure out whether y has a relative maximum, relative minimum or neither at $x = 0$. Explain your reasoning.

Question 6

t (minutes)	0	10	20	30	40	50	60	70	80
$v(t)$ (meters per minute)	0	180	172	160	158	164	166	152	170

The velocity of Runner A at selected times during a race are shown in the table above. At all times during the race, the runner's velocity was nonnegative. The runner had initial position 0 meters. (She was at the starting line.)

(a) Find the average acceleration of the Runner A from $t = 0$ minutes to $t = 80$ minutes. Label your answer with appropriate units.

(b) Explain the meaning of $\int_0^{80} v(t)\,dt$ as related to the runner, making sure to use appropriate units as a part of your explanation. Then use a midpoint Riemann sum with 4 subintervals of the same length to approximate $\int_0^{80} v(t)\,dt$.

(c) At time $t = 8$, Runner B leaves the starting line with a velocity of 160 meters per minute. Runner B accelerates by $a(t) = \dfrac{1}{\sqrt{t+1}}$ meters per minute per minute. Is Runner A or Runner B running faster at $t = 80$ minutes?

Section I

This section contains 45 multiple-choice questions and contains two parts: Part A and Part B. Part A has 28 questions that must be solved without a calculator. Part B has 17 questions, including some questions that require the use of a graphing calculator.

Part A Multiple-Choice

You may not use a calculator on this portion of the exam.

Directions: Solve each problem in the provided space. Then choose the best option from among the choices given. Be efficient with the use of your time.

Throughout this exam:

(1) The domain of each function f is the set of all real numbers for which $f(x)$ is defined. If the domain of a particular function differs from this, it will be specified in the problem.

(2) For trigonometric functions, the inverse may be represented with "$^{-1}$" or "arc". For example the inverse cosine function may be represented as $\cos^{-1} x$ or $\arccos x$.

1. If $f(x) = \dfrac{2x-1}{3x+2}$, then $f'(x) =$

(A) $\dfrac{-5}{(3x+2)^2}$

(B) $\dfrac{7}{(3x+2)^2}$

(C) $\dfrac{12x+1}{(3x+2)^2}$

(D) $\dfrac{2}{3}$

(E) $\dfrac{x+4}{(3x+2)^2}$

2. The third derivative of the function g is continuous on the interval (0,3). Values for g and its first three derivatives at $x = 2$ are given in the table below.

x	$g(x)$	$g'(x)$	$g''(x)$	$g'''(x)$
2	0	0	3	4

What is $\lim\limits_{x \to 2} \dfrac{g(x)}{(x-2)^2}$?

(A) 0

(B) $\dfrac{3}{2}$

(C) 3

(D) 4

(E) The limit does not exist.

3. What is the value of $\sum\limits_{n=0}^{\infty} \left(-\dfrac{7}{8}\right)^n$?

(A) -7

(B) $-\dfrac{7}{15}$

(C) $\dfrac{8}{15}$

(D) 8

(E) Does not exist

4. The length of the curve $y = x^3$ from $x = 1$ to $x = 5$ is given by

(A) $\displaystyle\int_1^5 \sqrt{1+3x^2}\,dx$

(B) $\displaystyle\int_1^5 \sqrt{1+x^3}\,dx$

(C) $\displaystyle\int_1^5 \sqrt{1+3x^4}\,dx$

(D) $\displaystyle\int_1^5 \sqrt{1+9x^4}\,dx$

(E) $\displaystyle\int_1^5 \sqrt{1+x^6}\,dx$

5. $\displaystyle\int_{\pi/4}^{3\pi/4} \frac{-e^{\cot x}}{\sin^2 x}\,dx$ is

(A) 1

(B) $\sqrt{2}$

(C) e

(D) $e^{-1}-e$

(E) $e-1$

6. A particle moves along the x-axis so that at any time $t \geq 0$, its velocity is given by

$v(t) = 2\sin t$. If the position of the particle at time $t = \dfrac{\pi}{3}$ is $x = 3$, what is the particle's

position at time $t = 0$?

(A) –2

(B) –1

(C) 0

(D) $\sqrt{3}$

(E) 2

7. A table of values for a continuous function f is shown below.

x	0	1.5	3	4.5	6
$f(x)$	4	2	3	7	12

If four equal subintervals of $[0,6]$ are used, which of the following is the trapezoidal

approximation of $\displaystyle\int_{0}^{6} f(x)dx$?

(A) 5

(B) 24

(C) 30

(D) 32

(E) 33

8. Let $y = f(x)$ be the solution to the differential equation $\dfrac{dy}{dx} = 2y$ with the initial condition $f(1) = -1$. What is the *approximation* for $f(1.2)$ if Euler's method is used, starting at $x = 1$ with two steps of equal size?

(A) –2

(B) –1.44

(C) –1.2

(D) –0.2

(E) 1.2

9. If $f'(x) = \dfrac{3}{x}$ and $f(e^2) = 1$, then $f(x) =$

(A) $f(x) = 3\ln|x| - 5$

(B) $f(x) = 3\ln|x| - 2$

(C) $f(x) = \ln|x| + 4$

(D) $f(x) = -\dfrac{3}{x^2} + e^2$

(E) $f(x) = -\dfrac{3}{x^2}$

10. For values of h very close to 0, which of the following functions best approximates $f(x) = \dfrac{\ln(x+h) - \ln x}{h}$?

(A) $\ln x$

(B) e^x

(C) $\dfrac{\ln x}{x}$

(D) $\dfrac{e^x}{x}$

(E) $\dfrac{1}{x}$

11. If $f(x) = \arcsin(e^x)$, then $f'(e^x) =$

(A) $\dfrac{1}{\sqrt{1-e^x}}$

(B) $\dfrac{e^x}{\sqrt{1-e^x}}$

(C) $\dfrac{e^x}{\sqrt{1-e^{2x}}}$

(D) $\dfrac{e^x}{1-e^x}$

(E) $\dfrac{-1}{\sqrt{1-e^{2x}}}$

12. Let f be the function given by $f(x) = \ln(2-x)$. The third-degree Taylor polynomial for f about $x = 1$ is

(A) $-x + \dfrac{x^2}{2} - \dfrac{x^3}{3}$

(B) $-(x-1) + \dfrac{(x-1)^2}{2!} - \dfrac{(x-1)^3}{3!}$

(C) $(x-1) + (x-1)^2 + (x-1)^3$

(D) $(x-1) - \dfrac{(x-1)^2}{2} + \dfrac{(x-1)^3}{3}$

(E) $-(x-1) + \dfrac{(x-1)^2}{2} - \dfrac{(x-1)^3}{3}$

13. Which of the following series converge?

I. $\displaystyle\sum_{n=1}^{\infty} \dfrac{2^n}{n!}$,   II. $\displaystyle\sum_{n=1}^{\infty} \dfrac{1}{n^4}$,   III. $\displaystyle\sum_{n=1}^{\infty} \left(\dfrac{\pi}{e}\right)^n$

(A) I only

(B) II only

(C) I & III

(D) I & II

(E) II & III

14. Find $\int x^2 e^{2x} dx$.

   (A) $2x^2 e^{2x} + 2xe^{2x} + C$

   (B) $\frac{1}{2}x^2 e^{2x} - \frac{1}{2}xe^{2x} + \frac{1}{4}e^{2x} + C$

   (C) $x^2 e^{2x} + xe^{2x} + e^{2x} + C$

   (D) $x^2 e^{2x} + 2xe^{2x} + 2e^{2x} + C$

   (E) $x^2 e^{2x} - 2xe^{2x} + 2e^{2x} + C$

15. What is the slope of the line tangent to the curve $y = x^2 - 3\cos y$ at the point $(1,0)$?

   (A) $-\frac{1}{2}$

   (B) 0

   (C) 1

   (D) 2

   (E) undefined

16. The slope field for a certain differential equation is shown below.

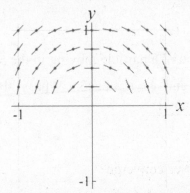

Which of the following could be a solution to the differential equation with the initial condition $y(0) = 1$?

   (A) $y = \cos x$

   (B) $y = 1 - x^2$

   (C) $y = \sqrt{1 - x^2}$

   (D) $y = |x|$

   (E) $y = \frac{1}{1 + x^2}$

17. $\displaystyle\int_{0}^{1} x\left(\sqrt{x}-1\right)dx =$

   (A) $-\dfrac{3}{2}$

   (B) $-\dfrac{3}{5}$

   (C) $\dfrac{3}{5}$

   (D) $\dfrac{3}{2}$

   (E) $\dfrac{7}{2}$

18. What are all values of x for which the series $\displaystyle\sum_{n=1}^{\infty}\dfrac{(x-1)^{n}}{\sqrt{n}}$ converges?

   (A) $-3 < x < -1$
   (B) $-3 \le x \le -1$
   (C) $-1 \le x \le 1$
   (D) $0 < x < 2$
   (E) $0 \le x < 2$

19. For time $t > 0$, the position of a particle moving in the xy-plane is given by the parametric equations $x = 4t^{2} + \sin 2t$ and $y = t^{2} + \cos 3t$. What is the acceleration of the particle at time $t = 0$?

   (A) $(8,11)$

   (B) $(8,2)$

   (C) $(8,-7)$

   (D) $(2,0)$

   (E) $(0,1)$

20. The figure below shows the graph of f', the derivative of the function f, on the interval $[-3,3]$.

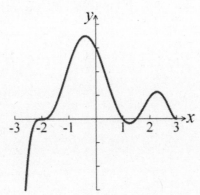

If the derivative of the function g is given by $g'(x) = 3f'(x)$, how many points of inflection does the graph of g have in the interval $[-3,3]$?

(A) One

(B) Two

(C) Three

(D) Four

(E) Five

21. $\int \dfrac{x}{x^2 - 9}\, dx$

(A) $\dfrac{1}{2}\ln\left|x^2 - 9\right| + C$

(B) $\ln\left|x^2 - 9\right| + C$

(C) $\tan^{-1}\left(\dfrac{x}{9}\right) + C$

(D) $\dfrac{1}{2}\ln\left|\dfrac{x+3}{x-3}\right| + C$

(E) $\dfrac{1}{2}\ln\left|\dfrac{x}{(x-3)(x+3)}\right| + C$

22. Evaluate $\displaystyle\int_1^x \frac{x}{\left(1+x^2\right)^3}\,dx$, if possible.

    (A) 3

    (B) $\dfrac{1}{2}$

    (C) $\dfrac{1}{4}$

    (D) $\dfrac{1}{16}$

    (E) Divergent

23. Solve the differential equation $y' = 0.05y\left(1 - \dfrac{y}{300}\right)$ subject to the condition $y(0) = 50$. Then evaluate $\displaystyle\lim_{t \to x} y(t)$.

    (A) 50

    (B) 100

    (C) 200

    (D) 250

    (E) 300

24. Give the first three nonzero terms in the Taylor series expansion about $x = 0$ for the function $f(x) = xe^{2x}$.

    (A) $1 + x + \dfrac{1}{2}x^2$

    (B) $1 + 2x + 2x^2$

    (C) $x + 2x^2 + 2x^3$

    (D) $1 - 2x + 2x^2$

    (E) $1 - 2x^2$

25. The figure below shows the graph of a function f.

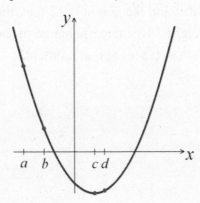

Which of the following has the least value?

(A) $\dfrac{f(b)-f(a)}{b-a}$

(B) $f(d)-f(c)$

(C) $f(d)$

(D) $f'(b)$

(E) $f'(a)$

26. If f is the function given by $f(x)=\displaystyle\int_{1}^{3x}e^{t}dt$, then $f'(\ln 2)=$

(A) 2

(B) 8

(C) 24

(D) $3e^{2}$

(E) $2e^{3}$

27. What is the slope of the line tangent to the polar curve $r=\sin\theta$ at the point $\theta=\dfrac{\pi}{3}$? .

(A) $-\sqrt{3}$

(B) $\dfrac{\sqrt{3}}{2}$

(C) $-\dfrac{1}{2}$

(D) $\dfrac{1}{2}$

(E) $\dfrac{\sqrt{3}}{2}$

28. The base, height and hypotenuse of a right triangle are strictly increasing with time. At the instant when the base is 5 feet and the height is 12 feet, the rate of change of the base is twice the rate of change of the height. If the rate of change of the height is $1/2$ ft/sec, find the rate of change of the hypotenuse (in ft/sec) at that moment.

(A) $\dfrac{5}{12}$

(B) $\dfrac{1}{2}$

(C) $\dfrac{11}{13}$

(D) $\dfrac{22}{13}$

(E) 3

Part B Multiple-Choice

This portion of the exam requires a graphing calculator for some questions.

This part of the exam contains 17 questions.

Directions: Solve each problem in the provided space. Then choose the best option from among the choices given. Be efficient with the use of your time.

Throughout this exam:
(1) Sometimes the exact numerical value of the solution is not given as a choice. In this event, pick the best numerical approximation from the given choices.
(2) The domain of each function f is the set of all real numbers for which $f(x)$ is defined. If the domain of a particular function differs from this, it will be specified in the problem.
(3) For trigonometric functions, the inverse may be represented with " $^{-1}$ " or "arc". For example, the inverse cosine function may be represented as $\cos^{-1} x$ or $\arccos x$.

29. Let f be the function given by $y = \sin x + \ln(2x)$. What is the least value of x at which the graph of f changes concavity?

    (A) 0.35
    (B) 2.07
    (C) 3.24
    (D) 4.49
    (E) 6.26

30. The function f is continuous on $[2,6]$ and differentiable on $(2,6)$. Which of the following statements must be false?
    (A) There exists c, with $2 < c < 6$, for which $f'(c) = 0$.

    (B) There exists c, with $2 < c < 6$, for which $f'(c) = \dfrac{f(6) - f(2)}{4}$.

    (C) f has a minimum value on $4 < x < 6$.
    (D) f has a maximum value on $4 < x < 6$.

    (E) $\displaystyle\int_2^6 f(x)dx$ exists.

31. Find the value of the limit $\lim\limits_{n \to \infty} \left(\dfrac{x + 3x^2}{2x^2 - 5} \right)^2$

    (A) 0

    (B) 1

    (C) $\dfrac{3}{2}$

    (D) $\dfrac{9}{4}$

    (E) ∞

32. The graph below shows the polar curve $r = \theta + \sin\theta$ for $0 \le \theta \le \pi$.

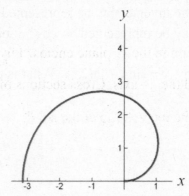

    What is the area of the region bounded by the curve and the x-axis?

    (A) 3.467

    (B) 4.283

    (C) 6.934

    (D) 9.095

    (E) 18.189

33. Let f be the function with first derivative defined by $f'(x) = \sin(e^x)$ for $0 \le x \le 2$. At what value of x does f attain its minimum value on the closed interval $0 \le x \le 2$?

    (A) 0.452

    (B) 1

    (C) 1.145

    (D) 1.550

    (E) 1.838

34. The rate at which a tank is being filled with water is given by $R(t)$, where t is in minutes and $R(t)$ is in gallons per minute. During the time interval $0 \le t \le 5$, which of the following expressions gives the average rate of water flow, in gallons per minute?

(A) $\int_0^5 R(t)dt$

(B) $\dfrac{1}{5}\int_0^5 R(t)dt$

(C) $\int_0^5 R'(t)dt$

(D) $R(5) - R(0)$

(E) $\dfrac{R(5) - R(0)}{5}$

35. The base of a solid is the region in the xy plane enclosed by the curves $f(x) = \cos(x), g(x) = \dfrac{1}{2}x$ and the y-axis. Cross sections of the solid perpendicular to the x-axis are semicircles. Determine the volume of the solid.

(A) 0.168

(B) 0.337

(C) 0.429

(D) 0.592

(E) 1.347

36. The graph of the derivative of f is given below. Which of the following is FALSE about f?

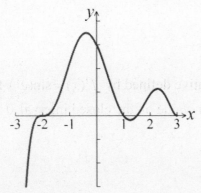

(A) A local minimum occurs at $x = -2$.

(B) A local maximum occurs at $x = 1$.

(C) A point of inflection occurs at $x = -2$.

(D) f is continuous on $[-2, 3]$.

(E) f is increasing on $[-2, 1]$.

37. Let $P(x) = 1 - x + 4x^2 + 5x^3 - 3x^4 + 6x^5$ be the fifth-degree Taylor polynomial for the function f about $x = 0$. What is the value of $f'''(0)$?

(A) $\dfrac{1}{6}$

(B) $\dfrac{5}{6}$

(C) 8

(D) 15

(E) 30

38. Give the length of the curve determined by $x = \sin t, y = e^t$ for t from 0 to $\dfrac{\pi}{2}$.

(A) 2.728

(B) 3.945

(C) 4.044

(D) 4.810

(E) 11.856

39. If $f(x) = g(x) + 5$ for $2 \le x \le 6$, find the value of $\displaystyle\int_2^6 [f(x) + g(x)] dx$.

(A) $\displaystyle\int_2^6 g(x)dx + 5$

(B) $\displaystyle\int_2^6 g(x)dx + 10$

(C) $2\displaystyle\int_2^6 g(x)dx + 5$

(D) $2\displaystyle\int_2^6 g(x)dx + 10$

(E) $2\displaystyle\int_2^6 g(x)dx + 20$

40. The table below gives selected values for a differentiable and increasing function f and its derivative.

x	$f(x)$	$f'(x)$
3	5	1
5	6	2
8	10	7

If g is the inverse of f, what is the value of $g'(6)$?

(A) $\dfrac{1}{7}$

(B) $\dfrac{1}{2}$

(C) 1

(D) 2

(E) 7

41. Let f be a function that is differentiable on the open interval $(-3,3)$. If
$f(-2) = -1, f(2) = -1$ and $f(3) = 4$, which of the following must be true?

I. There exists c, where $-3 < c < 3$, such that $f(c) = 0$.

II. There exists c, where $-3 < c < 3$, such that $f(c) = \dfrac{1}{2}$.

III. There exists c, where $-3 < c < 3$, such that $f'(c) = 0$.

(A) I only

(B) II only

(C) III only

(D) I and II only

(E) I, II, and III

42. The position of an object moving along the x-axis is given by $x(t) = e^{\sin(3t)} + \cos t$, where t is in seconds. In the first 4 seconds, how many times is the velocity of the object equal to 0?

(A) One

(B) Two

(C) Three

(D) Four

(E) Five

43. The function f has derivatives of all orders for all real numbers, and $f^{(5)}(x) = \dfrac{1}{e^x}$. If the fourth-degree Taylor polynomial for f about $x = 0$ is used to approximate f on the interval $[-1,0]$, what is the Lagrange error bound for the maximum error on the interval $[-1,0]$?

(A) 0.003

(B) 0.008

(C) 0.023

(D) 0.368

(E) 2.718

44. The population function in terms of t is given by $P(t) = \dfrac{20}{1 + 5e^{-t}}$. What is the population when it reaches its maximum rate of change?

(A) 1.609

(B) 2.872

(C) 4

(D) 10

(E) 20

45. Let f be the function defined by $f(x) = \displaystyle\int_0^x \left(t^2 - t + 1\right)dt$. What is the value of c for which the instantaneous rate of change of f at $x = c$ is the same as the average rate of change of f over $[0,2]$?

(A) 1.884

(B) 1.333

(C) 1.264

(D) 1

(E) 0.5

Section II

This section contains six free response problems and has two parts: Part A and Part B. Part A has three questions that may require a calculator. A calculator may not be used on the three questions in Part B.

Directions: Solve each problem in the provided space. Be efficient with the use of your time. A calculator may be used on Part A to solve equations, find derivatives at specific points, and evaluate definite integrals. A calculator may not be used on Part B.

Write neatly so that your work can be read. Cross out any mistakes. Work that is erased or crossed out will not be scored.

Before beginning work on Section II, you may want to look over all of the questions. Not everyone is expected to be able to complete every question.

As you work this exam, be sure to do the following:

- Show your work. Label tables, functions, and graphs that you create. Your solutions will be scored based on the correctness of the problem solving process used in addition to the final answer. To receive full credit, you must provide supporting work. When justifying your answers, use mathematical reasons.

- Use standard mathematical notation instead of calculator syntax. For example,

  $\text{fnInt}\left(x^2 - 2x, x, 3, 7\right)$ may not be used to represent $\int_{3}^{7}\left(x^2 - 2x\right)dx$.

- Numeric and algebraic answers do not need to be simplified (unless otherwise specified). Decimal approximations in final answers should be accurate to three decimal places.

- The domain of each function f is the set of all real numbers for which $f(x)$ is defined. If the domain of a particular function differs from this, it will be specified in the problem.

Part A   A calculator may be required to solve some problems.

Question 1

Let S be the region bounded by the graphs of $f(x) = \dfrac{1}{x^2 + 1}$

and $g(x) = x^2$.

(a) Find the area of the region S.

(b) Find the volume of the solid generated when the region S is rotated about the x-axis.

(c) The region S is the base of a solid for which each cross section perpendicular to the x-axis is a square with diameter in the xy plane. Find the volume of the solid.

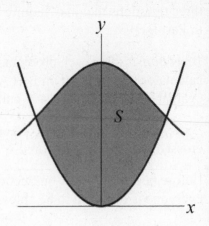

Question 2

Let $F(x) = \int_0^x \ln(t^2 + 1)\,dt$ on the interval $[0, 2]$.

(a) Approximate $F(2)$ using the trapezoid rule with $n = 4$.

(b) Find $F'(x)$.

(c) Find the average value of $F'(x)$ on the interval $[0, 2]$.

Question 3

The function f has derivative $f'(x) = (x-5)e^x$ for $x > 0$. Additionally, $f(1) = 4$.

(a) Given that $f'(5) = 0$, determine whether f has a relative maximum, relative minimum, or neither at $x = 5$. Show the work that justifies your answer.

(b) Is the graph of f simultaneously decreasing and concave up on any interval? Explain your reasoning.

(c) Determine the value of $f(5)$.

Part B   A calculator may not be used.

Question 4

Consider the differential equation $\dfrac{dy}{dx} = 4x^2 - \dfrac{3}{5-y}$ for $y \neq 5$. Define $y = f(x)$ to be the particular solution to this differential equation. Let the initial condition be $f(0) = 4$.

(a) Evaluate $\dfrac{dy}{dx}$ and $\dfrac{d^2y}{dx^2}$ at $(0, 4)$.

(b) Can the x-axis be a tangent line of the graph of f at some point? Explain.

(c) Determine the second-degree Taylor polynomial for f about $x = 0$.

(d) Starting at $x = 0$ and using two equally-sized steps, use Euler's method to approximate $f(1)$. Show all work leading to your solution.

Question 5

Let f be the function defined by the power series

$$f(x) = -1 + \frac{x}{2} - \frac{x^2}{3} + \frac{x^3}{4} - \ldots + (-1)^{n+1} \frac{x^n}{n+1} + \ldots \quad \text{for all real numbers } x \text{ for which the series}$$

converges. Let g be the function defined by the power series

$$g(x) = -\frac{x}{3!} + \frac{x^2}{5!} - \frac{x^3}{7!} - \ldots + (-1)^{n+1} \frac{x^{n+1}}{(2n+3)!} + \ldots \quad \text{for all real numbers } x \text{ for which the series}$$

converges.

(a) Find the interval of convergence of the power series for f. Justify your conclusion.

(b) The graph of $y = g(x) - f(x)$ passes through the point $(0,1)$. Find $y'(0)$ and $y''(0)$. Then figure out whether y has a relative maximum, relative minimum or neither at $x = 0$. Explain your reasoning.

Question 6

t (minutes)	0	10	20	30	40	50	60	70	80
$v(t)$ (meters per minute)	0	150	164	170	162	174	166	158	174

The velocity of Runner A at selected times during a race are shown in the table above. At all times during the race, the runner's velocity was nonnegative. The runner had initial position 0 meters. (She was at the starting line.)

(a) Find the average acceleration of the Runner A from $t = 0$ minutes to $t = 80$ minutes. Label your answer with appropriate units.

(b) Explain the meaning of $\int_0^{80} v(t)\,dt$ as related to the runner, making sure to use appropriate units as a part of your explanation. Then use a midpoint Riemann sum with 4 subintervals of the same length to approximate $\int_0^{80} v(t)\,dt$.

(c) At time $t = 7$, Runner B leaves the starting line with a velocity of 158 meters per minute. Runner B accelerates by $a(t) = \dfrac{1}{\sqrt{t+9}}$ meters per minute per minute. Is Runner A or Runner B running faster at $t = 40$ minutes?